D1368245

THE ARCTIC INSTITUTE OF NORTH AMERICA

Arctic

Environment

And Resources

JOHN E. SATER,
A. G. RONHOVDE, and L. C. VAN ALLEN

Price: $10.00

Library of Congress Catalog Card Number: 78-185066

Printed in The United States of America
November 1971

Foreword

Arctic Environment and Resources was prepared in accordance with the terms of a subcontract between the Systems Research Corporation and the Arctic Institute of North America. It is intended as a comprehensive presentation of arctic environmental conditions as they might be expected to affect resources development in northern areas as well as a report of current and planned development activities and an assessment of potential development and economic importance of arctic resources. For the sake of convenience it is divided into two distinct parts.

Part One, compiled by John E. Sater, describes the environment and character of the Arctic Basin and its near-shore areas as well as those of the arctic sectors of the North Atlantic and North Pacific and their shores. It is drawn from the available literature and represents a synthesis of the writings of many experts. The material presented is indicative of the conditions as they are known to exist. Subjects which lend themselves to small scale-large area treatment are presented at length, while those which require large scale-small area treatment are presented more briefly and the interested reader is urged to refer to the materials listed in the bibliographies. In addition to those materials, the reader is directed to works such as the *Arctic Bibliography*, the *CRREL Bibliography*, and *Government Reports Announcements* and to journals such as *Journal of Geophysical Research*, *Polar Record*, and *Arctic*.

Throughout the first section, all distances stated as miles are nautical miles, not statute miles.

Part Two on arctic resources, by A. G. Ronhovde and L. C. van Allen, is in part an expansion and updating of portions of an SRC report dated 18 December 1970, by L. C. van Allen, D. M. Tyree, and G. S. Sexton. Much of that report, including figures and tables, are incorporated in this study. Acknowledgement is due the authors of the December 1970 report in that much of the information therein on population, industry, and transportation were reasonably up to date and appear in the present volume with no significant changes.

After some investigation, it was concluded that in terms of potential economic and strategic importance, the major resources of the circumpolar arctic region were in the category of energy resources - more precisely, in oil and gas. In the light also of recent government and industry concern with the size and location of reserves of those fuels it was decided to place major emphasis on the oil and gas resources of the arctic region. In view of the evidence cited in the report, it is believed that the decision was warranted.

The projections made for the 1970-2000 period are primarily related to the oil and gas development because they were judged to be the arctic resources of greatest prospective economic and strategic concern to the United States and probably also to Canada and the U.S.S.R.

The financial support of the Office of Naval Research in carrying out the study is gratefully acknowledged.

Contents

CONTENTS (continued)

CONTENTS (continued)

REFERENCES

L I S T   O F   F I G U R E S

Page

CONTENTS (continued)

LIST OF TABLES

Page

Part One—Arctic Environment

Introduction

Definitions

In order to analyze the environment of the Arctic Basin it is first necessary to delineate its physical form or boundary. However, as a result both of remoteness from most population centers and of adverse climatic conditions, knowledge of the northern portion of our planet is still limited and has only partially been collated and verified. This circumstance has led to the discrepancies within the vocabulary which denotes and delimits various aspects of the region. A single expression often may have widely differing meanings. An excellent example is the phrase *Arctic Basin* (often referred to as *Polar Basin*). To many persons, especially to sailors and oceanographers, the term refers to the deep basin which is filled by the Arctic Ocean (also called Polar Ocean or Polar Sea), whereas to others it indicates the drainage basin in which water flows northward into the Arctic Ocean.

At the same time, the forces which act upon the Arctic Basin and which modify its internal conditions must also be comprehended, because a number of these, e.g. winds and currents, have their origins external to the Basin. Thus, the discussion will at times expand to include as well the Arctic, or the lands immediately surrounding the Arctic Basin. It follows that there must also be some objective discussion about the meaning of the word *arctic* and about other associated terms, because unlike the Arctic Basin, the Arctic does not appear to have an immutable boundary.

One certain characteristic of the Arctic is the cold. The term cold, unfortunately, may also be interpreted in a number of ways: it may mean extremely low temperatures (-40°F or lower) at which machines become relatively difficult to operate; or it may mean physiological cold - the combination of wind and low temperature which produces rapid heat loss from the body, generally referred to as wind-chill. It also may refer to the temperature at which plant growth ceases (near 32°F), or it may mean the temperature which permits the growth of only the relatively impoverished tundra vegetation (43°F) as compared with the more complex plant societies of the boreal forest. The upper limit of this temperature band forms a boundary line of considerable cultural significance as well because it marks the limit of agriculture, even the restricted agriculture of the taiga. Here, in fact, cold actually means only one thing - the heat deficit state of the atmosphere.

Climatologists have advanced a variety of climatic definitions to establish boundaries for the Arctic. These definitions are based for the most part on the relationship between atmospheric temperatures and the effects temperatures have on the ecology or, in some cases, the geomorphology. By establishing as arctic regions those areas in which the average temperature of the warmest month is below 50°F, Koppen suggested that the boundary of the Arctic coincides closely with the tree line. Furthermore, tundra regions were classified by him as those in which the average temperature of the coldest month is 32°F or below. In a second system, 43°F is a more significant plant growth temperature than is 32°F. On the basis of this criterion, the barren land or arctic regions were defined as those in which the mean monthly temperature throughout the year is less than 43°F while the tundra was taken to be that area in which the mean temperature is above 43°F for one to two months.

Nordenskjold's formulation of an arctic limit - also intended to coincide with the tree line - included those regions in which the average temperature of the warmest month plus one-tenth of the mean temperature of the coldest month is 51.4°F, which suggested that the winter temperatures also have an effect - if only a slight one - on the position of the tree line. However, it should be noted when considering these definitions that the tree line itself is in a state of flux and is not an ideal reference.

In terms of military operations, the U.S. Army defined the Arctic Operations Area as the area in which temperatures can be expected to reach -40°F. According to such a delimitation - which includes most of Canada and some parts of the United States - the significant characteristic of the so-called arctic area is its low temperature, whether of long or short duration. The Army's definition of the Arctic is: that portion of the northern hemisphere characterized by having an average temperature of the coldest month of less than 32°F and an average temperature of the warmest month of less than 50°F. The subarctic is defined as that portion of the northern hemisphere characterized by having an average temperature of less than 32°F during the coldest month and average temperature above 50°F for one to three of the warmest months.

Geomorphologically it is possible to approximate an arctic limit using the permafrost zone as a criterion. Permafrost, or perennially frozen subsoil, is a phenomenon closely associated with the Arctic and is of particular ecological interest because of the relationship of low soil temperature to plant growth. Geologists and geomorphologists have described the Arctic as the area of continuous permafrost, an area somewhat broader, particularly in western Canada and eastern Siberia, than the region delineated by Koppen.

Because it is a peculiarly polar phenomenon, the auroral zone has also been advanced as a criterion for the geophysical definition of the Arctic. The aurora borealis, observed in northern latitudes, is a luminous circumpolar phenomenon of the upper atmosphere. The center of auroral activity is located near Etah, Greenland, the point at which the geomagnetic pole intersects the earth's surface. From maps indicating the frequency and location of auroral observations, it appears that a specific line (isochasm) might easily be drawn to delineate the auroral or ionospheric Arctic.

Oceanographers consider the Arctic to be that region in which only pure Arctic water (the temperature of which is at or near 32°F and the salinity approximately 30°/oo) is found at the surface. Arctic water is formed in the Arctic Ocean by a combination of: (1) water from the Atlantic and Pacific oceans, (2) water drained from the surrounding land areas, and (3) water resulting from the melting of sea ice. Using these criteria, one can draw a line north of which all surface waters can be considered as Arctic waters and which can therefore be held to encompass the Arctic itself. That region, however, would be considerably less inclusive than those delimited on the basis of temperature, vegetation, permafrost, or ionospheric criteria in that it excludes land areas (Fig. 1).

Thus, the problem of a definitive boundary for the Arctic is a complex one. In its symbolic aspect, the Arctic coincides with that region which surrounds the North Pole; in its literal sense, it refers to the area

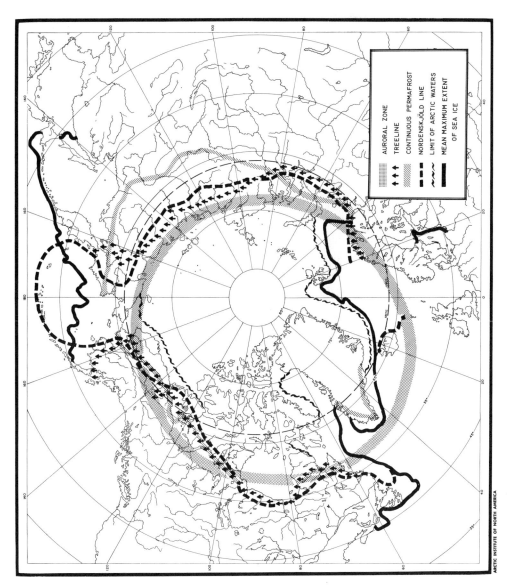

Figure 1. SOME SIGNIFICANT BOUNDARIES IN THE ARCTIC REGION

encompassed by the Arctic Circle. Its outer boundaries can, however, be
established only within a specific context, and even then the delimitation
is often arbitrary. In their specific forms the various delineations over-
lap and interplay, and rigorous definition is pointless. While its geographic and environmental features are peculiarly distinctive, the Arctic
has no boundary that is immutable and it cannot, therefore, be conclusively
defined.

In view of this, the Arctic must be considered as a region, not an area.
For the purposes of this study it will be defined as the portion of the
northern hemisphere in which sea ice may be encountered together with the
coasts which experience it. The term *Arctic Basin*, in contrast, will be
used to denote that basin which is filled by the Arctic Ocean and its peripheral seas, whereas the more inclusive drainage basin within which water
flows northward into the Arctic Ocean will be designated the *Arctic Drainage
Basin*.

Sovereignty

Today nearly all international misunderstandings and doubts regarding
sovereignty over arctic land areas have been resolved. The so-called "sector principle" proposed in Canada and promulgated by the USSR in 1926, while
neither renounced by them nor ever tested in litigation, is of doubtful va-
lidity and of no practical significance when accepted criteria of sovereignty already obtain, as they do in most instances. This principle would
permit a nation bordering on the Arctic Ocean to claim sovereignty over lands
within that segment of the ocean lying between the easternmost and the westernmost meridians bounding its territory to the point where those meridians
meet at the North Pole. The principle has served *de facto* rather than *de
jure*, for a short period, to delimit areas of sovereignty of the respective
countries over land areas north of the mainland. However, Canada now claims
sovereignty on the basis of exploration, occupancy, and administration; and
her claim is recognized over all islands except Greenland north of the mainland of North America between longitude 62°W and 141°W. Under the same pattern such islands and island groups as Wrangel, Zemlya Frantsa Iosifa,
Novaya Zemlya, and Novosibirskiye Ostrova fall in the Soviet sector and are
not disputed. Overall, the Soviet Union controls approximately the same
amount of the territory bordering the Arctic Ocean as do the United States,
Canada, Norway, and Denmark combined.

In 1926 the Soviet government published a decree claiming all land,
including ice formations that are more or less immovable, and all islands
in the triangle that lay between the meridians of 32°4'34"E and 168°49'30"W
and had as its apex the North Pole. The eastern islands of the Svalbard
Archipelago and Little Diomede that lie within this triangle were accepted
as belonging to Norway and the United States of America, respectively. In
articles in 1928 and again in 1950, the Soviet press advanced claims to the
open polar seas, including drifting ice; and the entire triangle has long
been shown on USSR maps as constituting Soviet territory. While the USSR
has not made her official position wholly clear as regards the arctic seas
north of her mainland, it is significant that she has not demonstrated a
proprietary interest in the area defined in the decree of 1926 despite numerous incursions into the area by other nations' vessels and aircraft. In
a separate claim the USSR defined as territorial waters a 12-mile zone off
her entire coast, including islands.

Greenland became an integral part of the Danish State in 1953. Jan Mayen was occupied and claimed by Norway in 1929. Svalbard was awarded to Norway in 1925 by an international treaty, which at the same time restricted her sovereignty in several respects. Military installations are forbidden, and in the case of Vestspitsbergen there is a somewhat complicated dual-occupancy arrangement with the USSR for the exploitation of the Longyearbyen coal.

Two other situations should be considered: ice floating on the sea and ice on the sea that is attached to land. It has now been demonstrated clearly by both the USSR and the United States that it is possible to establish relatively large camps for long periods both on the sea ice of the Arctic Ocean and on the much thicker ice of the ice islands that are broken from land-fast ice and are adrift in the ocean. In spite of the ability to operate from these floes and islands, such operations have not led to the assertion of claims to sovereignty over any area of ice or over any specific geographic location. They appear, rather, to be considered by their occupants to be analogous to ships drifting without control. A similar position seems to have gained general acceptance in regard to shelf ice, the ice that is attached to the land and extends to sea beyond the generally accepted limit of territorial waters.

Because of the possibility of petroleum deposits and other mineral resources lying under the continental shelves of the Arctic Ocean and for other reasons as well, there is considerable interest in learning more about these areas. In this connection the agreements reached a decade ago at the International Conference on the Law of the Sea at Geneva are of interest. The right of a nation to develop minerals on the bordering continental shelf to the outer practical limit of development was not held to be of sufficient practical importance to justify special regulations. Thus the ownership of these resources is still not established and the question is likely to be raised in future international discussions.

Daylight

The "long darkness of winter," more than anything else except perhaps the fear of cold, has prevented people from going to the Arctic. Actually, it is only at the Pole that the extreme condition exists; and even there the sun shines for about 28 weeks each year and remains invisible for the remaining 24. Moreover, the season of "useful light" is much longer than this would indicate. If daylight is defined as the amount of light sufficient to enable one to read newspaper print out-of-doors under a clear sky, there are 32 weeks of continuous daylight at the Pole and over 8 weeks more during which there is at least some twilight all the time. This leaves only about 80 days of real night. At the North Pole there are about 140 more hours of sunlight each year than at the equator. On the Arctic Circle there are about 230 more. The following figures (2 and 3) may be used to determine the various periods of light experienced in the Arctic.

Bibliography

Baird, P.D., 1964. *The Polar World*. New York: John Wiley. 228 pp.

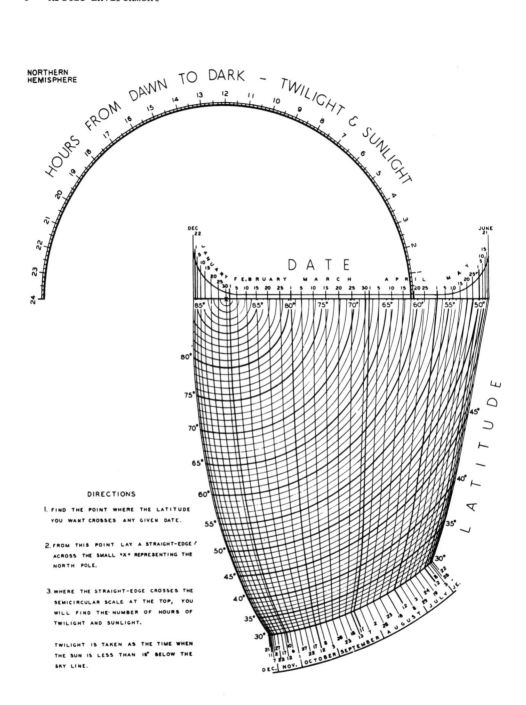

Figure 2.   HOURS OF TWILIGHT AND SUNLIGHT

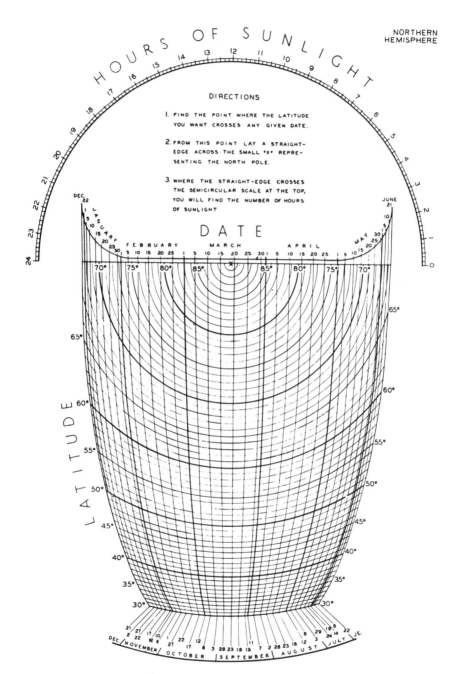

Figure 3.   HOURS OF SUNLIGHT

MacDonald, R. St. J., ed., 1966. *The Arctic Frontier*. Toronto: University
    of Toronto Press. 311 pp.

Sandford, B. P. and L. R. Doan, 1969. *Graphs of the Solar Depression Angle
    from 0° to 32° vs Local Hour Angle for Latitudes 0° to 90°*. Bedford,
    Mass.: Air Force Cambridge Research Laboratories. Report AFCRL-69-
    0543. 112 pp.

Sater, J. E., 1969. *The Arctic Basin*. Washington, D. C.: Arctic Institute
    of No. Amer. 337 pp.

U. S. Navy, 1956. *The Dynamic North*. Washington, D. C.: Technical Assist-
    ant to the Chief of Naval Operations for Polar Projects.

Geophysics

Gravity

Observations of the strength of the earth's gravitational field are used both to determine the precise shape and size of the geoid and to establish the nature and thickness of the crustal materials. The principal goal of geodesy has been to determine the parameters of an ellipsoid of revolution that best fits the figure of the earth as a whole. The resulting determinations are now converging to a point beyond which there will be little change, and attention is being directed to determination of the earth's actual shape, or the relationship between the ellipsoid and the geoid. Different types of geodetic analysis may be used. A classical method involves astronomic observations for latitude and longitude which, in connection with geodetic positions, determine the deflection of the vertical or the slope of the geoid at the point in question. A second method involves observations of gravity at more or less uniformly spaced points over the area of concern. Many gravity measurements have been made in the principal countries of the world and across the oceans, particularly in the middle latitudes, but there is a paucity of such data from the Arctic.

In Alaska a continuous scheme of triangulation extends from the British Columbia-Alaska boundary through southeastern and southwestern Alaska to the western extremity of the Aleutian Islands, to the shoreline and the islands of the Bering Sea to the Arctic Ocean, to the international boundary near the Demarcation Point. The elevations above mean sea level of established bench marks have been determined by lines of precise levels along the Alaska Highway from Whitehorse to Fairbanks, on the Richardson Highway from Fairbanks to Valdez, and on the Steese Highway to Circle.

The main triangulation net of arctic Canada is tied to the Alaskan network at the boundary near the Alaska Highway. A loop has been completed north of 60°N from the vicinity of Great Slave Lake to east of Fort Reliance. From the latter point an arc has been completed to close the loop east of Lake Athabasca. Another loop has been extended north from Great Slave Lake to a connection with Victoria Island. A triangulation network using short-range navigation by radar (SHORAN) covers all of northern Canada while a satellite triangulation net is nearly complete which ties Canadian and U.S. stations with accuracies near one in one million. SHORAN points have been established from the Alaska boundary to the Atlantic coast and north over the Canadian Arctic Archipelago to Ellesmere Island and northwestern Greenland.

A tie between the geodetic surveys in North America and Europe was completed by HIRAN trilateration across the North Atlantic. This network extends from Baffin Island, across southern Greenland to Iceland, to the northern British Isles and from there to the coast of Norway. The European data were thus carried from the three Norwegian triangulation stations through the trilateration net to Canada. The North America data were, at the same time, carried from the Canadian SHORAN stations to Norway. The astronomic positions of the points in the HIRAN net have been determined.

It is known that the European data have been carried through Czechoslovakia on to the USSR (the Krassowsky triaxial ellipsoid) and it can be assumed that in this manner the Alaska-Canada-Greenland-Norway triangulation and trilateration net has been carried to its arctic coast.   There is no tie across the Bering Strait.   After the worldwide geodetic satellite triangulation network is completed, these various surveys in high latitudes can be interconnected.   Even without the geometric results, considerable geoidal information has been obtained from dynamic studies of satellites with Doppler techniques.

Gravity observations can be obtained rapidly with airborne gravity meters.   The data collected by satellites over areas not readily accessible by other means are of a generalized nature, however, and can determine only the long-period undulations of the geoid, not the detailed undulations that may be arrived at through work on the surface of the earth.   A sea-gravity meter has been developed for observations from a surface vessel.   In dealing with the problems of the Arctic, there is a need for a greater density of gravity observations, both on land and sea; such observations should be accomplished with the support of aircraft and surface vessels or submarines. For the proper interpretation of these observations, geodetic positions to about one kilometer and elevations to about five meters must be known.

The published data on arctic gravimetry, such as that compiled at the University of Wisconsin and the Lamont-Doherty Geological Observatory cover limited areas   (Fig. 4).   Other western nations have published results of traverses over parts of the oceans dealt with here but a complete picture is lacking.   Presumably the most extensive records to date are those collected on the cruises of the U.S. Navy's nuclear submarines across the Arctic Ocean, but the data are not published.   A recently published report discusses the most recent studies of both the Wisconsin and Lamont groups.   The observations of gravimetric forces continue on Fletcher's Ice Island, T-3, but the station has been relatively stationary for some time.

Magnetic Phenomena

The magnetic field measured on the earth's surface originates from three sources: (1)   the self-exciting dynamo action within the earth's liquid core that produces the main magnetic field,   (2)   the magnetic induction of rocks within the earth's crust, and   (3)   an external and rapidly changing field generated by solar effects that disturb the ionosphere and give rise to a number of related upper-atmosphere phenomena such as magnetic storms and aurorae.   All of these magnetic fluxes have important consequences for operations in the Arctic.

The earth's magnetic field is almost entirely of internal origin.   It can be fairly closely represented by a small number of harmonics; and the first-order harmonics, much the most important, have a physically simple description.   They correspond to the potential of a small magnet or dipole located at the center of the earth and inclined at a small angle to the axis of rotation, and they produce the main dipole field.   This dipole field is a useful simplification of the mathematically described geomagnetic field, which is computed by a harmonic analysis of the magnetic intensity measured at many locations on the earth's surface.

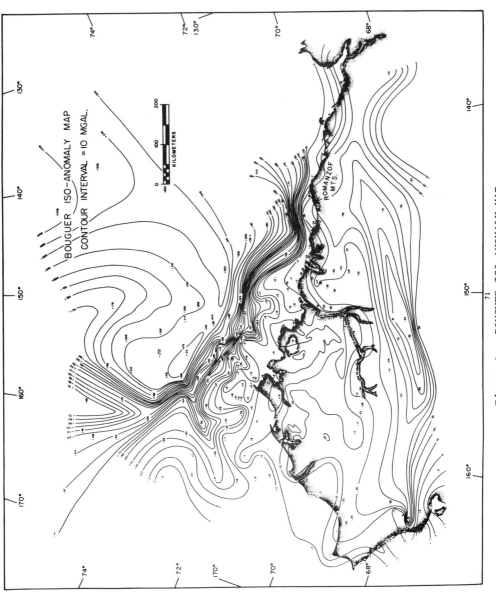

BOUGUER ISO-ANOMALY MAP
CONTOUR INTERVAL = 10 MGAL.

Figure 4.   BOUGUER ISO-ANOMALY MAP

The poles of the dipole are called the geomagnetic (or dipole) poles.
They should not be confused with the magnetic (or dip) poles, whose changing
geographic locations on the earth's surface are influenced by the composite
of all magnetic sources. Even though the dipole field differs from the magnetic field actually observed at the earth's surface, the difference diminishes rapidly with elevation. Thus those concerned with operations on or
near the earth's surface must concern themselves with the complex total magnetic field, whereas those studying and working in the earth's outer environment are well served by the dipole field. In correlation studies and
theoretical analyses the magnetic field has not been widely used, but its
acceptance will grow now that the electronic computer makes the use of the
actual field coordinates practical. In addition, new coordinates, such as
the magnetic shell parameter, have been invented. They describe the motion
of particles trapped in the magnetic field, and their principal use is in
studies of the interaction of particles in the ionosphere.

Being mathematically determined, the dipole poles are diametrically
opposed and their projections to the earth's surface are at approximately
78.5°N 69°W, near Thule, Greenland, and 78.5°S 111°E, near Vostok, Antarctica. The geocentric dipoles are inclined at an angle of 11.5° to the
earth's rotational axis, an angle sufficiently small for the earth's rotation to be considered to play a dominant role in the creation of this magnetic field. Contrastingly, the magnetic (dip) poles are not diametrically
opposed, each being about 800 mi from the point antipodal to the other.
The line joining the two dip poles misses passing through the center of the
earth by about 400 mi. The horizontal intensity can also vanish at other
points within small areas on the earth's surface because of the magnetic
susceptibility of crustal rocks. Such local north and south poles are not
to be confused with the main dip poles that affect the compass on a global
scale.

The earth's magnetic field is a vector quantity, having both magnitude
and direction. The orientation of the total intensity vector (F) is defined by the angles of inclination or dip (I) and declination (D). Inclination is measured relative to horizontal, i.e. tangent to the earth's surface, and is downward in the northern hemisphere and upward in the southern
hemisphere. Declination is measured in degrees of arc east or west of geographic or true north. Mariners commonly refer to declination as a variation
of the compass. This value constitutes an important correction for navigation. The horizontal and vertical components of F are denoted by H and Z,
respectively. H is always considered positive, whatever its direction,
whereas Z is considered positive downward and thus has the same sign conven-
tion as I. The various components of the total field vector are geomet-
rically relatable by the equations
$$H = F \cos I, \quad Z = F \sin I, \quad \text{and} \quad \tan I = Z/H.$$

By definition the dip poles are at the sites where, on the surface of
the earth, the total field vector is vertical (H = C, I = ± 90°). At these
sites a freely suspended compass needle points straight down; hence they
are commonly referred to as dip poles. The magnetic (dip) equator is the
circumglobal line along which F is tangent to the earth's surface (Z = 0,
I = 0°). Strictly speaking, the magnetic field strength is measured in
fractions of an oersted but is commonly referred to in terms of the gauss,
which is the unit of magnetic induction. Another frequently used and often
more convenient unit is the gamma, which is 100,000 times smaller than an
oersted. The maximum value of the earth's total field is just over 0.7

oersted and occurs in a region that includes the southern dip pole. The field at the northern dip pole is considerably smaller, being less than 0.59 oersted.

The northern dip pole is now located at approximately 75°N 98°W in northern Canada. From it a strong ridge of high horizontal magnetic intensity reaches across the Arctic Basin into Siberia, seriously distorting the magnetic meridians in this region (see Fig. 5). The maximum value of the total field intensity (over 0.6 oersted) occurs not at the principal dip pole, but at a secondary focus in Siberia. Locally over the earth's surface (e.g. above some outcropping iron ore bodies in central and northern Sweden and in places in Norway) the magnetic intensity is as great as 1 to 4 oersted but these are exceptional conditions. Elsewhere the varying rocks of the earth's crust can cause local distortions of the main magnetic field. These distortions, or anomalies, can amount to as much as 10% of the normal field strength. Also the oceans, because they are floored with basalt, have an associated magnetic field that is particularly disturbed and may produce rather large anomalies.

There is a slow change in the magnetic field with time, now called the secular variation, which is observed in all the components. If successive annual mean values of a magnetic component are obtained for a particular station, it is found that the changes are in the same sense over a long period of time, although the rate of change is not usually constant. Over a period of years this change may be considerable. Thus H at Cape Town has decreased by 21% in the hundred years following the first observation in 1843. The secular drift of the northern dip pole since 1831 is shown in Figure 6.

The northern and southern dip poles have wandered at different rates and in different directions. The northern dip pole is now moving in a northeasterly direction at about 6 mi/yr whereas the southern dip pole is moving in a northwesterly direction at approximately 7 mi/yr. During the past century, secular variation has decreased the movement of the geomagnetic dipole at a rate of 0.05% a year and caused a westward precessional rotation of the dipole of 0.05°/yr, plus a northward shifting of the dipole by 1 mi/yr.

Lines of equal secular changes (isopors), in any component, form sets of ovals centering on points of local maximum change (isoporic foci). Considerable changes take place in the general distribution of isopors in periods as small as 10 or 20 years. The secular variation is a regional rather than a planetary phenomenon and is anomalously large and complicated over and around Antarctica.

Superimposed on the growth and decline and random movement of the isoporic foci pattern is an overall average motion of the whole pattern from east to west at an average rate of about 0.2 degree of longitude per year. The angular velocity of this westward drift appears to be independent of latitude but is closely related to the irregularities in the observed rate of rotation of the earth, after allowance has been made for the regular slowing-down due to tidal friction. Secular variations have been related to convective motion within the earth's core.

Within the past few years the aeromagnetic surveys of the Arctic Basin made by the Naval Oceanographic Office, the University of Wisconsin, and Dominion Observatory of Canada have shown the degree of disturbance of the

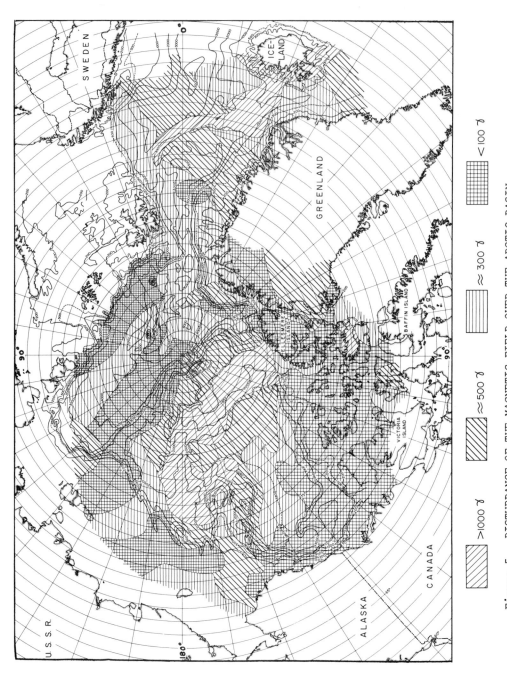

Figure 5.   DISTURBANCE OF THE MAGNETIC FIELD OVER THE ARCTIC BASIN

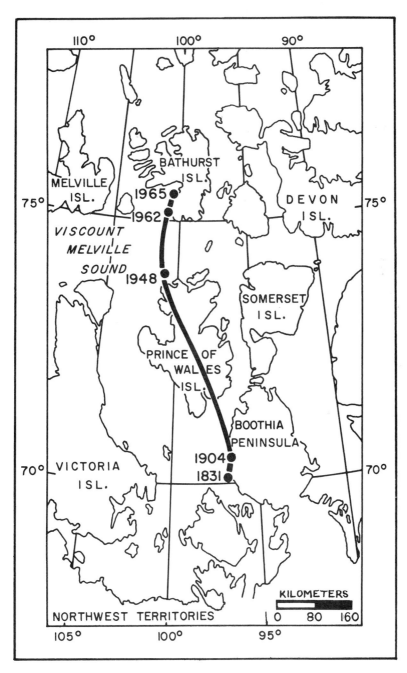

Figure 6.   MIGRATION OF THE NORTH MAGNETIC (DIP) POLE
BETWEEN 1831 AND 1965

magnetic field to be regionally variable in reflection of the complex geologic structure of the Arctic Basin (Fig. 5). Over large areas the field is virtually undisturbed, whereas in other areas anomalies exceeding 1,000 gamma are common and gradients as steep as 2 gamma a meter are encountered.

Other salient observations are: (1) the magnetic field is much more disturbed over the Amerasia Basin than over the Eurasia Basin; (2) intense magnetic disturbance characterizes the Alpha Cordillera and suggests that it is composed of crystalline rock of high magnetic susceptibility; (3) contrastingly, the Lomonosov Ridge produces but little magnetic disturbance; and (4) the northward projection of the Mid-Atlantic Ridge into the Arctic Basin is indicated by a band of relatively intense magnetic disturbance, but its anomalies are not nearly so great as, and neither do they have the orderly arrangement of, those associated with the Mid-Atlantic Ridge proper.

Bibliography

Chapman, S. and J. Bartels, 1962. *Geomagnetism*. 2 vol. Oxford: Clarendon Press. 1049 pp.

Dawson, E. and E. I. Loomer, 1963. The north magnetic dip pole. *Dominion Obs. Publ.* 28:195-208.

Haines, G. V., W. Hannaford and P. H. Serson, 1970. Magnetic anomaly maps of the Nordic countries and the Greenland and Norwegian seas. *Publications of the Dominion Observatory, Ottawa*. Ottawa: The Queen's Printer. Vol. XXXIX, No. 5: 123-49.

King, E. R., I. Zietz, and L. R. Alldredge, 1966. Magnetic data on the structure of the central arctic region. *Geol. Soc. Amer. Bull.* 77:619-46.

Ostenso, N. A., 1962. *Geophysical Investigations of the Arctic Ocean Basin*. Madison: The University of Wisconsin. Geophysical and Polar Research Center Research Report No. 4. 124 pp.

Sater, J. E., 1969. *The Arctic Basin*. Washington, D. C.: Arctic Institute of No. Amer. 337 pp.

Tarr, A. C., 1970. New maps of polar seismicity. *Bulletin* of the Seismological Society of America, 60: 1741-47.

U. S. Navy, 1956. *The Dynamic North*. Washington, D. C.: Technical Assistant to the Chief of Naval Operations for Polar Projects.

Vogt, P. R. and N. A. Ostenso, 1970. Magnetic and Gravity Profiles Across the Alpha Cordillera and Their Relation of Arctic Sea-Floor Spreading. *J. Geophys. Research* 75:4925-37.

Atmospherics

Aeronomy

The atmosphere above the stratopause is of operational importance in the Arctic, particularly as regards communications, radiation backgrounds, and transient magnetic variations. The time and space variations of electron densities in the ionosphere reach their widest limits over the polar (ionospheric) cap. The aurora is occasionally as bright as the full moon. Aurorae occur in both polar regions, the polar aurora of the northern hemisphere being termed aurora borealis and that of the southern hemisphere aurora australis.

The magnetic fields in the space immediately surrounding the earth are contained within the magnetosphere. Figure 7 illustrates our present knowledge, which is based on a large number of satellite observations. The solar wind, a stream of fully ionized hydrogen blowing continuously with varying intensity, compresses the sunward side of the magnetosphere to a minimum thickness of approximately 32,500 miles. In the direction away from the sun, however, the earth's magnetic field is drawn out far behind the earth in a magnetic tail that extends to at least 1,000 earth radii. The magnetic field lines terminating on the day and night sides over the polar caps go into the magnetic tail where they may or may not connect. However, some of the high-latitude magnetic field may be connected, at times, directly with the interplanetary magnetic field. Satellite observations have established the existence of a neutral sheet inside the magnetic tail and also a shock front toward the sunward side of the magnetosphere that can be understood by using the methods of hypersonic gas dynamics.

The "normal polar ionosphere" is unique because of two independent factors found nowhere else on the globe. The first is the presence of the dip poles within the polar regions and may be considered accidental. The second factor, arising from sun-earth geometry and the tilt of the earth's rotational axis, produces the seasons and long periods when the sun is continuously absent above the polar circles. Even at ionospheric altitudes, a given layer, depending upon its altitude and latitude, may be sunlit or dark for periods of months. Thus, the polar ionic layers enjoy the constant presence or absence of solar ionizing radiations for periods of months; and they encounter a situation appreciably different from that presented to the lower-latitude ionosphere.

Figure 8 shows the behavior of incoming solar radiation, which creates the layers of the ionosphere. Infrared radiation of relatively long wave length (1 in the Figure) is perceived as heat. Intermediate to this and the ultraviolet (2) is the visible radiation, light. The lethal ultraviolet would profoundly influence life on earth were it not absorbed at altitudes above 12 mi. Other ultraviolet radiations (3 and 4) of shorter wave length create the D and F layers (or regions) of the ionosphere by ionizing some of its constituent gasses. Of still shorter wave length are X-rays (5, 6, and 7), the longest of which (5) ionize gasses to form the E layer. Medium-length X-rays (6) appear during solar flares and cause depressions of the D and E layers that severely restrict radio telecommunications. Ultrashort X-rays (7) do not reach the earth's surface.

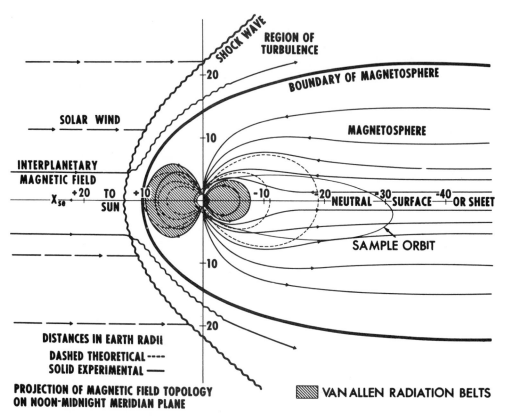

Figure 7. MAGNETIC-FIELD TOPOLOGY WITHIN THE MAGNETOSPHERE IN THE NOON-
    MIDNIGHT MERIDIAN PLANE. The relative positions of the neutral surface
    or sheet in the earth's magnetic tail and the co-rotating magnetic
    field lines supporting trapped-particle motion are indicated. These
    include the classical Van Allen radiation belts. A cylindrical sym-
    metry about the earth-sun line has been assumed for the boundary of the
    earth's magnetic tail in this presentation. A major problem for
    conjugate-point studies is determining from observations whether the
    field line connecting a conjugate pair is connected simply (as in the
    shaded region) or in a complex manner, for example with the field lines
    going out into the tail region.

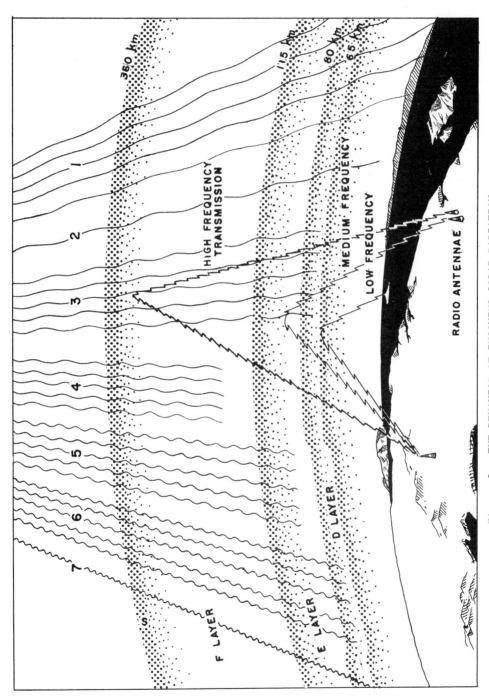

Figure 8.   THE BEHAVIOR OF INCOMING SOLAR RADIATION

Under quiet conditions, the E and F_1 layers of the polar ionosphere
are well behaved and conform to the general predictions of the Chapman
theory. The diurnal variation of electron density at the maximum of the
layers is fairly symmetrical around local noon; the layers appear continuously during summer when the sun remains constantly above the horizon and
are absent during the polar night when no solar ionizing radiation is
present. Average values of noon median critical frequencies, determined
over one sunspot cycle range at a number of North American arctic sites
from 1.6 to 3.6 mHz for the E layer and 3 to 5.5 mHz for the F_1 layer.

The F_2 layer is highly irregular in many respects. It does not follow
the simple Chapman theory requiring a dependence of electron density on the
solar zenith angle. At many places the maximum of ionization does not occur, for example, near local noon. During summer, when the sun constantly
illuminates the layer, the critical frequency is almost constant near 5 to
6 mHz during sunspot maxima and 4 mHz during sunspot minima; and it displays
a very small variation throughout the 24-hour period. In winter, the diurnal critical frequency increases in range markedly, attaining its greatest
amplitudes of 8 to 10 mHz at the geographic pole during the maximum of solar
activity. The amplitudes decrease with decreasing solar activity to about
half the above-stated values.

In the absence of sunspots, the average values of the noon F_2 layer
median frequency during winter portray the non-solar contribution to the
layer's electron density. The same type of data gathered during the summer
reveals the solar influence. The maintenance of the polar ionosphere in
winter indicated the dominant role played by non-solar electron-ion production processes. These processes include diffusion that is due to density
gradients and gravity; horizontal and vertical drifts caused by electric
fields; movements of ionization induced by neutral air winds; and the redis-
tribution of ionization caused by changes in ion or electron temperature.
All these processes in the F region are not yet well understood.

Because it is immediately evident to the unaided eye, the visual
aurora has been observed and described for millennia. It probably results
from the bombardment of the upper atmosphere by solar protons and, more
importantly, by energetic electrons and protons accelerated by processes
still unknown that probably occur in the tail of the magnetosphere. The
bombarding particles excite or ionize the atmospheric gasses. Aurora
activity occurs most frequently in zones about 23° from the geomagnetic
poles. The average annual overhead occurrence of aurorae in the northern
hemisphere is shown in Figure 9. The zone of maximal auroral activity
covers a latitude band called the auroral oval. This zone corresponds to
the outer boundary of the region of electrons trapped in the magnetic field.
During magnetic activity this zone moves southward by several degrees.

By far the most common altitude of the lower border of the aurora is
50 mi, but lower heights have been reported. The maximum altitude has been
found to be over 550 mi. Visual auroral forms include homogeneous arcs and
bands, arcs and bands with ray structure, pulsating arcs, diffuse and pulsating surfaces, glows, draperies, rays, coronae, and flaming coronae.
Homogeneous arcs and some other forms frequently lie along, or at a small
angle to, the dipole latitude.

The luminous aurora, in the usual connotation, includes the emissions
resulting from interactions between precipitating electrons and protons and

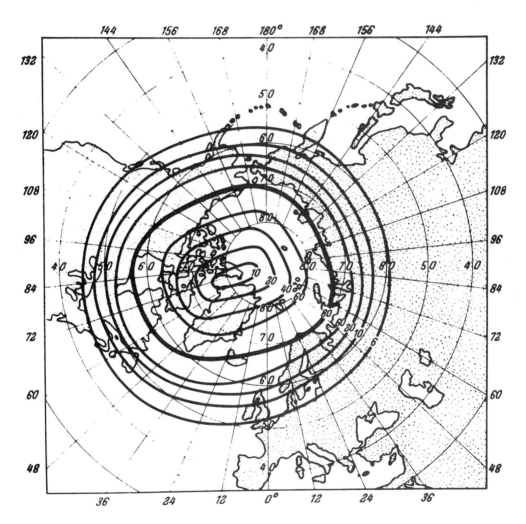

Figure 9.   ISOAURORES IN THE NORTHERN HEMISPHERE.   Note the low
number of overhead aurorae in the vicinity of the dipole
pole.

the atmospheric constituents. These excitations include not only the
visual aurora (that detected by the naked eye) but also those other emissions detectable by spectroscopes in the near-ultraviolet and infrared
regions. Some of the collisional interactions produce not only excitation
but ionization as well. In many cases the resulting electron densities are
sufficiently large and persistent to allow their examination by high-
frequency (HF), very high-frequency (VHF), and ultrahigh-frequency (UHF)
probings.

A radio aurora is an ionization that gives rise to certain characteristic types of radio reflection. If both the luminous and ionized (radio)
aurorae are caused by the same stream of bombarding particles, they should
exhibit a correspondence in time and space. This correspondence, however,
is not always found; and probably this is true for at least two reasons.
First, since the cross section for excitation or ionization is energy-
dependent, an incoming stream may on some occasions produce excitation at
one location and ionization at another, or it could produce ionization without excitation, etc. Secondly, a radio wave that is probing auroral ionization is sensitive to the geometry of the ray path involved - that from
sender to aurora to receiver. Roughly speaking, a reflection from an ionized aurora will be detectable in the radar receiver if the incident ray is
closely perpendicular to the ionized auroral sheath. If this aspect sensitivity in detecting the ionized aurora is neglected, the conclusion could
be reached that no relationship exists between the luminous and ionized
aurorae.

On reflection from the ionized aurora, radio waves usually acquire a
random fading rate (100 to 400 Hz at frequencies of 50 to 150 mHz) that
shifts their spectrum to either side of the carrier frequency. This
aurorally induced modulation may restrict the information bandpass of the
ionized aurora to about 1 kHz or even less, depending upon the fading present. Bandwidths of this size prohibit radiotelephone communications by
seriously garbling the signal; nonetheless, CW, radioteletype, and similar
narrow bandwidth systems may be received with little loss of intelligibility.

The ionized aurora is generally considered to lie along the earth's
magnetic lines of force, which in polar regions may be inclined about 20 to
$30°$ to the vertical. If Snell's law is observed, the reflection of radio
waves with respect to the earth is then different on the poleward and
equatorward sides of the aurora. On a number of occasions, reports have
been issued on the reception of radio noise from the ionized aurora. Thus,
increased noise levels have been noted (at distances of 300 miles from
aurorae) at frequencies of 46 and 72 mHz and also at 3,000 mHz. Noise
bursts at 3,000 mHz have been found to correlate with geomagnetic disturbances.

Fluctuations in magnetic recordings may usually be associated with
strong outbursts of solar activity, and they may be time-related to ionospheric storminess, polar-cap absorption, auroral occurrences, and cosmic-
ray events. While these correlations also may be noted at lower latitudes,
the variations occur with greatest frequency in the polar regions where the
interdependence is more marked.

Small-scale variations of the magnetic field occur nearly all the
time. The regularly repeated diurnal variation of magnetic activity shows
a dependence on magnetic time with maxima occurring around magnetic noon
and midnight within the auroral zone during winter and only around noon

during summer. South of the auroral zone the magnetic noon maxima disappear. The seasonal variation has a major maximum during the vernal
equinox, a minor maximum in the autumnal equinox, and a minimum during
the solstices.

Large changes of the magnetic field are called magnetic storms. They
are caused by solar plasma ejected from the sun during solar flares im-
pacting on the magnetosphere. Such an impact causes the magnetosphere
first to become compressed, then to expand and vibrate. A part of the
plasma energy enters deep into the magnetosphere and creates a storm-time
belt, the ring current. Its effect on the magnetosphere has been expressed
as an inflation. Another part of the plasma energy is converted into the
energy of energetic electrons, which by interacting with the polar (neutral)
atmosphere causes the oval band-shaped light of the aurora around the dipole
and an intense magnetic current, the polar electrojet.

Most storms begin with a very abrupt rise in H intensity, usually of
about 10 to 20 gamma, which lasts only a fraction of a minute and is observed simultaneously throughout the world. This feature is called the
"sudden commencement." Following a sudden commencement the field remains
at an enhanced level for two to six hours, exhibiting a slightly pulsating
character. This is the "enhancement phase." The field then begins to
weaken while undergoing a series of large erratic pulsations. These pulses
are spectacularly large and erratic both in amplitude and period. This
"main phase" lasts from a few hours to a whole day, after which the pulsations diminish in amplitude and the field slowly rises back to its normal
level in an exponential manner. This "recovery phase" generally takes one
to two days, although complete normality may not be reached for a week or
more.

Since the incident particles that cause severe disturbances in the
lower ionosphere are charged, they are affected by the existence of the
magnetic field, resulting in a particular precipitation pattern over the
polar cap. Measurements from scientific satellites close to the earth as
well as several earth's radii away, together with ground-based observations
of ionospheric and geomagnetic parameters, continue to provide information
about the interaction between the solar-flare emission, variations in the
solar wind, and the expansion and contraction of the magnetosphere resulting
in ionospheric and magnetic variations over the polar regions.

The normal daytime radio-wave absorption in the middle and high
latitudes is approximately proportional to some power (0.75) of the cosine
of the solar zenith angle. In high latitudes several types of abnormal
absorption are encountered; their existence and prolonged prevalence has
long been known to communicators employing high frequencies. It became
known more recently that this absorption can also cause communication out-
ages on high-power, VHF forward-scatter circuits. Roughly, it is usually
considered that radio-wave absorption will occur during magnetically active
periods for those radio circuits whose great circle paths are tangent to or
intersect the auroral zone. Abnormal polar radio-wave absorption may be
categorized in three groups: sudden ionospheric disturbances (SID), polar-
cap absorption (PCA), and auroral absorption (AA). The first two types
correlate with solar-flare events.

Sudden ionospheric disturbances are associated with visible solar
flares. They are confined to daylight hours and occur not only in polar
regions, but simultaneously throughout the entire sunlit hemisphere. They

are caused by solar ultraviolet radiation that is absorbed in the D region
(45 mi) and creates large ionization. Since the magnitude of the absorption
depends on the zenith distance of the sun, it is normally not very important
in the polar regions. It starts within minutes of the beginning of a solar
flare and lasts for only several minutes to about one hour.

Polar-cap absorption is the most severe absorption event. It starts
one to several hours after the solar flare well inside the polar region
around the magnetic pole. Its geographic extent increases with time until
it covers the polar regions inside the auroral zones, arctic and antarctic.
The absorption is much stronger over the sunlit portion than over the dark
portion. Therefore, the magnitude and geographic extent of a PCA event
change over the polar cap with the change of illumination during the course
of a day. Solar protons with energies greater than 10 MeV can enter the
polar cap to be absorbed in the D region without any worldwide magnetic
disturbances, which start much later. The absorption of HF wave energy
can be so strong that HF communication becomes impossible; this is called
polar blackout. Such a blackout lasts for several hours, or several days
in extreme cases, especially when two strong solar flares and therefore two
PCA's occur within a day or two, which happens during periods of sunspot
maxima. The mechanism by which solar protons enter the polar cap near the
magnetic pole at the beginning of a PCA event is known, but the physical
processes that lead to the geographic spreading of absorption during the
following phase is not yet understood.

Those absorption events are called auroral absorption (AA) when they
occur at latitudes above 50° in either hemisphere and are measurable by
radio techniques. They are short-lived, i.e. lasting mostly only a few
minutes and rarely up to a few hours; and are not related to PCA's and
SID's. They are commonly associated with magnetospheric substorms (magnetic
"bays") and aurorae. They display a very pronounced maximum in occurrence
around dipole latitude 65°, with the magnitude of the absorption usually
largest in winter (in both hemispheres) and their diurnal variation peaks
a few hours before local magnetic noon. The average absorption in winter
is twice that in summer, but from the zone of maximum occurrence their
amplitude decreases toward the pole. The absorption has a well-defined
peak a few degrees south of the visual auroral oval. Some events cover
relatively small areas and others very wide areas. Some events occur more
or less simultaneously in both hemispheres, but others do not.

Auroral absorption is only one of the many manifestations of precipitating particles (electrons and at times protons) coming from the magnetosphere into the ionosphere. For example, other effects are: visible
aurorae, magnetic substorms, micropulsations, VLF hiss and chorus, sporadic
E, and spread F. Recent satellite measurements have shown that precipitating electrons with energies of about 1 to 1,000 keV and protons above 100
keV are related to auroral absorption events. A discrete event is intense,
is limited spatially, shows rapid and deep fluctuations, and in general can
be thought of as a "splash." The diffuse event, on the other hand, can be
associated with a particle influx that is steady and widespread and that
can be aptly described as a "drizzle." Most of the evidence suggests that
the discrete event arises from soft electron fluxes and the diffuse from
relatively hard fluxes. The discrete event occurs roughly along the
auroral oval, whereas the diffuse event occurs in a separate ring several
degrees farther south.

Radio Propagation

Radio systems in the Arctic employ transfers of energy by most of the normal propagating modes. Those modes involving contact with the earth's surface or the ionosphere will, in many cases, behave quite differently in the Arctic than in the temperate zone. Those portions of the arctic land surface that are covered with snow and ice can introduce great losses of surface waves. Since the arctic ionosphere has ionization profiles that differ greatly from those in temperate regions, there are times when high-frequency ionospheric losses in the Arctic are much greater than at low latitudes. At these same disturbed times, low-frequency ionospheric losses are often less than at low latitudes. A listing of the types of propagating modes that may be important for arctic paths together with the significant earth parameters is given in Table 1.

Once a given communication path has been established and its distance determined, there are usually several types of propagation mode that can be employed and a range of frequencies for each mode. The choice of frequency and propagating mode will be influenced by the specific path-terrain and the data rates and reliability required. For example, in the VLF range, as in the LF range with a ground-wave mode, propagation is much more effective over arctic sea ice than over an ice cap or a permafrost region. In addition, line-of-sight systems have ranges that vary greatly depending upon terminal and on-path elevations. Some of the types of propagation mode and associated frequency ranges that are useful for arctic propagation paths of given lengths are summarized in Table 2.

Since most communication systems or sorts of equipment are designed to operate in specific frequency ranges (Table 3), anticipated propagation conditions are described in the following sections for specific frequency ranges.

VLF communication systems are primarily for broadcasting over a large area with path lengths up to about 6,000 mi. Because of the noise levels at these frequencies, the transmitting installations employ large antennae with transmitter powers ranging from 100 kW to 2 MW. These systems carry only 10 to 100 words a minute. Because of the cost of such installations, VLF is not used for point-to-point communications in the Arctic; but since the fields exist throughout the Arctic, VHF communication does provide a useful broadcast service as well as a means of navigation.

Arctic ionospheric conditions modify VLF propagation characteristics slightly. For most applications other than precise navigation, this effect is rather negligible. The primary modifier is the conductivity of the lower portion of the earth-ionosphere wave guide. Around 15 kHz, the normal attenuation rate over temperate-zone seawater ranges from 1 to 2-1/2 db/600 mi. When the path is over normal land, an attenuation of about 1 to 2 db/600 mi must be added to the seawater rate, and when the path is over a region of deep permafrost or an ice cap, an attenuation of about 6 to 20 db/600 mi must be added. The attenuation increase is usually much greater during the day than at night. This is particularly true at the higher frequencies (near 30 kHz) where during the night most of the energy is contained high in the earth-ionosphere guide; and as a result, a loss-prone surface at the lower boundary does not appreciably affect the attenuation rate.

Table 1

PROPAGATING MODES USED IN THE ARCTIC AND GEOPHYSICAL
PARAMETERS THAT MAY INFLUENCE THE PROPAGATING WAVE

Propagating mode	Earth's Surface		Ionosphere	Troposphere
	near antenna	along path		
Ground wave	x	x		
Sky wave	x		x	
Earth-ionosphere duct	x	x	x	
Ionospheric scatter			x	
Tropospheric scatter				x
Auroral scatter			x	
Meteor scatter			x	
Space wave				*
between elevated points				*
airborne relay				*
satellite relay			x	*
reflection (passive relay)				*
refraction (mountain type)		x		*

* Only at some frequencies

Table 2

TYPES OF PROPAGATION AND FREQUENCY RANGES USEFUL IN
THE ARCTIC FOR VARIOUS PATH LENGTHS

Path Lengths (miles)	Propagation Modes	Frequency Ranges
1 to 5	ground wave (surface)	MF, HF
	direct (line of site)	VHF, UHF
5 to 50	ground wave (surface)	MF, HF
	point to point and refraction	VHF, UHF
50 to 500	ground wave (surface)	LF
	sky wave	LF, HF
	tropo-scatter	UHF
	iono-scatter	VHF
	line of site (with relay)	VHF, UHF, SHF
500 to 5,000	ducted wave	VLF, LF
	sky wave	LF, HF
	auroral scatter	HF, VHF
	meteor scatter	VHF
	line of site (satellite relay)	UHF, SHF

Table 3

FREQUENCIES AND THEIR USES

Longline: (Open wire line or multiple pair cable)	Very short inter-building and inter-site (less than 10 miles)
Very Low Frequency: (3 to 30 kHz)	Standard frequency measurements WWVL 20 kHz, Boulder
Low Frequency: (30 to 300 kHz)	Radio beacons; radionavigation WWVB 60 kHz, Boulder
Medium Frequency: (300 to 3,000 kHz)	Radionavigation; station-to-station mobile
High Frequency: (3 to 30 mHz)	Long-distance skip; station-to-station mobile; distress, emergency
Very High Frequency: (30 to 300 mHz)	Ionospheric scatter; station-to-station mobile; radionavigation
Ultra High Frequency: (300 to 2,000 mHz)	Tropospheric scatter; station-to-station mobile; microwave
Super High Frequency: (3 to 30 gHz)	Milimeter wave

LF systems are used for both broadcast and point-to-point communications and also for navigation in the Arctic. The very low conductivity of some of the land considerably modifies the design procedures for antenna installations as well as the overall system design. Although in many cases the low-conductivity regions present additional problems, very efficient transmitting antenna systems are feasible in spite of the low conductivity at the surface. In addition, there are some advantages to be gained by using horizontal wire antennae of the Beverage type for transmitting and receiving. The horizontal and vertical positioning available with these antennae makes the installation relatively economical in many cases. Low-frequency systems also have a low data rate of 100 to 500 words a minute. The transmitting antenna installations can be large (330 to 1,300 ft high). Fortunately the receiving antennae can be small (less than 3 ft high), although in some cases Beverage receiving antennae over a mile long are employed.

At LF, the propagation mode involved is primarily the ground wave or a combination of ground and sky waves. Typical ground-wave curves show that the fields produced for ice-cap paths are very highly attenuated compared with fields over seawater. In addition, when sky-wave propagation is involved, the conductivity for a few wave lengths in the foreground of the antenna can become very important. This factor must be very carefully considered in the design of any LF system in the Arctic. At present there are installations where a relocation of several miles would increase the effective radiated power for the sky-wave paths involved by factors of 10 to 20 db. Typical transmitter powers range from 10 to 50 kW with useful path lengths ranging from 150 to 1,500 mi. Ionospheric disturbances that frequently interrupt normal HF communications in the Arctic have very little effect upon LF and, in fact, in the lower portion of this band the field strength may actually be enhanced during such disturbed periods.

The MF portion of the frequency spectrum is of limited usefulness in the Arctic because of the rapid attenuation of the ground-wave mode as well as the high attenuations on reflections from the ionosphere. The upper portion of the MF band is useful during undisturbed nighttime conditions and can also be employed for communications along paths that are primarily over seawater. The MF band has the advantage over VLF and LF bands in that the transmitting antennae are much smaller and the atmospheric noise levels are lower. The ranges available, however, are also considerably smaller; but for some short paths, usually 60 mi or less, MF systems may be the most economical solution. There are some short-range mobile systems operating in this band. Other uses include navigation systems such as A-N beacons and LORAN.

At high frequencies, it is possible to obtain good communications over long distance (up to several thousand miles under good conditions) with much lower transmitter powers than at the lower frequencies. The antennae required are relatively small (about 6 to 65 ft long), and very simple configurations are useful. For seawater paths, the ground-wave propagation mode provides useful communication for up to several hundred miles. Over poor arctic soil or ice caps, the useful range is much less - in some cases less than 6 mi. The sky-wave mode, useful in the region from 60 to 1,000 mi, makes use of ionospheric reflections from the E and F layers. In this frequency band, an appreciable amount of sky-wave energy is absorbed as the rays traverse the D layer. Since this absorbing layer has to be traversed twice for each sky-wave hop and the absorption for each traverse becomes quite high in polar regions, HF communication links are highly susceptible to blackouts due to auroral and other corpuscular-associated ionospheric disturbances. Since this type of attenuation decreases with increasing frequency, it is usually desirable to use as high a frequency as will effectively be reflected from the E or F layer under disturbed conditions.

The sky-wave mode also suffers two additional disadvantages. First, multi-path scattering, particularly that occurring during aurorae, can result in severe fading with rates roughly proportional to frequency. The rather large time delays can be so severe as to make voice signals unintelligible. Second, depending upon ionospheric conditions and the length of the path, the radio wave may penetrate the E and F layers completely instead of being reflected. This tends to limit operations to that part of the HF band below about 15 mHz. The upper limit of 15 mHz can be exceeded a large percentage of the time over transmission paths to the south. Occasionally, particularly during the summer months, sporadic-E propagation permits the use of higher-than-normal frequencies. This is often the case during ionospheric disturbances. The maximum usable frequency will depend, of course, on the time of day, the season, the terminal locations, and the phase of the sunspot cycle. Contrary to conditions at VLF, where the atmospheric noise levels are rather low, the antenna noise levels in the Arctic can be high, primarily because of cosmic radio noise that has penetrated the ionosphere, although in some cases atmospherics and manmade transmissions from distant stations may be the limiting factor.

The rather simple installations required, the low radiated powers and appreciable bandwidth (typically several Hz), and the wide range of path lengths that can be employed make HF systems a fairly useful means of communication in the Arctic. The disadvantages include frequent communication failures that are due to excessive absorption, multi-path, or maximum usable frequency failure. The possible means of reducing these failures include: (1) decreasing the receiver bandwidth at the expense of the data rate, possibly causing frequency stability problems; (2) using vertical polarization which would be significant, however, only for frequencies at or near the gyro-frequency, i.e. between 1 and 3 mHz; (3) using care in the selection of frequencies; (4) careful siting of antennae to permit high-conductivity paths where possible for short ranges, or launching over a short section of high-conductivity soil; (5) using receivers with very low noise figures; and (6) using SSB modulation for voice and data systems.

The application of real-time propagation information operationally to communications circuits by oblique-incidence ionospheric sounding of the transmission path removes the unknown variable from high-frequency propagation. In general, where a choice of operating frequencies is available, it is preferable to use the highest frequency during blackout or near-blackout conditions. This is due to the (approximately) inverse frequency-squared dependence of the ionospheric absorption, which causes the lower portion of the HF band to be more highly absorbed than the higher portion. Maximum usable frequencies tend to be increased in the Arctic during disturbances, and for this reason it may be beneficial to try a higher frequency at times when a lower frequency has failed during disturbed conditions.

For radio communications a technique of forecasting disturbed ionospheric conditions by electronic computer has been developed and tested and should become operational within the next few years. However, the relationship of sunspot activity to magnetic storms and the usual orderly development of the storms makes it possible to forecast the quality of radio propagation with reasonable accuracy. Short-term radio propagation forecasts are broadcast on each of the standard radio carrier frequencies of WWV (at 19.5 and 49.5

minutes past each hour) and WWVH (at 9.4 and 39.4 minutes past each hour).
Those forecasts (at 1700 and 2300 GMT for WWV; 0600 and 1800 GMT for WWVH)
predict communication conditions expected for the succeeding six or more
hours. The WWV announcement is for the North Atlantic region and the WWVH
announcement is for the North Pacific. In the near future it may be possible to establish a mathematical model of the arctic ionosphere which will
permit still better forecasts.

A type of propagating mode called ionospheric scatter makes use of
scattering by irregularities in the ionized D region. The effective
forward-scattering coefficient at VHF is quite low and such systems require large directional antennae and powerful transmitters. For this
reason, ionospheric forward-scattering is not an effective communication
system for small mobile groups or ships. Its advantages include long path
lengths - roughly up to about 1,000 mi - and a number of data links. Because both absorption and scatter are critically dependent upon frequency,
the optimum frequency range in the Arctic is fairly narrow and lies somewhere between 50 and 70 mHz. Because of the rather high cost and inflex-
ibility of such systems, their use is quite limited. VHF propagation may
also involve the scattering of radio waves from meteor trails. In this
technique, transmitters operate continuously on closely spaced frequencies
at each end of the circuit until a trail of meteor ionization occurs with
a position and orientation that permit a predetermined energy level to be
exceeded at the receiving terminal. The receipt of such a signal is used
as an indication that good propagation is available, and the message is
immediately transmitted at high speed until the adjoining receiver shows
that the propagation mode has faded below some preset level. This intermittent communication system has the advantage of lower radiated power
requirements than the standard ionospheric forward-scatter system. Also,
because of the character of the propagation, it is relatively private.
Path lengths of up to 1,200 mi may be used. It has been found that, like
the VHF ionospheric forward-scatter mode, meteor-burst communication links
are much less affected by high-latitude ionospheric disturbances than are
HF communication links.

Both types of VHF ionospheric scatter can be disturbed by the major
polar cap events. Such events have occurred several times each year during
sunspot maxima and are likely to cause severe attenuation or even complete
failure of the link during daylight hours for periods of up to two to four
days. The obvious defect of meteor-burst communication systems is the intermittent nature of the propagation path. The delay time is dependent
upon the sensitivity of the system which is a function of the operating frequency, the radiated power, the bandwidth, and the sensitivity of the receiving system. Under some circumstances, when instantaneous communication
is not required, meteor-burst communication is acceptable.

Another form of VHF communications employs the direct or space wave
with some intermediated high-elevation relay - an airborne relay, passive
reflectors, or diffraction over a mountain or mountain range. The last
mode is, of course, subject to multi-path and to some tropospheric fading,
and its bandwidth capacity is limited to a few hertz. It is relatively
little-used except under unique circumstances, such as when a high mountain is surrounded by a large plain. The airborne relay is useful for
distances of up to 300 mi. A suitably located aircraft can be used for
short-term relay work to provide communications along a very broad band
with rather low ambient noise levels. When high-gain antennae are used
on the ground, the transmitter power requirements are fairly low.

One additional method of arctic VHF propagation is scatter from auroral ionization. This form of scatter decreases rapidly in intensity with increasing frequency; even so, the high frequency of 3,000 mHz has been observed. As a communication technique it has numerous disadvantages, primarily those of a rapid fade rate and a very intermittent and unpredictable occurrence of the propagation mode. Under certain conditions, in the lower portion of the VHF band (30 to 60 mHz), quite strong auroral-scatter signals can be expected during ionospheric disturbances and then such a propagation mode can be of particular value as a HF circuit back-up. Any such link must take into account the pronounced directional sensitivity and limited height of the auroral ionization. Such ionization tends to act rather like a metallic mirror inclined parallel to the magnetic field lines and is most common at heights of about 60 miles. In general, east-west propagation in the Arctic would be via auroral forms to the north of the midpoint. North-south auroral-scatter propagation would involve scatter from auroral ionization several hundred miles to the north of the northern station. In other words, for north-south auroral-scatter modes, both antennae should be directed northward at low angles of elevation toward a common scattering column in which the line of sight is approximately perpendicular to the earth's magnetic field lines.

UHF frequencies are useful for short-range line-of-sight systems where the antennae are small and the powers low enough that mobile or hand-carried equipment can be employed. For conditions where the line of sight does not obtain between the transmitter and receiver terminals, it is possible to use some type of relay mode, such as passive reflectors, mountain diffraction, airborne relays, and satellite relays. Most of these modes, with the possible exception of mountain diffraction, have very wide bandwidth capabilities. At the greater ranges directional antennae are usually employed, but for moderate gains, their size fortunately is not great.

An additional useful type of propagation mode in this frequency range is tropospheric scatter, which has found wide application in the Arctic. When properly engineered, such systems are very reliable, are not subject to failure because of ionospheric disturbances, and may have an unusually wide bandwidth capacity (up to a few megahertz) depending upon the system parameters. The major disadvantage is the high cost of the large antennae and powerful transmitters needed to overcome the rather high losses of the tropo-scattering mode.

Although it is possible to use the SHF region for short-range direct and line-of-sight communications, it is usually more economical to use VHF or UHF systems for such applications. The primary present-day application for SHF is in satellite relays although some of the satellite systems are also active in the UHF region. In the future, however, use of SHF may expand vastly, as it offers the broadest bandwidth yet to accommodate the proliferating need.

Bibliography

Bean, B.R., B.A. Cahoon, C.A. Samson, and G.D. Thayer, 1966. *A World Atlas of Atmospheric Radio Refractivity*. Washington, D.C.: Government Printing Office. ESSA Monograph 1. 130 pp.

Blacker, H.L., ed., 1971. *Conference Record,* IEEE International Conf. on
     Comm's. (1971). New York: The Institute of Electrical and Electron-
     ics Engineers, Inc. 1,116 pp.

Buchau, J., E.W. Pettinger, and A.H. Sizoo, 1970. *Arctic Ionosphere and
     Aurora: Airborne Investigations.* Bedford, Mass.: Air Force Cambridge
     Research Laboratories. Report AFCRL-70-0280. 60 pp.

Grassman, G.J., 1970. *An Ionospheric Model for the Arctic.* Bedford, Mass.:
     Air Force Cambridge Research Laboratories. Report AFCRL-70-0562.
     15 pp.

Landmark, B., ed., 1964. *Arctic Communications.* New York: Macmillan.
     297 pp.

Watt, A.D., 1967. *VLF Radio Engineering.* Oxford: Pergamon Press. 703 pp.

Sea Ice

Physical Properties

Sea ice is the dominant element in surface operations in the Arctic Basin. Its presence or absence determines the areas where conventional shipping may operate, and the nature of its upper surface limits the types of airborne vehicles which may land on it. The properties of sea ice are derived initially from the presence of dissolved salts in seawaters. The composition of these salts is sufficiently uniform throughout the world's oceans that it can be described by a single parameter known as the salinity (S). Salinity is the weight of the salts contained in 1 kilogram of seawater expressed as grams per kilogram (^{o}/oo) and varies from 36°/oo or more in tropical waters to 31°/oo or less in arctic waters.

Pure water reaches its maximum density at 39.2^{o}F and expands on further cooling. The effect of this inversion in density on the formation of an ice cover over fresh water is well known. For seawater, both the freezing temperature and the inversion temperature decrease linearly with increasing salinity, until at a salinity of 24.7^o/oo each of these temperatures is equal to 29.7^{o}F. This critical salinity may conveniently be taken as the division between brackish water and true seawater. Seawater in the Arctic usually has a salinity at the surface of between 28 and 32°/00, and it freezes at about 29°F. This is well below the critical salinity and temperature so that the density of arctic seawater increases continually with decreasing temperature down to the onset of freezing. As a result, a seawater column of uniform salinity, cooled from the top, will develop a vertical circulation so that the entire column must cool to the freezing point before freezing begins. The column of uniform salinity may extend to the bottom of the sea or may terminate at a thermocline or halocline where a denser layer underlies the surface water. As an example, in the fall following the summer melt period, the surface water is of low salinity and will begin to freeze without turnover to any appreciable depth. As the freezing continues, the surface waters are enriched in salt, and turnover penetrates to greater depths, reaching 160 ft by the end of winter over most of the Arctic Basin. Immediately after open water begins to freeze, there is usually a rapid buildup of the first foot or so of ice. This occurs because ice reflects the incoming radiation better than water but, at the same time, continues to emit radiant energy with about the same efficiency as water so that the net heat loss is initially rapid. Both the temperature of the ice surface and that of the overlying air drop rapidly. As the ice cover thickens, its own low thermal conductivity, together with any snow cover that may accrue, slows the rate of heat loss from the sea and limits the thickness reached.

The crystal structure of ice is intolerant of impurities such as the inorganic salts which make up most of the dissolved material in seawater. If seawater is frozen very slowly, the result is a layer of pure ice from which the impurities have been rejected into the seawater below it. Natural freezing is never this slow, however, and sea ice always contains a certain amount of entrapped salts. The actual amount is dependent upon the freezing rate, but new sea ice generally has a salinity of 4 to 6°/oo. Thus freezing of seawater in nature is a refining process with about 80 to 90% of the salts being excluded from the ice cover.

The presence of the salt in sea ice is of such importance that the physical properties of sea ice are almost entirely determined by the salt content. The peculiar structure which results dominates the physical parameters to the extent that one can relate any of them to brine volume with little regard to the properties of pure ice, except in the limiting case where the brine volume is equal to zero. Brine volume is defined as that portion of the volume of sea ice occupied by fluid, either liquid brine or air bubbles.

It is known that the atoms in ice are arranged with hexagonal symmetry. This atomic-scale symmetry appears microscopically in the hexagonal pattern of most snowflakes. The unit cell is in the form of a prism whose cross section is a regular hexagon which has one main axis of symmetry along the length of the prism. This is known as the c-axis and any plane perpendicular to this axis is called a basal plane. Frazil ice is a single crystal with its c-axis accurately perpendicular to its areal extent. From this we deduce that ice growth is much more rapid along a basal plane than along the c-axis.

When seawater is cooled to its freezing point and more heat is then removed, the initial ice forms in very thin disks or platelets known as frazil ice. On the average, these platelets are about 1 in. wide and about 0.02 in. thick. Their shapes vary considerably, ranging from hexagonal dendrites through irregular shapes to almost square. Frazil ice generation is not confined to the surface but may occur anywhere within the top few inches of water. The frazil crystals are pure ice so they float to the surface and form a slush which gives the water a slightly oily appearance. With continued cooling, the crystals consolidate into a solid but extraordinarily flexible surface ice cover about one inch thick. The bow wave of a ship may cause transverse waves in this cover which will not fracture the ice until an amplitude of several inches is exceeded.

When frazil ice first forms, if there is no wind or current, each crystal will float to the surface and lie with its c-axis vertical because of buoyancy. Such conditions are rare in nature, and normally the frazil crystals are jammed together by wind and waves so that the first crust is consolidated from masses of frazil crystals with a great variety of orientations. As growth continues, the frazil particles act as seed crystals and some of them grow. The growth potential of an ice crystal depends critically on the angle between its c-axis and the vertical. The larger this angle, the more rapid the growth of the crystal. This geometrical selection results in the bulk of a sea ice cover consisting of crystals with nearly horizontal c-axes.

A single crystal of sea ice is defined as one which shows a uniform brightness in polarized light. A crystal has a pronounced internal structure and consists of a large number of thin parallel platelets of pure ice separated by rows of cells of liquid brine. Typical platelet thickness and brine cell diameter are of the order of 0.02 and 0.002 in. respectively. Each platelet may be an inch or more in length. The platelets grow downward into the water and thicken near the ice cover. When the brine film separating the platelets becomes thin enough, surface tension causes it to break into individual vertical columns interrupted by ice bridges linking the platelets. The sea ice thus solidifies into a compact mass threaded through by very large numbers of brine cells. Almost all the brine entrapped in sea ice is situated in these brine cells within crystals.

The average salinity of the oceans is about $35^{\circ}/oo$ which is taken as the "standard" salinity of seawater. The three principal dissolved salts in the order of their concentration are NaCl ($23.48^{\circ}/oo$), $MgCl_2$ ($4.98^{\circ}/oo$), and Na_2SO_4 ($3.92^{\circ}/oo$). The phase diagram of seawater below its normal freezing point is quite accurately known down to a temperature of -13 to $-22^{\circ}F$. At any given temperature there is a unique salinity at which ice and brine can remain in equilibrium with each other. This is the freezing point for this brine. Thus, ice at $28.6^{\circ}F$ can remain in equilibrium with standard seawater, the amount of ice neither increasing nor decreasing with time. When seawater trapped in ice is cooled, in the range from its freezing point down to $17.3^{\circ}F$, all of the salt is in solution in the brine. At $17.3^{\circ}F$ sodium sulfate starts to precipitate as a hydrated solid, $Na_2SO_4 \cdot 10$ H_2O. On further cooling, the amount of precipitated sodium sulfate increases, but no other salt is precipitated until a temperature of $-9.2^{\circ}F$ is reached. This temperature marks the onset of precipitation of solid $NaCl \cdot 2H_2O$ and the apparent initiation of ice strength reinforcement by this solid salt. Below $-9.4^{\circ}F$ the characteristics of sea ice change notably - the ice is whitish because of the sodium chloride crystals, more brittle but harder to drill or chisel, and significantly stronger.

Ice is a visco-elastic material that flows readily under sustained stress, so that its strength varies with the rate of stress application. The following discussion of the various ultimate strengths is valid only for a rapid application of stress. Experimentally it is found that ice strengths appear to be independent of stress rate for loads applied at rates greater than approximately 3 $lb/in^2/sec$. The table shows the average results obtained at $23^{\circ}F$ for such loads on freshwater ice samples with a minimum dimension of 2 inches (test samples smaller than this tend to give higher values). The word *average* must be emphasized. Individual test results may easily differ from these averages by a factor of two or even three. Although interest here is with sea ice, the table can serve as a basis for discussing the corresponding strength in sea ice, which cannot be tabulated in this way because of the dependence on brine volume. The most extensively studied property is the ultimate tensile strength, and the commonest measurement is the ring-tensile test in which a hollow cylinder of ice is broken by a load applied along the full length of the cylinder in a direction perpendicular to its axis. As a result of this load the cylinder fails in tension. The maximum tensile stress in this test is applied to a very small volume of ice, and the results observed are appreciably higher than those obtained by the conventional "simple" tensile tests. However, because of the convenience of the test it lends itself to mass production, and a very large number of tests have been made by a considerable number of observers. In general the values are in good agreement with the comparable value for sea ice.

Ultimate Strengths of Freshwater Ice
(lb/in^2)

Unconfined Compression	Shear	Tension		Flexure	
		Simple	Ring	Small beam	*In situ* beams and cantilevers
210	90	102	174	102	42

Two other principal experimental methods have been used. In the first, small ice beams (typically 20x3x3 inches) are sawn from the ice and, with their ends freely supported, are broken in flexure. The figure of 102 lb/in^2 for the flexural strength of pure ice comes from these tests. A number of large-scale, in-place cantilever beam tests have also been made. For such a test three vertical cuts are made through the ice cover, thereby leaving a rectangular beam of ice, still attached at its base to the cover but otherwise floating freely. The beam is then broken by pushing down or pulling up on the free end. Such a test, at first sight, seems ideal for determining the actual flexural strength and hence bearing capacity of an ice cover because there is a minimum disturbance of the temperature and salinity profiles of the ice and the effect of buoyancy is automatically included in the depression tests. There are difficulties, however. In theory, bending a cantilever beam produces stress concentrations in the fixed end. Fortunately, comparisons of *in situ* cantilevers with *in situ* simple beams suggest that the actual stress concentration is about 10% or less. Also the shape of the ice beam, particularly in thick ice, is far from the theoretical ideal (of width much greater than thickness), so that uncertainties enter into the calculations. The results of such tests always show much lower strength values than ring-tensile or small-beam tests, typically about 12 to 30 lb/in^2.

Unconfined compression and shear tests on sea ice are much less numerous than tensile or flexural tests. In general, the strength decreases with increasing salinity or temperature of the ice, although data are sparse. In the light of present knowledge the best estimate is that any ultimate strength of sea ice should be calculated from the equation
$$\sigma = \sigma_0 \ (1 - 1.9v)$$
using the appropriate value from the table for σ_0. When calculating the bearing capacity of an ice cover, the σ_0 determined from *in situ* beam and cantilever tests should be used. A safety factor should also be added by the person making the calculation.

The response of ice to a periodic force with a frequency greater than one cycle per second is elastic, provided, of course, that crushing does not occur. Sound transmissions, responses to moving vehicles, and impacts resulting from aircraft landings all fall within this category. Deflections caused by parked vehicles or aircraft do *not*. Almost the only reproducible values for Young's modulus E are found from seismic and acoustic measurements. On the basis of small-sample tests the best approximation is
$$E = (1.02 - 3.56v) \times 1.32 \times 10^6 \ \text{lb/in}^2$$
where v is the fractional brine volume. Less is known about Poisson's ratio, but it appears to be essentially constant for sea ice over a wide range of values of v, with a value $\mu \sim 0.30$.

Ice subjected to a steady or slowly varying load flows plastically. This plastic flow has been studied extensively in connection with glaciers, but few data are available for sea ice. The most practical problem - that of parking or storing heavy loads on an ice cover - can as yet be handled only empirically. As an example, if the ice surface temperature is 14°F a thickness of 3 ft of sea ice is considered safe for parking of a DC-3 aircraft of about 25,000 lb weight. At this thickness the ice cover does flow slightly, i.e. it sags, but over such a large surface area that the increased buoyant force of the seawater supports the load. Caution must be exercised nevertheless.

Seismic methods can be used to measure the average thickness of an ice cover if E is known. A detonation at or above the ice surface generates several types of wave including an air-coupled flexural wave whose frequency is inversely proportional to the ice thickness. This wave can be used to measure the ice thickness from the air. A second method of making this measurement from the air, by electromagnetic waves, is under study by several groups. Considerable success has been achieved in measuring the thicknesses of glaciers and ice caps, but so far it has not been possible to obtain a satisfactory reflection from the interface of the sea ice and seawater.

Since sea ice in its natural state always contains cells of liquid brine, any change in the temperature of the ice will result in a phase change in a portion of the ice, either from water to ice or ice to water, depending on the sign of the temperature variation. For this reason the concepts of latent and specific heats are closely interrelated, and in reality a definite latent heat of fusion cannot be established since the phase change from solid to liquid is a continuous process. The quantity of heat required to raise the temperature of a given amount of sea ice is always greater than that needed to raise the temperature by the same amount of an equal mass of pure ice. While the difference is small for ice of low salinity at temperatures below $14^{\circ}F$, the specific heat of sea ice rises rapidly as the melting point is approached, especially as the salinity increases. Because the thermal properties of sea ice are controlled primarily by its salinity and because the salt content depends principally on the rate of freezing, the phase change from sea ice to seawater is not thermodynamically reversible. Consequently, if a sample of sea ice is melted and then cooled to its original temperature, there is very little chance that it will retain its original saline and thermal properties.

Pure ice has an essentially constant specific heat of 0.50 in the range 32 to $14^{\circ}F$, but the specific heat of sea ice rises very rapidly with increasing temperature, becoming infinite at the melting point. Consequently it is necessary to integrate the specific heat from any desired temperature up to the melting point to obtain the quantity of heat needed to melt sea ice. Another useful quantity is the latent heat of freezing, L_S. This is the quantity of heat which must be removed from unit mass of seawater of salinity S to produce sea ice of salinity σ. The empirical equation, which can also be justified theoretically, is

$$L_S = (1 - \frac{\sigma}{S}) L_i$$

where L_i is the latent heat of pure ice (about 80 cal/gm). The other important thermal property of sea ice is its thermal conductivity, k. Because of the brine, k is always smaller for sea ice than for freshwater ice but it approaches the value for the latter at a temperature of +5 to $-4^{\circ}F$. Either form of ice is a poor heat conductor, as can be seen in the relative thinness of ice covers on water.

Nowhere does the dominant role of the brine in sea ice show more strikingly than in the peculiar electrical behavior of this material. The first systematic observations of dielectric properties and electrical conductivity have appeared in the last few years. For sea ice of salinity $10^{\circ}/oo$ at a temperature of $-7.6^{\circ}F$, the dielectric coefficient is extremely large (of the order 10^6) at 20 Hz. It decreases approximately as the reciprocal of the frequency in the audio range and more slowly above 100 kHz, reaching a value of about 10 or less at 50 mHz. The effective electrical conductivity over the same range increases slowly with frequency, from about 8 micro-ohms/in at 20 Hz to about 80 at 50 mHz.

Sea ice transmits acoustic energy readily, particularly at low audio frequencies. Furthermore, the skeleton-layer structure below an ice sheet helps match the acoustic impedances of sea ice and seawater so that little reflection occurs at the sea ice-water interface. This has been used to permit bathymetric observations through an ice cover. If a flat transducer of a conventional echo sounder is bonded to the surface of sea ice with a thin film of a non-freezing liquid, acoustic power can be transmitted through the ice with little attenuation and with the only significant reflection occurring at the bottom of the water. In one test, the frequency used was 37 kHz. Actual data on the acoustic absorption in sea ice are sparse. Other studies suggest that the attenuation rises from a negligible value at 20 kHz to about 5 or 6 db/m at 100 kHz. An abrupt increase in attenuation occurs between 100 and 200 kHz. This is to be expected since the longitudinal wave velocity in sea ice is about 2 mi/sec, corresponding to a wave length of 2 cm at 175 kHz. This is just about the mean minimum dimension of sea ice crystals, and the attenuation would be expected to be much larger for wave lengths equal to or less than the size of the obstructions. Above 200 kHz a typical attenuation coefficient is of the order of 50 to 60 db/m.

The complete annual cycle of a cover of sea ice, restricted here to a discussion of a shorefast ice cover which remains in place throughout its history, is of value. The maximum thickness of ice in a given locality is quite constant from season to season. The first attempt to relate ice thickness to the temperature regimen of a particular area was made in 1891. The analysis showed that

$$h = \left[\frac{2k}{L_s p} \cdot E_t \right]^{1/2}$$

where h is the thickness of the ice cover with density p, L_s the latent heat of freezing of salt water of salinity S, and E_t the freezing exposure in the accumulated degree-days of ice surface temperature below the freezing point of seawater. This analysis has several weaknesses in that it ignores the specific heat of the ice, which cools after it is formed and thereby releases a considerable amount of heat, and it is based on the generally unknown surface temperature of the ice. In practice it is generally necessary to use the air temperature, which may be considerably lower than the ice temperature because of the insulating effect of snow cover and other parameters. Nevertheless, the equation works well. If E_t is calculated using air temperatures h is usually found to vary quite closely with $\sqrt{E_t}$, and most forecasts of ice thickness are based on climatological records and a modification of the equation. The simplest modification is to substitute an empirical coefficient for the theoretical coefficient E_t. The appropriate coefficient depends on the area of the world in question and reflects the prevailing local conditions such as snow cover. A number of suggested coefficients have been computed.

A more valid but more difficult approach to the problem of ice growth and decay is to study the micrometeorology of the sea ice-air boundary and to attempt to measure the quantities of heat transferred across this boundary. Many such studies have been made; and one interesting conclusion is that, in the Arctic at least, radiation is the almost completely dominant factor in determining the ice surface temperature. The ice cover will continue to grow until some time in spring when the increasing value of incoming solar radiation changes the heat budget of the ice cover to positive - that is, it starts to gain heat from above rather than lose it. This usually happens before the air temperature rises above the melting point of the snow cover. Pure white snow will reflect as much as 90% of the radiation incident on it, and the quantity of heat absorbed by the snow and ice cover is at first quite small but does have the effect of modifying the crystal structure of the snow cover and of starting to raise the temperature of the ice. After a few weeks the air temperature reaches the melting point and the snow surface suffers an abrupt drop in albedo, to about 40%. The result is particularly dramatic in the high Arctic where at this season the sun is above the horizon 24 hours a day and the sky is normally cloudless in the spring. As a consequence of the large amount of incident radiation and the high percentage of absorption, the snow cover melts rapidly (usually in one day or less) producing a "flash" flood. To be caught on the ice at this time is unpleasant, although the ice cover itself is still intact and strong.

The next stage is the deterioration of the ice cover. The heat absorbed gradually raises the temperature of the ice cover to the melting point, and flaws and cracks develop through which much of the surface water drains away, leaving dry hummocks of white ice separated by ponds and streams of water. When the ice has this appearance, operations on it must be carried out with caution. The bearing strength is uncertain and a strong wind may cause it to break into floes of various sizes.

In sufficiently low latitudes, the floes finally melt and the cycle is completed. Farther north the summer is too brief for complete melting to take place, and by late August or September the ice floes start to grow again. A floe formed in one year which has survived the following summer differs chemically and physically from ice that is less than one year old. Over the course of a year, most of the salt drains out of sea ice so that the typical salinity pf perennial or polar ice (more than one year old) is about 0.5 to $1^o/oo$. Thus melted polar ice is quite potable. The crystal structure of polar ice (particularly when several years old) is less regular than that of annual ice. Polar ice crystals are smaller and somewhat more rounded, and their c-axes are no longer uniformly horizontal. The most important result is that polar ice is extraordinarily resilliant. Standard icebreakers would experience extreme difficulty in attempting to "break" polar floes, even in summer. It can be done, but there is an excellent chance of breaking the plating on the icebreaker as well.

In summer, polar floes may be distinguished from annual ice by their color. The meltwater pools on a polar floe have a characteristic pale blue color which persists after the pools freeze. Annual ice is generally grey in summer. Also, annual ice is comparatively smooth, except perhaps for occasional remnants of pressure ridges, while polar ice typically has a hummocky appearance with gently rounded hummocks, each approximately 3 ft in height, spaced at intervals of about 100 to 150 ft. The origin of this relief is the difference between the high albedo of white ice and the low albedo of meltwater pools. Differential melting increases the height contrast each year. Polar floes vary considerably in thickness but have an equilibrium value of about 10 ft in the Arctic Ocean. Each summer about 3 ft of the surface melts and drains off, and each winter about 3 ft freezes onto the bottom.

Occurrence and Classification

Sea ice rarely forms in the open ocean below 60^oN but is important in more enclosed bays, rivers, and seas farther south, such as Hudson Bay, the

Gulf of St. Lawrence, and the Sea of Okhotsk. It may also drift south from
higher latitudes. Between about 60°N and 75°N, the occurrence of sea ice
is a seasonal matter; and there is usually a period during the year when the
water is ice-free. Above 75°N there is a more or less permanent ice cover.
It must be recognized that generalizations such as these are subject to
modifications because of local conditions and seasonal variations. As an
example, the Parry Channel (Northwest Passage) cuts through the Canadian Arctic Archipelago at 74 to 75°N. Its eastern end is usually ice-free for 3
to 5 weeks each summer. Its western end is almost invariably ten-tenths
covered with ice the year around, partly because of drifting Arctic Ocean
ice entering through M'Clure Strait and partly due to local ice. Other examples of waters which are nearly ice-free at some season of the year are
Davis Strait and Baffin Bay, the Norwegian Sea, and the near-shore portion
of the Barents, Beaufort, Kara, and Laptev seas. The Arctic Ocean is never
totally ice-covered. One estimate, based on infrared temperature measurements is that even during winter as much as 10% of the area of the ocean
is either open water or a thin ice cover over refreezing leads.

Most northern countries have developed elaborate terminology and codes
for reporting sea ice. The World Meteorological Organization has attempted,
without complete success, to standardize the terminology. Most of the terms
defined below are in fairly general use. Sea ice is classified by age into
young ice (less than 6 inches thick), annual or 1-year ice, and perennial
or polar ice. The size of unbroken pieces determine its classification into
ice fields (more than 1 mi across), ice floes (33 ft to 1 mi across), ice
cakes (6 to 33 ft across), and brash (pieces less than 6 ft in diameter).
Other terms relate to the nature of the surface which may be smooth, ridged
(when ice pressure has forced ice to buckle upward), or rafted (when one
floe has overridden another). Few of the terms above relate specifically
to thickness. Some orders of magnitude for typical regions may be useful.
The average maximum thicknesses of unbroken, unrafted floes are as follows:
approximately 6 ft in Parry Channel; approximately 8 ft in the northern
Canadian archipelago; approximately 10 ft in the Arctic Ocean; and approximately 6 ft in Eurasian arctic seas.

Pressure ridges and rafted ice may be much thicker than these typical
figures. There are few accurate data on the height and frequency of pressure ridges, but in the Arctic Ocean heights of 26 to 33 ft are occasionally
seen and heights of 13 to 16 ft above the average ice surface are common.
To date it has not been possible to determine a roughness coefficient, although the work undertaken by Project AIDJEX should produce many valuable
insights. The number of pressure ridges per mile may vary from zero to 60
or more. Because of its density, uniform sea ice floats with 87% of its
volume below sea level. When a pressure ridge is formed it tends to sag
or slump because of the plasticity of ice. Hydrostatic equilibrium would
be reached when 87% of its volume was below water level. Thus, at equilibrium a ridge reaching 13 ft above the water surface should extend 85 ft below the surface. Pack ice is usually too active for equilibrium to be
reached but submarine observations show that the bottom relief is similar
to that of the top surface except that it is magnified in scale by a factor
of 3 to 5.

The date on which freeze-up commences depends on both the oceanographic
and meteorologic regimens encountered in an area, but only rarely is the
knowledge of ocean dynamics in a particular region extensive enough to forecast the values of the relevant parameters accurately. Consequently, in
important areas, it is the practice to dispatch a ship in the fall to take

a number of oceanographic stations to determine the depth of the thermocline
(if any) and the temperature and salinity profiles above it. From these
data may be calculated the quantity of heat per unit area which must be removed for ice to form. The climatological records of the area together with
theories on the rate of heat transfer from the ocean to the atmosphere are
then used to forecast the date of freeze-up. This is the ice potential
method introduced by Zubov in 1938.

While it is possible to forecast with fair accuracy the thickness at
any time after freeze-up and the maximum thickness which will be attained,
it is much more difficult to predict the rate at which ice will decay,
break up into floes, and melt. In most areas affected by sea ice, the earliest date at which a ship can navigate safely varies greatly from year to
year as well as from place to place. The approximate opening and closing
dates of some arctic ports for conventional ships with some icebreaker support are:

Ambarchik	Late July to late September
Amderma	Late June to late October
Anadyr	Late June to mid-October
Churchill	Mid-July to late October
Dikson	Early July to mid-October
Dudinka	Mid-July to mid-October
Frobisher	Early August to early October
Igarka	Mid-July to mid-October
Kozhevnikova	Mid-July to early October
Pevek	Mid-July to late September
Provideniya	Late June to mid-October
Pt. Barrow	Early August to mid-October
Resolute	Late July to early October
Tiksi	Mid-July to early October
Thule	Mid-July to early October
Tuktoyaktuk	Mid-July to early October

Icebergs are fragments of ice which originated on land. Their average
size is the largest of that category - in the Arctic they are about as big
as a city block. Smaller fragments are bergy-bits (about the size of a
small cottage) and growlers (about the size of a piano). The greatest number of icebergs in the northern hemisphere is found in Baffin Bay and the
Labrador Sea. Predominantly of irregular shape, they are calved principally
from the glaciers of Greenland and consequently never reach the central portions of the Arctic Ocean; nevertheless they are of considerable importance
because of their movement into the North Atlantic shipping lanes. The principal sources of icebergs within the Arctic Ocean itself are Svalbard,
Zemlya Frantsa Iosifa, Novaya Zemlya, and Severnaya Zemlya, but these bergs
are relatively small in number and size. Their limited frequency and small-
ness is attributed to the size of the parent ice caps characterizing the
Eurasian arctic archipelagos, which are considerably smaller than the Greenland ice sheet, and also to the relative shallowness of the shelves surrounding those archipelagos.

The largest individual pieces of freshwater ice circulating in the central Arctic Ocean itself are tabular bergs known as ice islands. The source
of ice islands is believed to be an ice shelf, or series of ice shelves, off
the northern coast of Ellesmere Island. As recently as 1961-62 the largest
of these, the Ward Hunt Ice Shelf, lost an area of 300 mi^2 by the breaking
away of five large ice islands and a great many fragments. Ice islands

first became known when the USAF identified and followed the drift of three
of them in 1946 and the years following.

Perhaps the most significant characteristics of both kinds of floating
ice are their vast extent and the extreme short- and long-term variability
of their distribution. Mainly on the basis of material contained in the
U.S. Naval Oceanographic Office's atlases, a recent estimate in thousands
of miles of the areal extent and volume of ice of land and sea origin is:

| | Icebergs | | Sea Ice | | Areal extent, ignoring varying concentrations | |
| | Volume | | Volume | | | |
	Maximum	Minimum	Maximum	Minimum	Maximum	Minimum
N. Hemisphere	-	-	8	4	7,000	4,000
S. Hemisphere	-	-	10	2	12,000	6,500
Total	4	3	18	6	19,000	10,000

The maximum and minimum extent of sea ice in the northern hemisphere is
shown on the map in Figure 10. The drift and deformation of ice are primarily determined by the vertical and horizontal transfer of momentum. This
is an area of study that has been neglected, perhaps because of the com-
plexity of the problems to be solved as well as the inadequacies of environmental data coverage. The forces involved in the drift of ice are those
represented by (1) the stress imparted by the wind to the ice-air interface,
(2) the water stress at the water-ice interface, (3) the Coriolis effect,
(4) the pressure-gradient force that is due to the tilting of the sea surface on which the ice floats (or "permanent current" effect), and (5) the
internal ice resistance. The most comprehensive models for sea ice drift
which have been published still do not permit a definite solution. Less
sophisticated and considerably simplified studies are generally used in
formulating practical forecasts of drift and movement. Although displaying
fair reliability, these forecasts do leave much to be desired according to
the few evaluations published to date. In the subjective forecasts, drift
and deformation are expressed as empirically derived functions of the geo-
strophic wind, the isobaric gradient, the permanent currents, the quantity
of ridging in the pack ice, and the concentration of the ice. The last two
parameters are determined from recent aerial observations.

From data obtained by the U.S. Navy's Project BIRD'S EYE it has been
found that the arctic pack ice has no consistent thickness; and this is confirmed by the upward-beamed acoustic data obtained during the 1957 through
1962 under-ice cruises of submarines. The constant fracturing, diverging,
and compacting motions result in a spectrum of thicknesses ranging from a
few inches to more than 15 ft. The data further indicate that the ridges
and hummocks - whose drafts may average 40 ft in the summer and 55 ft in
the longer winter period - contribute significantly to the total ice volume.
Indeed on rare occasions, sea ice ridges may attain a total thickness of
200 ft.

Zones of Open water

Coastal configurations, especially geographic constrictions occurring
in the path of a current or a wind-driven stream of moving ice, profoundly
affect sea ice distribution. The famous North Water, which in mid-winter
occupies an area of up to 14,000 mi^2 is found in northern Baffin Bay and

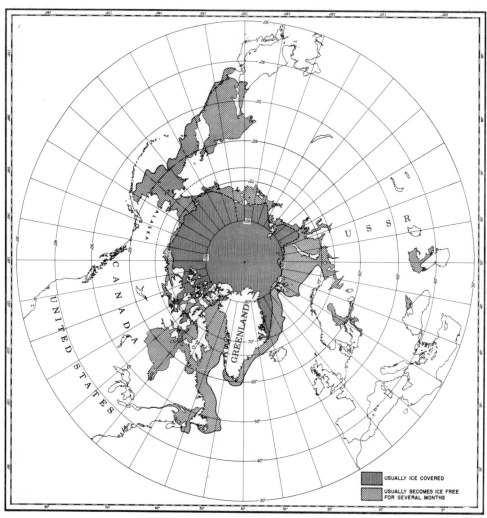

Figure 10. THE MAXIMUM AND MINIMUM EXTENT OF SEA ICE
IN THE NORTHERN HEMISPHERE

Smith Sound. It has long been known by whalers as a prime example of an
area of reduced ice concentration that can occur near arctic coasts or
coastal regions faced with pack ice. Common smaller-scale coastal phenomena
of this type are flaw leads, or zones of navigable size between the fast ice
(ice attached to the shore) and the moving pack ice. Both the flaw leads
and the large-scale zones such as the North Water may be open or covered
with thin ice. They may also contain fragments of thicker drift ice commonly called clutter. These phenomena are not completely understood but
are believed to be caused mainly by coastal configurations and currents.
Tidal openings, however, are also an important contributing cause in regions whose tidal ranges are high or where tidal currents attain a considerable magnitude. Perhaps the waters of Frobisher Bay and Foxe Basin
exemplify most outstandingly the considerable effects of tidal parameters
on ice conditions and behavior.

Reporting and Forecasting

The practical or operational basis for the need to understand sea ice
behavior is the desire for an ability to forecast ice conditions. Three
types of prediction are involved: general climatic predictions of probable
conditions at a given time of year and place, long-term forecasts of conditions at a specific time and place, and short-term operational forecasts.
General climatic predictions are provided by the various available ice
atlases, but the quality of the atlases still suffers from the insufficiency
of accumulated data.

Denmark produced the first annual survey of arctic ice conditions in
1901 and subsequently issued one each year without interruption, except for
the years of World War II, until 1956. Since then she has confined her
interest to the regions surrounding Greenland, where U.S. groups are now
also making visual aerial observations.

The U.S. Naval Oceanographic Office and the Canadian Meteorological
Service have been issuing both long- and short-term ice forecasts for some
years, and they have had considerable success in rather generalized forecasts. The U.S. Navy is continuing aerial surveillance of the Bering,
Chuckchi, and Labrador seas and of Baffin Bay. Canada has an active ice
surveillance program in progress over the waters of the Canadian archipelago
and from the coast of Newfoundland to the Great Lakes. In the Sea of
Okhotsk, the Japanese Hydrographic Office is conducting an aerial observation
program. In addition, the British Meteorological Office summarizes and pub-
lishes hemispheric maps of ice conditions on both a monthly and a shorter-
range basis.

While USSR scientists have produced considerable literature dealing
with the general patterns of drift within the arctic regions as well as
with the theory of ice drift, divergence, and behavior, they have not made
available any regular reports of ice conditions or any systematic data concerning the areal distribution of openings in the ice, pressure-ridges,
degree of melt, or other ice-water features. The USSR conducts an aerial
program in the marginal seas of the Eurasian Arctic and in the central Arctic where it probably overlaps with Project BIRD'S EYE. The USSR's high-
latitude airborne expeditions are of considerable magnitude as a mechanism
for the synoptic collection of sea ice data.

Reconnaissance Techniques

Ice reporting and forecasting techniques have been continually developed in the USSR since the 1930's. In the collection of near-synoptic distribution data by aircraft, and in the theory of what may be deduced from it, the USSR is presumed ahead of all other countries. The effect on forecasting theory of the data received from the drifting stations and from the radio beacons left on drifting ice since 1953 (291 up to 1967) has surely been great. But the effectiveness of the forecasts cannot be checked in the west, since neither forecasts nor detailed reports of actual conditions are published regularly. Far from new to the western specialist, however, are the newest aids in the ice reporting system - the use of helicopters from icebreakers and radio facsimile transmission of ice charts. The USSR system has always relied principally on frequent reports from highly skilled observers. Forecasting techniques include the use of computers, but the results are as yet apparently far from infallible.

At present most ice observations are made visually by trained observers who record their observations with conventional signs on a map and make periodic entries on prepared forms for spot observations. This is a most unsatisfactory method, subject to a great deal of human error and dependent on good visibility. The use of aerial photography has been suggested, but the number of photographs required makes it an impractical aid for daily operational reconnaissance and it is also restricted by visibility conditions. For longer-term synoptic purposes, photography should not be discarded for reconnaissance without much more thorough investigation than it has so far received; in particular, it should be considered as a medium for the new techniques of remote-sensing imagery.

The new advanced Vidicon, automatic picture taking (APT), and high-resolution infrared camera systems contained within the new ESSA and Nimbus polar-orbiting weather satellites promise ultimately to provide the necessary hemispheric - indeed global - sea ice data required not only for operational support by surface ships and submarines but also for a final evaluation of the sea ice mass balance. However, the resolution of the satellite imagery is not now sufficiently accurate to obviate the need for an arctic aerial reconnaissance program. Infrared-scanning imagery sequences now permit a more objective description of water and ridging features in periods of darkness as well as light. Side-looking radar imagery can penetrate cloud layers 20,000 ft thick and promises to provide data during periods of complete undercast when stresses on the ice are at a maximum. Also, a passive-microwave system is under development, the primary objective of which is to acquire imagery which will distinguish sea ice and icebergs from ship hulls.

The relatively wide use of remote sensors in studying sea ice is just beginning at this writing. Orvig's tabulation of areas of open water within pack ice (Table 4), which relied on remotely sensed data, is in general agreement with the earlier theoretical studies (roughly 1% open water) and the observations of the British Trans Arctic Expedition. Thus the 10% reported by the BIRD'S EYE Program may not be representative. More accurate figures await a rigorous study of satellite-collected data and the more extensive use of microwave sensors in satellites.

Both the Naval Oceanographic Office and the Cold Regions Research and Engineering Laboratory (CRREL) are analyzing the frequency, distribution,

Table 4

AREAS OF OPEN WATER WITHIN PACK ICE

ICE AREA (I) OF CONCENTRATION 1.0, AND OPEN WATER (W) WITHIN THE PACK ICE (km² · 10³)

Region	Jan.		Feb.		Mar.		Apr.		May		June		July		Aug.		Sept.		Oct.		Nov.		Dec.	
	I	W	I	W	I	W	I	W	I	W	I	W	I	W	I	W	I	W	I	W	I	W	I	W
Norwegian–Barents Sea	1,600	150	1,756	85	1,901	77	1,736	140	1,600	147	1,290	305	856	510	256	362	214	217	613	322	1,223	205	1,475	105
West Siberian coast	472	15	472	15	472	15	472	15	472	15	472	15	383	59	182	140	152	100	370	92	472	15	472	15
East Siberian coast	743	23	743	23	743	23	743	23	743	23	741	25	635	105	318	148	481	150	670	65	743	23	743	23
Beaufort Sea	407	13	407	13	407	13	407	13	407	13	382	38	357	21	151	89	134	78	349	41	407	13	407	13
Canadian Archipelago	941	29	941	29	941	29	941	29	932	38	915	47	871	68	665	175	607	115	886	69	937	33	941	29
Davis Strait–Baffin Bay	693	20	722	22	726	20	722	34	631	47	479	72	242	116	63	120	30	159	149	50	355	51	663	39
Central Polar Ocean	5,320	61	5,320	61	5,320	61	5,320	61	5,320	61	5,320	61	5,209	172	5,193	188	5,190	191	5,208	173	5,320	61	5,320	61
East Greenland Sea	757	31	807	21	908	31	907	41	733	48	718	44	499	117	230	194	242	103	334	45	391	44	527	33
Total Arctic Ocean	10,933	342	11,168	269	11,418	269	11,248	356	10,838	392	10,317	607	9,052	1,168	7,058	1,416	7,050	1,113	8,579	857	9,848	445	10,548	318

and orientation of pressure ridges from information collected with laser profilometers. The extreme accuracy of measurement of this instrument offers considerable promise in providing quantitative, rather than quali- tative, data concerning these parameters. The reports available are pre- liminary in nature; however, the studies are continuing.

Studies carried out on the surface of the ice by personnel from CRREL and the Johns Hopkins University and their contractor indicate that side- looking radar will prove to be a viable tool at this inclination as well as in the higher, airborne mode. Cross-sectional measurements have been made but the low grazing angle mutes pressure ridges and complicates the masking of a snow cover, especially at 94 GHz. The preferred ranges appear to be X-band and 35 GHz. The initial reports of these studies should be available in the summer of 1971.

Under-ice observations of ice distribution have been made for many years by the U.S. Navy but the data are difficult to obtain. Fortunately, the March 1971 cruise of the British nuclear submarine *Dreadnaught* from Svalbard to the Pole has resulted in a wealth of data for that sector. To quote Swithinbank, "A preliminary analysis of some of the data indicates that the roughest ice bottom topography was found between latitudes 86° and 88°N; this agrees with findings from earlier United States submarine voyages. A simple ice keel count between latitudes 80° and 90°N yields an overall average of 1.65 ice keels per km of linear track with drafts of 10 to 15 m, 0.32 keels per km with drafts of 15 to 20 m, 0.06 keels per km with drafts of 20 to 25 m, and 0.007 keels per km with drafts of 25 to 30 m. The deepest ice keel reached a depth of 30 m (100 ft). About 5% of the total under-ice part of the track consisted of open water or young ice."

Behavior

Wind stress appears to be the most important factor in ice drift. The ice moves in a direction about 25° to 30° to the right of the wind direc- tion, because of the Coriolis force. A rule of thumb is that the speed of ice drift is about 2% that of the average wind speed. For the Arctic Ocean, Zubov's rule is frequently used. This purely empirical quotation is:

$$V = a_i \cdot d_p$$

where V is the drift vector of the ice in km per month, d_p is the magnitude of the pressure gradient in millibars per kilometer (calculated from the average monthly map), and a_i is the isobaric coefficient. The direction of V is assumed to be parallel to the direction of the isobars on the weather map - that is, at right angles to the direction of the pressure gradient. Zubov's original value for a_i, 13,000, was later modified by taking a_i = 9,100 for the period February to April and 12,900 for the months from August to October. Zubov's rule appears to be applicable only to the Arctic Ocean itself, and cannot be used for the North Atlantic Ocean or Bering or Okhotsk seas.

The pattern of ice movement in the Arctic Ocean is shown in Figure 11. The two main features are an east-to-west drift on the Soviet side of the North Pole and a clockwise circulation called the Beaufort Gyral in the area between Canada, Alaska, and the Pole. In the Soviet seas there are also local ice circulations which are too complex to show in detail in this fig- ure. The existence of the central current was first established by the voyage of the *Fram* in 1893 to 1896. This ship was deliberately frozen into the ice near the Novosibirskiye Ostrova and allowed to drift with the ice.

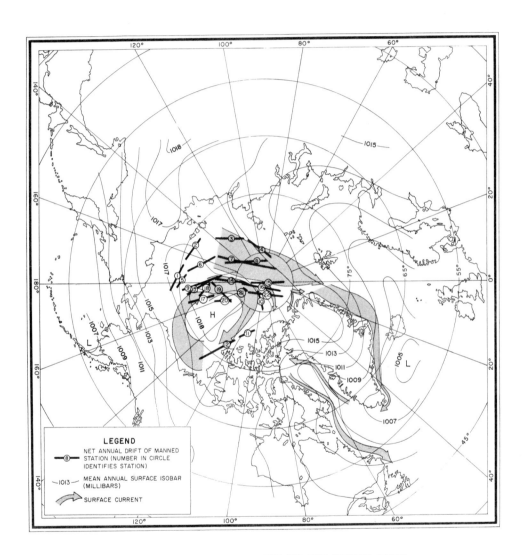

Figure 11.   ICE MOVEMENT IN THE ARCTIC OCEAN

Three years later she became free of the ice near Svalbard. This central current is the main discharge route for ice from the Arctic. After passing between Greenland and Svalbard, the ice follows the coast closely and is borne by the East Greenland Current. Each year the ice of this current reaches and passes Kap Farvel, but usually it melts before penetrating far into the Labrador Sea or Davis Strait. However, this does not mean that Labrador and Newfoundland are ice-free. Sea ice formed in Baffin Bay, Davis Strait, and along the Labrador coast is carried southeastward by the Labrador Current, blocking the Strait of Belle Isle (and often the east coast of Newfoundland) until early summer. This is also a region of high incidence of icebergs.

The Beaufort Gyral is a quasi-permanent circulation driven largely by the arctic high-pressure system. Ice on the outer edge of the gyral takes about 10 years to complete a circuit, whereas near the center the period of revolution may be as little as 3 years. Ice on the periphery of the gyral may get caught in the central arctic stream and be discharged from the Arctic Ocean, but ice nearer the center circulates indefinitely. This area therefore contains the oldest sea ice in the Arctic.

In addition to the ice discharged in the East Greenland Current, a certain amount of sea ice moves out of the Arctic Basin to the southeast through the channels of the Canadian archipelago. There is little data available to estimate the fraction of ice discharged by this route. Closely connected with the rate of discharge of ice from the Arctic Ocean is the question of the average age of the ice there. Again the data are too sparse for anything but a very rough estimate of about 10 years.

The ice in estuaries and near them may present more of a hazard to shipping than the usual sea ice. There are a number of major rivers discharging into the Arctic Ocean, including the Mackenzie in Canada and the Lena, Yenisey, and Ob in Siberia. Since settlements tend to occur on and near these rivers, it is a great inconvenience that the estuaries with their freshwater ice usually remain frozen after the nearby sea is open. The Russians have had some success with dusting the ice to hasten the breakup. In this technique any dark, local material is spread, usually by aircraft, on the ice to decrease its albedo and make as much use of solar radiation as possible.

Sea ice in the central arctic grows to a thickness of 6 ft during the first year. Subsequently, it grows more slowly, reaching an equilibrium thickness of 10 to 13 ft after a period of 5 to 8 years. The ice cover is marked by leads and pressure ridges which form as the wind and currents deform it. On the Eurasian side, the ice moves directly toward the opening between Svalbard and Greenland. The drift of ice station ARLIS II (Fig. 12) illustrates this pattern. The swiftest part of the drift occurred off eastern Greenland where steady speeds in excess of one knot were logged. Ice on the Canadian side moves circularly in a clockwise gyre. The drift of Fletcher's Ice Island, T-3, provides an example of this. The ice island made two orbits of the gyre in 17 years. In the vicinity of the North Pole there is an ice divergence which separates the two patterns of drift. The exact location of the divergence varies from year to year. Even though the tracks of ARLIS II and T-3 were similar on the Canadian side, one exited into the East Greenland Current and the other remains locked in the gyre.

Superimposed on these broad patterns are many irregularities of drift. The small-scale motions are due to wind and are particularly noticeable in

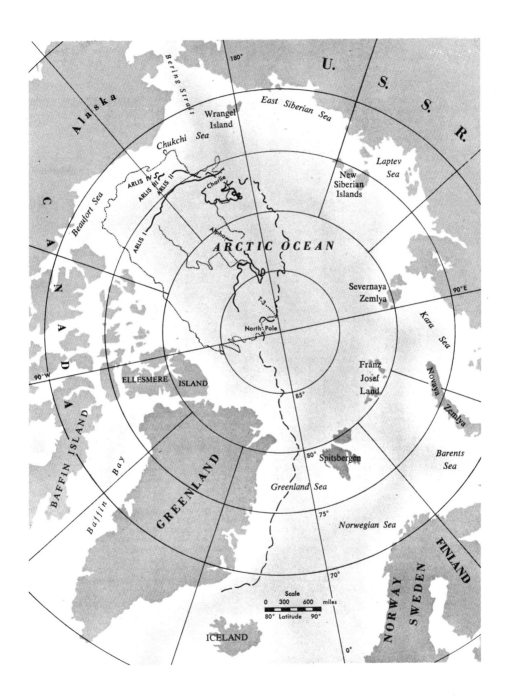

Figure 12.   DRIFT OF ICE STATION ARLIS II

the T-3 track. There is a still-smaller scale of ice motion with a period of about 12 hours which can only be detected with the more precise and frequent fixes obtained with satellites. The ice describes clockwise circles with a diameter of approximately one-half mile. These are inertial motions representing the transient response of the ice to changing wind conditions.

In many areas around the Arctic Basin there is, for greater or lesser parts of the year, a belt of ice which is fastened to the shore. This ice is commonly smooth and unbroken, but there may be deep snow drifts or large meltwater pools depending on the season. As the season progresses the shorefast ice breaks apart and either melts or joins the drifting pack. The amount of shorefast ice varies greatly. In most parts of the Arctic Basin some knowledge exists of where and when it has occurred over several years, where it is consistent and dependable, and where it is extremely variable from year to year. The most extensive areas of smooth ice, not strictly shorefast but included here in this general classification, are found in the Greenland fiords, especially in Peary Land, and on bays and sounds of the Canadian archipelago, Svalbard, and Zemlya Frantsa Iosifa.

Distribution

The geographical distribution of sea ice in the northeastward extension of the Atlantic Ocean is highly asymmetrical at all seasons. The striking feature is the absence of ice in the southern and eastern sectors of this part of the ocean, the Norwegian Sea, resulting from the ameliorating effect of warm water and air. The most extreme example is northwest of Svaldbard where open water is normally found in winter as far north as 80°. This is over 800 mi closer to the North Pole than any other open circumpolar sea at this season.

The seas around Iceland occasionally were reached by pack ice before the climatic improvement of most of the present century. In an unusual year in the nineteenth century, ice appeared off the north coast in December 1887 and by the following June had spread clockwise round the island until only the west coast was ice-free. In the last thousand years the island has been surrounded by ice probably several times each century, although the variations from one century to another have been considerable. Since 1920 sea ice has appeared off the north coast of Iceland on only a few occasions, except for the last three years during which conditions have deteriorated considerably.

Jan Mayen and Bjornoya are normally reached by pack ice and remain surrounded for 2 to 4 months. Inasmuch as the ice margin is not far away during this period, conditions are variable.

The sea ice off East Greenland originates primarily in the Arctic Basin. Together with smaller amounts of ice that freeze locally and icebergs from glaciers, pack ice is carried south between Svalbard and Greenland by the East Greenland Current as a broad belt of ice that is about 270 mi wide north of Scoresby Sund (70°N) in late winter. North of this latitude there is sea ice at all times of the year, although the belt narrows and contains open water in late August. Beginning in September the southern and southeastern margin of the pack ice expands southward until by December or January a tongue of pack ice has reached as far as Kap Farvel and has effectively blocked the east coast. While the pack ice develops offshore, the fiords begin to freeze in October, and this ice remains until the following

June or July. When the fiords clear of fast ice they are commonly filled
with pack ice blown in by onshore winds. The maximum extent of East Greenland ice is reached in March and April, and in very heavy ice years there
is continuous pack ice from southern Greenland to Svalbard and eastward to
Novaya Zemlya. The margin of the ice off Greenland begins to withdraw in
May by melting on the outer side and by the developing inshore leads between
the coast and the open pack.

In the most favorable years, the limit of pack ice in August may be as
far north as 75°, while in a bad year ice may still reach Kap Farvel at
this time. Great fluctuations have been recognized in the extent of the
East Greenland ice, and this is clearly related to the rate of transport by
the current and amount of ice that exits from the Arctic Ocean. Although
in general it appears to have been less in the 20th century than in the
previous three centuries, forecasting the quantity and distribution of the
East Greenland ice is still not possible.

Only three glacier systems in East Greenland are significant producers
of icebergs. The most active glaciers calve into Scoresby Sund and may
contribute 40% of the total iceberg production. Iceberg calving begins in
July and continues through the latter part of the summer. Few icebergs
actually reach the polar pack and move south with it as the majority become
stranded in the fiords or trapped in the many offshore islands. The smaller
the concentration of pack ice, the more icebergs move south because they are
less apt to be blocked by the pack.

In Peary Land, fast ice remains in the fiords from September until the
end of July and is rarely broken up by winds once it has formed. In unusually cold summers it may fail to melt. This ice may survive several decades
and becomes fresh and re-crystallised; only with difficulty can it be dif-
ferentiated from glacier ice. It is found in several fiords, including
J. P. Koch's Fiord and Independence Fiord. On some coasts in North Greenland the fast ice is practically permanent, but the ice breaks up in most
fiords and for a short period there is open water along the coast. Throughout the year heavy pack ice is present off the coast.

The west coast of Svalbard is free of ice or experiences only limited
severe ice conditions, while the east and north coasts experience very
heavy pack ice. Fast ice generally develops on the west coast of Vestspitsbergen in December, but in some years a continuous ice cover fails to
form in winter. This inshore ice melts in April or May; it may be replaced by pack ice later in the summer in the south, but the area north
of Isfjorden is normally ice-free. On the east coast, local fast ice, icebergs from glaciers, and pack ice that has been carried from the east block
the coast for the first half of the year. Storfjorden and Hinlopenstredet
between Vestspitsbergen and Nordaustlandet may remain blocked throughout
the summer. When the ice begins to loosen up with summer melting, it is
carried by currents round the southern tip of Vestspitsbergen (Sorkapp) and
north along the west coast, in some years reaching Prince Karls Forland by
the beginning of July. The northwest part and the western part of the
north coast are generally the most accessible.

The opposing coasts of Baffin Bay and Davis Strait show startling contrasts in sea ice conditions. Due to the warm current the southwest coast
of Greenland is commonly ice-free even in winter, except for the inner
fiords, as far north as Disko Bugt. In summer the whole coast may be free
of pack ice although in Melville Bugt icebergs occur. However, in bad years

ice is carried round Kap Farvel from East Greenland in summer and blocks the southwest coast.

Ice conditions on the Canadian side are much less favorable. In winter heavy fast and pack ice blocks all coasts and moving pack stretches across Baffin Bay. Open water may occur, particularly in late winter in the extreme north of Baffin Bay and off Baffin Island between the moving pack and the fixed inshore ice. Conditions improve only slowly in early summer and heavy pack may continue to be carried south well into August. In favorable years the ice will disappear about this time except for icebergs. In bad ice years some pack remains inshore and heavy pack ice may survive in the middle and north of Baffin Bay.

The northern channels that lead to the Lincoln Sea have great ice variations from day to day and from one year to another. In general, Kane Basin, Hall Basin, and Robeson Channel provide greatest difficulty to ships. Robeson Channel in particular may be so jammed with ice throughout the summer that it remains impassable even to icebreakers.

Jones Sound which is the normal route for ships making for Eureka can be entered either through Glacier or Lady Ann straits. The ice begins to loosen in July and in good years will be clear from mid-August until the second half of September.

Parry Channel normally shows a range of ice conditions from heavy ice at the western end throughout the summer to navigable conditions in Lancaster Sound in the east end beginning in mid-June and lasting until the end of September. Summer conditions in Lancaster Sound are helped by the presence of open water early in the year and sometimes throughout the winter in Barrow Strait.

The ice in the coastal waters of Labrador has three sources: local freezing, Baffin Bay ice carried into the area by the Labrador Current, and icebergs which originated in northwest Greenland. The pack ice extends southward with the onset of winter and is off south Labrador by early December. A month later it is off Notre Dame Bay (Newfoundland), and by March when the sea ice is at its maximum the whole Labrador-Newfoundland coast as far as the Avalon Peninsula is infested. Breakup begins in the southern part in April and slowly extends northward in the next two months to Strait of Belle Isle and more rapidly by mid-July to Hudson Strait.

Freeze-up in the Gulf of St. Lawrence begins on the north shore in December and extends southward with the addition of ice that enters through the Strait of Belle Isle. By late January the Gulf is 80% ice-covered except for the southwest corner of Newfoundland which remains clear a few more weeks. There is sufficient open water throughout the winter for shipping to be possible through the Gulf, although it may be locally restricted by large ice fields, particularly in Cabot Strait. The ice cover decreases rapidly in early April and within a few weeks ceases to be a hazard except in the northeast corner of the Gulf.

Ice conditions in Hudson Strait are highly variable. In addition to that which develops *in situ*, ice is carried into Hudson Strait from Foxe Channel, Hudson Bay, and Davis Strait at different times of the year. At the beginning of the season, pack ice is often present at the west end of Hudson Strait where it has been brought in from Foxe Channel. Inshore ice on the Baffin coast begins to form in mid-October but there is not much

growth until early November in the west and until the middle of the month
at the east end. Much of this early fast ice breaks away to form the winter pack ice in the Strait. There is a heavy cover of moving pack ice between early December and the end of May. There is often appreciable open
water, particularly on the north side, but navigation is impossible. The
breakup is prolonged as the ice that moves out into the Atlantic is replaced
from the west. In an average year the straits are open in the third or
fourth week of July.

Sea ice usually begins to appear in Hudson Bay about the middle of
October and reaches a thickness of about 5 ft by December. Most harbors
on the west coast are normally blocked by late October, but Churchill may
remain open into November. An ice-covered zone gradually builds up along
the shores with moving ice fields in the middle of the Bay. The Bay is not
covered until late December or January; and even then in the northern part
of Hudson Bay temporary ice-free areas may develop after continuous northwesterly and northerly winds. Melting begins in May and open water increases rapidly in early June. Winds play an important part in slowing down or
speeding up the removal of the ice; on the whole the prevailing winds tend
to clear the northern part earlier. Ice fields are still present in many
years during late July, but by August the ice has usually disappeared.

Ice conditions in Foxe Channel and Foxe Basin are generally severe.
The ice is extremely rough and often dirty in appearance because of the in-
corporation of bottom muds as it forms in shallow water. Fast ice begins
to develop in the east side of the Basin early in October. Pack ice in the
center and west extends the ice cover until, by late December, Foxe Basin
and Channel are completely covered. The pack on the west and south sides
is on the move throughout the winter, and open water may be found at many
points. The first significant clearing of sea ice occurs in late June in
Frozen Strait and Foxe Channel. This is, however, temporary; and when the
main pack becomes mobile in late July, areas that were formerly open are
again closed. Ice conditions remain difficult even on the west side during
the first half of August, and only by late August is part of the Basin (depending on winds) likely to be open.

The channels of the Queen Elizabeth Islands present ice conditions for
surface navigation second in difficulty only to those of the Arctic Ocean.
Throughout most of the straits there is a continuous ice cover at practically all times of the year, and only in the more favorable summers are there
openings in the form of small leads. Ice conditions are best in the east.
Parry Channel, which forms the southern margin of the area, has relatively
clear summer conditions in Lancaster Sound, but these deteriorate further
west.

At the west end of Barrow Strait the ice is at a minimum in mid- and
late August, although generally a good deal of ice remains throughout the
summer, particularly if strong westerly winds blow it eastward from Viscount
Melville Sound. Farther west in Parry Channel, there are considerable quantities of ice at all times of the year; and M'Clure Strait has never been
known to be ice-free, although in occasional and unusual years small inshore
leads develop. Generally, conditions along the north side of Parry Channel
are better than the south because of the tendency for northwesterly winds to
blow the ice southward. In winter, and especially in spring, areas of open
water may be found in the eastern part of Parry Channel, particularly at the
west end of Barrow Strait.

The best approach to the inner channels is through either Wellington Channel or Jones Sound. The former has experienced several areas of open water in spring, and the expansion of these produces fairly early melting. Thus, by late June there may be considerable open water in the north of Wellington Channel and in the vicinity of Belcher Channel; however, the ice may not clear from the southern part until late in the summer. Norwegian Bay, between Axel Heiberg, southwestern Ellesmere, and Grinnel Peninsula, is normally ice-covered from late September to late July. Navigation may be possible during mid-August, and conditions improve northward toward Eureka Sound, where the strong currents contribute to an early breakup. Elsewhere the channels remain ice-covered throughout the year. The movement of ice islands through the channels from the north and northwest shows that the ice tends to move as a unit, although probably only in good years. From all practical points of view the remaining waters may be considered unnavigable by surface ships at all times.

The character and distribution of the sea ice in the southwestern portion of the archipelago is profoundly influenced by the low tidal range which permits fast ice to develop in all but a few localities during the winter. The absence of strong tidal currents except in a few of the narrower straits (e.g. Dease Strait) enables the ice to form quickly in the fall; and it is only where there are strong tidal currents that channels remain open as late as December. The comparative summer warmth of the southern channels and the presence of many large rivers flowing off warm land contribute to early and continuous melting of the sea ice. In contrast, the channels that open to the north become jammed with ice under the influence of the northwesterly winds, and some waters - notably M'Clintock Channel - may never be clear of ice. In the northerly channels it is often true that ice conditions are better in the early summer than later in the year, by which time much of the ice has broken up farther north and blown into them.

Along the mainland coast the first open water appears near the mouths of the large rivers. The southern part of Bathurst Inlet normally has extensive open water by the end of June, and in an average year much more open water is evident by the second or third week of July when, except in very bad years, navigation is possible all along the coast. Heavy pack ice may exist until well into August in Coronation Gulf and until even later at the east end of Queen Maud Gulf. The freeze-up in these areas begins in late September or early October and spreads comparatively quickly on the brackish water close to the large rivers. Hence, by the end of October the coasts are frozen again, and by early November there is once more continuous ice except in narrow channels.

In contrast to the ice conditions in mainland waters, the south sides of Viscount Melville Sound and M'Clintock Channel contain the most heavily ice-infested waters south of the Queen Elizabeth Islands. The winter ice in this area, except in the bays, is rough and contains a proportion of perennial pack ice. There is some evidence that ice in the middle of M'Clintock Channel is on the move even in midwinter. Leads may develop in early August in these areas, particularly adjacent to the river mouths; and with favorable offshore winds, a shore lead may persist although it can never be relied upon. The larger bays (e.g. South Hadley Bay) begin to open at the head by the end of July and become ice-free toward the end of most summers, but there is always a danger that ice will be pushed back in. The conditions at the south end of M'Clintock Channel are made more difficult by the inability of the ice to escape from it. In the early 1960's an ice island from the Arctic Ocean moved south through M'Clintock Channel and became wedged in the Victoria Strait area.

Prince of Wales Strait has extremely variable ice conditions. In most summers passage is possible at some time, although long periods of waiting may be expected. It is likely that small craft can negotiate the straits in late August after the ice has melted in the northern part of the Strait and before it is filled from Viscount Melville Sound. Similar conditions are found in the east where Peel Sound has an extremely variable record. In Franklin Strait conditions are not as good; and it seems unlikely that this sector is ever completely clear of ice, although in late August a shallow-draft vessel may occasionally achieve a successful passage.

The sea ice conditions in the Beaufort Sea during the summer vary greatly and only general statements are possible. The clockwise current tends to force the permanent polar pack into the southeastern Beaufort Sea. However, this drift is counteracted effectively by the dominant southeasterly winds. Therefore, at freeze-up in late fall, the margin of the pack has retreated about 100 mi from the mainland near the Mackenzie Delta. Normally it is close off northern Banks Island and Point Barrow.

During the first week of June the only open water along the coast is found in Shallow Bay on the west side of the Mackenzie Delta. By the following week Kugmallit Bay opens on the east side, and Tuktoyaktuk is usually accessible from the Mackenzie by the end of the month. Along the Yukon coast the open water extends slowly westward, affording the possibility, in an average year, of reaching Herschel Island during the second week of July and Point Barrow by the third week. Large leads in Amundsen Gulf absorb solar radiation and contribute to an early breakup in this area. The Thesiger Bay coast is usually free of ice by July first. Summer ice conditions off Banks Island depend on the location of the polar pack. At the end of July ships can normally proceed north of Cape Kellett. Beyond Storkerson Bay, however, the sea is never free of ice, and in bad years only shore leads are open.

Between Herschel Island and Point Barrow the edge of the polar pack closely approaches the Alaskan coast, generally leaving a channel several miles wide in late summer that may be closed at any time if the pack surges south. The polar pack in this area has a clockwise movement and may contain large ice islands.

Drifting pack ice covers most of the Arctic Ocean. In the pack there are four areas where the ice is quite distinct from that in the other areas. In the southern Beaufort gyre where it impinges on Point Barrow and across the head of the Bering Strait, the ice, having come slowly down along the Canadian archipelago and across the Beaufort Sea, is relatively old. It is mostly thick ice blocks or floes which have been jostled and compressed by being squeezed by the northward trend of the Alaskan coast, and the thin ice has been pushed and pressed onto the thicker ice. It is fairly warm north of Alaska compared to many other parts of the Arctic, so melting of the thin ice takes place there. Nevertheless, the pack ice, from having been under compression, is rough-surfaced, and what is there is mainly fairly old ice. This ice remains almost unchanged as it goes past the northeastern coast of Siberia and drifts toward the North Pole. Through that area, there are many old ice floes. Quite often these floes are measured in fractions of a mile, but in most areas there are some that are measured in miles. The floes are separated by pressure ridges; by and large,

the larger the floes, the larger are the pressure ridges between them. For
most of the year this region is nearly completely ice-covered with only small
areas of open water. This region gives us the classic picture of Arctic
Ocean sea ice.

In the middle of the Beaufort gyre there are from several hundreds to
thousands of square miles where the ice does not move as much and is not
subjected to great shearing stresses. Usually turning more or less on its
axis, the ice does move, of course, when subjected to the considerable
stresses due to storms, but there is not a constant translatory motion.
Here the ice floes are thicker and generally smaller than in the outer parts
of the gyre; the pressure ridges are not so well defined and are mostly
short and branching, running in various directions; and the general topography is rougher with not very much open water.

Still within this western gyre, there is another zone in the southeastern Beaufort Sea itself where the ice pack expands after having been
compressed against the Canadian islands and is allowed to diverge and spread
out as it moves on toward the delta of the Mackenzie River. This is also
a warm area - the amount of sea ice melting is perhaps as great as anywhere
in the whole of the Arctic - so every autumn along the shore there are large
regions of open water that later freeze into young ice. As the ice passes
Banks Island and turns the right-angle corner to go westward past Alaska,
the flow pattern which has been generally in extension changes to a compres-
sive pattern of movement. Because most of the pack consists of pieces of
multi-year ice separated from one another with the spaces in between filled
with one- or two-year-old ice, the result is a frozen mixture perhaps 6 ft
thick of varying ice types. It is very difficult for a ship to get through
this ice, although it is not as thick as ice elsewhere, and it has a fairly
uniform surface roughness in comparison with the wide range of roughness in
the middle of the ocean where there is a greater contrast between smooth
floes and well-organized ridges.

On the Eurasian side of the Arctic Ocean, the U-shaped current pattern
comes out of the Atlantic and goes back into it again. By the very nature
of this pattern the ice does not stay long in the Arctic Ocean. The average
ice thickness therefore is less than in the Beaufort gyre. On the basis
of the observations that have been published, mostly by the USSR, the ice in
a smooth floe is seldom more than 7 ft thick. It is difficult to determine
the age of this ice, but extremely thick old floes are not a conspicuous
part of the pack ice in this area. In the areas from about 85° latitude to
the North Pole there are, depending on the local history, fairly smooth regions with well-organized ridges separating them. Sometimes it is possible
to see a regional pattern in the organization of ridges through the area.
Satellite photographs often give a good indication of the texture of this
part of the pack and these seem to be fairly constant.

The marginal seas of the northern Pacific have no direct, unrestricted
link with the Arctic Basin, and ice from the polar pack never reaches them.
In the Bering Sea the local pack ice reaches its maximum extent in April
when its margin lies roughly from the tip of the Alaskan Peninsula slightly
south of the Pribilof Islands to the east coast of Kamchatka. Open pack
ice present along the Kamchatka coast poses no problems to navigation at
this time. The ice in Bristol Bay begins to break up in May. By early June,
Bristol Bay is completely ice-free, and the ice has retreated to St. Lawrence Island. By mid-June Norton Sound is ice-free and by July the Bering
Sea is completely free, the Siberian side clearing before the Alaskan. The

first pack ice reforms in Bering Strait during the first two weeks in October.

Ice conditions in the Sea of Okhotsk closely resemble those in Hudson Bay. Ice usually forms in the northern bays in late October or early November. It covers the bay completely by December, and by this time there is floating ice throughout the northern half of the sea. Ice continues to form under the influence of the intensely cold continental air mass until April, and the strong winds carry it toward the Kuril Islands until the whole sea is covered. There is drift ice in the Kuril Straits from January until March, the amount depending on the strength and duration of the winter monsoon. Sometimes the ice moves well into the Pacific before melting completely. In the north the breakup comes in May, starting with the river meltwater which forces the landfast ice out to sea. The Shantar Islands are sometimes blocked until July, but in general the sea is ice-free in June.

Ice conditions are also variable in the Chuckchi Sea as in the Beaufort Sea. When the volume of water coming through Bering Strait in summer is large, it forces the margin of the polar pack ice north toward the edge of the continental shelf, at 72 to 73°N; but continuous strong northerly and easterly winds will drive the ice back to the coast near Point Barrow and into Proliv Longa. Ice begins to form in September in northern coastal parts of the sea while in sheltered inlets such as Kotzebue Sound, freeze-up occurs by mid- or late October. On open coasts fast ice may not form for another month. Offshore, roughly beyond the 80-ft submarine contour, heavy pack ice is on the move all winter. Breakup in coastal areas occurs during June, and the southern half of the sea is navigable from mid-July to mid- or late September. Farther north shipping is restricted until mid-August.

The ice conditions of the Laptev and the East Siberian seas are more severe than in any other of the peripheral seas off northern Asia. Sea ice forms unusually quickly as the water temperatures of the shallow seas drop rapidly in the autumn. A zone of hummocky ice as much as 30 ft high is common at the boundary of the fast ice and pack ice and is most strongly developed in the western Laptev Sea and in Proliv Longa. In the spring the ice melts first at the mouths of rivers and along the nearby coasts. The rivers freeze between October and December, and their flow throughout the winter either ceases or is quite low. Breakup is at the end of May or the beginning of June. On large rivers, with ice up to 8 ft thick, this involves violent movement, ice dams, and flooding. The ice on the smaller rivers melts in place. The navigation period for the lower reaches of the rivers lasts from 3 to 4 months.

In summer, Proliv Dmitriya Lapteva tends to have favorable ice conditions but Proliv Sannikova and Proliv Longa are rarely completely free of ice, and Proliv Vil'kitskogo has the worst ice conditions. This is caused by drift of ice with the current from the Kara Sea and by pack ice and icebergs that drift southeast from Severnaya Zemlya.

Breakup begins in June off the deltas of the Lena and Yana Rivers. The eastern side of the Laptev Sea is the first to be free of ice because of the influx of river water and the action of winds blowing the ice offshore. Changes in the western part are slower because of the deeper water and the cold current that flows south along the east coast of Severnaya Zemlya. Once the ice has broken up in the west, the ice margin retreats at 10 to 25 mi a day. The southern part of the Laptev Sea is navigable in July, but

there may not be access to it from the seas on either side. Heavy pack ice
from the Arctic Basin does not extend far into the Laptev Sea (unlike the
East Siberian Sea) and only small quantities find their way south. The
navigation season is effectively August and September.

Freeze-up begins at Tiksi, in Guba Buorkhaya, in early October and
spreads both east and west from there. By December the sea is completely
frozen over. Ice conditions vary from the west to the east. In the west
there is much hummocky and rafted ice caused by wind stress. There are
often large fields of heavy sea ice off Severnaya Zemlya and Poluostrov
Taimyr where heavy floes and icebergs may run aground as they are driven
southward. In the eastern part, the ice is generally smoother and from 60
to 90 inches thick. The fast ice is 10 to 15 mi wide off the northeastern
parts of the Taimyr, 50 to 60 mi wide along the southern shores of the sea,
and 250 mi wide from the mainland to north of the Novosibirskiye Ostrova.

In the East Siberian Sea the first open water appears in late June off
the Kolyma delta. Open water expands rapidly west of the Kolyma and the ice
edge moves to the north. In the eastern sector of the sea, the ice does not
begin to clear for 1 to 2 weeks longer. The navigation season is 8 to 10
weeks long in the west and 6 to 8 weeks in the east. During this period,
ice conditions in the western sector are usually favorable for navigation.
Proliv Dmitriya Lapteva is clear of ice and in the late summer it is sometimes possible to pass north of Novosibirskiye Ostrova. The Ostrova De
Longa are usually surrounded by drifting ice and bergy bits that have calved
from small glaciers on the islands. In the eastern section, conditions are
generally neither as good nor as predictable. The heavy pack of the Arctic
Basin approaches the coast more frequently here than anywhere else along the
whole north Siberian shore. However, during the late summer, there is
usually an open lead close to the shore up to 20 mi wide.

Freeze-up begins in the west and by late November there may be an unbroken surface extending 180 to 300 mi offshore in the west and narrowing
to 10 to 20 mi off Mys Shmidta. Ice is constantly on the move in Proliv
Longa.

Around Ostrov Vrangelya navigation is possible only during the last
half of August and September. Proliv Dmitriya Lapteva is normally open for
navigation from late July or early August through September. The seas surrounding the Novosibirskiye Ostrova are rarely free to pack ice, although
the concentration is at its minimum in September.

There is floating ice all year in the Kara Sea, the amount and distribution depending largely on the strength and direction of the prevailing winds.
Most of the ice originates in the Kara Sea itself, because currents and shallow water in the north act as barriers to the heavier pack ice of the Arctic
Basin. Breakup advances from the south, where it is essentially open by
July. Optimum navigation conditions are in August and September, but in
good years they last from July to October. The worst conditions for navigation are usually encountered near Poluostrov Taimyr where ice collects in
the narrow straits separating the islands of Arkhipelag Nordenshel'da and
blocks the area immediately west of Proliv Vil'kitskogo. Conditions are
quite variable elsewhere in the Kara Sea, but ice is apt to be heavy either
in the northwest or in the southwest. Small icebergs may be found off
northern Novaya Zemlya and Severnaya Zemlya. Mainland rivers begin to freeze
in October at the river mouths, and at the same time fast ice develops around

their mouths. Fast ice forms quickly and, anchored by the many islands, remains all winter. Along eastern Novaya Zemlya fast ice is 3 to 5 mi wide,
and north of the mainland it may exceed 15 mi in width. The pack in the
central Kara Sea is 6 to 10 ft thick but considerably thicker where it is
ridged or hummocked by pressure. Grounded hummocks, called 'Stamukhi,'
are common off Novaya Zemlya and Severnaya Zemlya. They reach heights of
30 ft and tend to retain the surrounding ice cover in position. Ice conditions around Severnaya Zemlya are variable. The navigation season is usually from mid-August to mid-September. East of the archipelago there is ice
all year, including some icebergs. East winds drive much of this ice between the islands making those straits impassable.

The Barents Sea is exceptionally ice-free when compared with the other
peripheral seas of northern U.S.S.R. This is a consequence of the warm
Atlantic water which enters the sea. The inflow is sufficient to keep the
southwestern sector free of sea ice all year, and it causes ice conditions
in the rest of the sea to be much less severe than is normal for the latitude. Ice conditions may be predicted by measuring the flow of the North
Atlantic Drift north of Scotland. Warmer water there is followed 2 years
later by better ice conditions in the Barents Sea. Negligible quantities of
ice enter the Barents Sea from the Kara Sea and the Arctic Ocean, and all
sea ice may be considered local. Maximum ice cover is in April, when the
sea is 75% covered. The mean southerly limit of unnavigable ice at this time
runs from the southwest coast of Svalbard to Bjornoya and east to 73° 30'N,
40°E and the mainland at Mys Svatoy Nos. Significantly the Murman coast
is always open. In the spring the ice margin recedes east and north, and
by mid-June it can be navigated north of Bjornoya and east to 50°E. At
Ostrov Kolguyev in the southeast of the Barents Sea, ice lasts until the
end of July. Ice conditions are best in September when the mean ice limit
runs from southern Svalbard to Zemlya Frantsa Iosifa and continues east-
southeast to 40 mi north of Novaya Zemlya. Occasionally in late August
the Barents Sea is entirely free of ice.

Freeze-up begins in October in the shallow waters around Zemlya Frantsa
Iosifa, Novaya Zemlya, Svalbard, and the estuary of Pechora. During November the west coast of Novaya Zemlya freezes, and by December most of the sea
north of 75°N is frozen. The ice margin moves gradually south and west as
the winter progresses. Winds and currents have a strong effect on the ice
conditions because there is much open water in the west. Between February
and April, if southeast winds are unusually strong, the ice will be driven
to the northeast, leaving much open water in the southwestern quadrant of
the sea. Zemlya Frantsa Iosifa is rarely clear of ice. The southern portion
of the archipelago may be ice-free for a few weeks but the narrower straits
are icebound all year. Western Novaya Zemlya is clear of ice from the end
of July until October. In January there is much loose pack ice to the west
of the island. From February to April Novaya Zemlya and Zemlya Frantsa
Iosifa are completely surrounded by landfast ice, with breakup beginning in
May. Small icebergs may be found in the vicinity of both island groups since
both have glaciers which reach the sea.

Ice conditions in the White Sea vary radically from year to year as a
result of the strength and direction of prevailing winds. In October fast
ice begins to spread from gulfs and bights. By January the sea is frozen
over, but ice is very thin in the central part and the entrance to the sea
is still ice-free. Maximum ice occurs in February and March and by then ice
is thickest in the entrance which is still blocked in May. Grounded hummocks form a chain north of Ostrov Morzhovets. Breakup begins in late April

and by June the sea is ice-free again. The ice is usually forced out into
the Barents Sea to melt, and consequently Mys Kanin Nos is often surrounded
by floating ice until the end of June.

Drifting Stations

Because of their relative durability and availability, ice floes and
ice islands have been used for many years as platforms from which to study
the arctic oceanic environment. Since the early 1950's over 20 such stations
have been occupied, primarily by the Soviet Union, on a long-term basis
(see Table 5). Semi-permanent living and working quarters were erected
and a varying number of vehicles provided. As many as 8 to 10 disciplinary
studies may be conducted at a station and, in the Soviet case, helicopters
and small fixed-wing aircraft may add immensely to the areal extent of the
programs. The only limitation on the number of personnel is budgetary although the usual complement is from 20 to 40. If conditions permit, the
station may be supplied by icebreaker, but usually a landing strip is required for long-range aircraft. In this the Soviets excel as witnessed by
their high-latitude expeditions which are mounted each spring and involve
tens of aircraft and hundreds of people.

Drawbacks to the use of such stations include their susceptibility to
fracturing and the inability to control their course. There is, of course,
no assurance that a suitable site will be available in a given area at a
specific time, so planning must be flexible. Nevertheless, drifting ice
stations provide a valuable base for selected operations in the Arctic Basin.

Bibliography

Bilello, M. A., 1960. *Formation, Growth and Decay of Sea Ice in the
    Canadian Arctic Archipelago*. Wilmette, Ill.: U. S. Army Corps of
    Engineers. SIPRE Research Report 65. 36 pp.

Campbell, W. J., 1965. The wind-driven circulation of ice and water in a
    polar ocean. *J. Geophys. Research* 70:3279-3301.

Koerner, R. M., 1971. Ice balance in the Arctic Ocean. *AIDJEX Bulletin*,
    6:11-26.

National Academy of Sciences, 1958. *Arctic Sea Ice*. Washington, D.C.:
    National Research Council Pub. No. 598.

Pounder, E. R., 1965. *The Physics of Ice*. Oxford: Pergamon Press. 151 pp.

Reed, R. J. and W. J. Campbell, 1962. The equilibrium drift of ice station
    Alpha. *J. Geophys. Research* 67:281-97.

Sater, J. E., 1968. *Arctic Drifting Stations*. Washington, D. C.: Arctic
    Institute of No. Amer. 475 pp.

Schule, J. J., Jr. and W. I. Wittmann, 1958. Comparative ice conditions in
    the North American Arctic, 1953-1955, inclusive. *Trans. Amer. Geophys.
    Union* 39:409-19.

Table 5

DRIFT POSITIONS OF SHIPS AND DRIFTING STATIONS

VECTOR NO. (Fig. 3-3)	STATION	DATE Begin	DATE End	POSITION Begin	POSITION End	SPEED (cm/sec)
1	Maud	24 Sept 22	24 Sept 23	73.0°N 173.3°W	75.5°N 163.7°E	2
2	Maud	24 Sept 23	8 Aug 24	75.5°N 163.7°W	76.5°N 143.2°E	2
3	Fram	25 Nov 93	24 Nov 94	78.6°N 139.1°W	82.0°N 112.0°E	2
4	Fram	24 Nov 94	22 Nov 95	82.0°N 112.0°W	85.8°N 64.2°E	2
5	NP-6	19 Apr 56	19 Apr 57	74.5°N 177.0°W	76.0°N 171.7°E	1
6	NP-6	19 Apr 57	8 Apr 58	76.0°N 171.7°E	80.9°N 150.2°E	2
7	NP-6	8 Apr 58	12 Apr 59	80.9°N 150.2°E	86.3°N 39.6°E	5
8	NP-5	16 Apr 55	16 Apr 56	82.2°N 156.2°E	86.3°N 89.3°E	3
9	T-3*	July 50	July 51	75.5°N 175.0°W	83.0°N 169.0°E	3
10	T-3	1 June 52	4 June 53	88.5°N 140.0°W	85.2°N 92.0°W	1
11	T-3	14 July 57	14 July 58	82.2°N 102.2°W	79.5°N 116.6°W	1
12	T-3	14 July 58	2 July 59	79.5°N 116.6°W	72.0°N 132.5°W	3
13	T-3	9 June 59	7 Mar 60	72.3°N 130.5°W	71.8°N 150.5°W	3
14	NP-4	8 Apr 54	17 Apr 55	75.8°N 171.6°W	80.6°N 176.1°E	2
15	NP-4	17 Apr 55	19 Apr 56	80.6°N 176.1°E	87.4°N 178.5°W	2
16	NP-4	19 Apr 56	20 Apr 57	87.4°N 178.5°W	85.9°N 0.0°	2
17	NP-3	9 Apr 54	20 Apr 55	86.0°N 178.0°W	86.4°N 24.0°W	3
18	NP-2	12 Apr 50	11 Apr 51	76.0°N 166.6°W	81.8°N 163.8°W	2
19	NP-8	15 July 59	15 July 60	78.1°W 168.0°W	80.4°N 177.8°E	1
20	NP-8	15 July 60	15 July 61	80.4°N 177.8°E	83.4°N 146.2°W	2
21	Alpha	8 June 57	10 June 58	80.9°W 159.5°W	84.1°N 149.7°W	1
22	NP-7	13 Apr 58	11 Apr 59	86.7°N 150.0°W	85.2°N 33.1°W	2
23	ARLIS II	Nov 63	Nov 64	87.8°N 13.5°W	84.6°N 10.5°W	2
24	ARLIS II	12 Nov 64	12 Feb 65	84.6°N 10.5°W	78.5°N 6.5°W	9
25	ARLIS II	12 Feb 64	16 Apr 64	78.5°N 6.5°W	69.3°N 20.0°W	20
26	WH-5	13 June 62	13 Dec 62	83.2°N 69.0°W	83.0°W 65.0°W	0.3
27	WH-5	29 July 63	29 Sept 62	80.4°N 67.9°W	77.5°N 76.5°W	7
28	WH-5	29 Sept 63	29 Nov 63	77.5°N 76.5°W	71.1°N 67.0°W	15
29	WH-5	29 Nov 63	25 Jan 64	71.1°N 67 °W	66.4°N 60.0°W	12

*Fletcher's Ice Island

Swithinbank, C., 1971. *Arctic Pack Ice From Below*. Paper presented at International Sea Ice Conference, Reykjavik, Iceland. (Abstract)

Untersteiner, N., 1964. Calculations of temperature regime and heat budget of sea ice in the central Arctic. *J. Geophys. Research* 69:4755-66.

Welsh, J. P. and W. B. Tucker, 1971. *Sea Ice Laser Statistics*. Paper presented at Seventh International Remote Sensing Symposium, Ann Arbor. (Abstract)

Wittmann, W. I., 1966. U. S. Naval ice observations in the seas of the northern Pacific: past and future. Abstracted in *Proceedings of the 11th Pacific Science Conference*, vol. 2. Conference held Tokyo, Japan, 22 Aug.-10 Sept. 1966. Tokyo: Science Council of Japan. p. 40.

Wittmann, W. I. and G. P. MacDonald, 1964. *Manual of Short-Term Sea Ice Forecasting*, App. B. Washington, D. C.: U. S. Naval Oceanographic Office. Special Publ. 82.

World Meteorological Organization, 1970. *Sea Ice Nomenclature. Terminology, Codes and Illustrated Glossary, Edition 1970*. Geneva: The Secretariat. 134 pp.

The Ocean

Structure

The Arctic Ocean surrounds the North Pole and is bordered by Scandinavia, Siberia, Alaska, Canada, and Greenland. Its area, approximately 4 million sq mi, is about five times that of the Mediterranean Sea, but its volume is only three times as great. Unlike its southern antipode, the polar region above 80°N is a basin, some of which is over 14,000 ft below sea level, while most of the immense expanse between 55 and 80°N is an area of northward-flowing drainage - the arctic drainage basin. In an oceanographic sense it is a single, large, nearly enclosed basin connected primarily with the Atlantic Ocean through 2 other major arctic seas, the Norwegian Sea and the Greenland Sea. The water characteristics can be traced in large part to North Atlantic water characteristics which have been modified through surface-acting processes associated with the unique climatic conditions of the Arctic. The characteristics of the peripheral continental arctic seas are highly variable and are discussed in greater detail below. The connection of the Arctic Ocean with the Pacific Ocean through Bering Strait is of relatively minor importance oceanographically.

The generalized bathymetry is given in Figure 13. The continental shelf on the North American side of the Arctic Ocean is narrow (20 to 50 mi), whereas the half bounded by Scandinavia and Siberia is very broad (up to 600 mi) and shallow with peninsulas and islands separating it into five marginal seas - the Barents, Kara, Laptev, East Siberian, and Chukchi. Even though these marginal seas occupy 36% of the area of the Arctic Ocean, they contain only 2% of its volume of water. With the exception of the Mackenzie River in northern Canada and the Yukon River, which enters via Bering Sea and Bering Strait, all the major continental rivers reaching the Arctic Ocean flow into these five seas. Thus, these shallow seas, which have a high ratio of exposed surface to total volume and a substantial input of fresh water in summer, greatly influence surface water conditions in the Arctic Ocean.

The major structural features of the floor of the Arctic Ocean are shown in Figure 14. The continental shelf is indented by numerous submarine canyons. The principal canyons are the very large Svyataya Anna and Voronin troughs in the northern Kara Sea and the Hope Valley and Barrow Canyon in the Chukchi and Beaufort seas. The edge of the continental shelf, particularly in the Laptev and East Siberian seas, is poorly surveyed; and undoubtedly there are canyons yet to be defined. These canyons have an oceanographic importance as preferential pathways for the egress of water from the relatively warm Atlantic layer onto areas of the continental shelf, where it comes within the influence of strong mixing processes. Hence they can influence locally, but significantly, the surface waters and ice cover.

The Arctic Basin is a true ocean basin. Beneath its deepest parts, the thickness of the earth's crust is about 5 mi, a figure that is typical of the other oceans. The relief of the Arctic Basin, too, is much like that of the other oceans in that it has two predominant levels: the conti-

Figure 13.   BATHYMETRY OF THE ARCTIC OCEAN AND ITS SEAS
              (depths in fathoms)

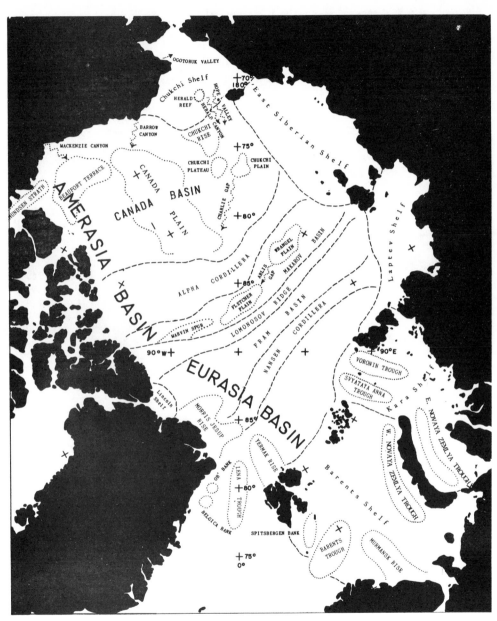

Figure 14.   MAJOR FEATURES OF THE FLOOR OF THE ARCTIC OCEAN
AND ITS SEAS   (The boundaries are approximate)

nental shelves with water depths of a few hundreds of feet and the deep
basins with depths of thousands of feet. A sharp break in slope where
the continental shelf meets the continental slope marks the boundary between
the shelves and basins and defines the edge of the central Arctic Basin.
In most oceans, the shelf break is at about the 650-ft depth, but in the
Arctic it is deeper in some places (1,300 to 1,600 ft).

The continental margin on the Eurasian side contains some of the broadest continental shelves in the world. The East Siberian Shelf is 250 to 450
mi wide, and the Barents and Kara shelves are 350 to 600 mi wide. In contrast, the shelf off Greenland and northwestern Canada is only 15 to 35 mi
wide. North of Alaska the continental slope has a gradient comparable to
that in other parts of the world. In contrast the continental slope between
the Novosibirskiye Ostrova and the Chukchi Sea is apparently formed of several level surfaces. The continental shelf along East Greenland, south to
77°N, is broad (150 mi) and contains a system of banks no deeper than 650
ft. South of 77°N the shelf narrows until between 75°N and the Kap Farvel
it is less than 50 mi wide. The shelf is marked, particularly in the southern part, by several deep indentations. At about 79°N the Greenland Sea is
separated from the Arctic Basin by a rise with a sill depth of about 9,200
ft. South of the rise the Greenland Sea contains 2 deep basins. At 71°N
the Jan Mayen Ridge extends toward Greenland at a maximum depth of about
5,000 ft. In Denmark Strait, however, the sill depth is about 1,800 ft.

Around Baffin Bay the shelf is relatively narrow and never exceeds a
width of 50 mi. The shelf is widest off central Baffin Island, Labrador,
and West Greenland south of 78°N. Central Baffin Bay is a basin with depths
exceeding 6,500 ft. The sill across Davis Strait is about 2,000 ft deep.
Baffin Bay is connected with the Arctic Ocean through a network of channels -
Smith, Jones, and Lancaster sounds. The Jones Sound connection is quite
restricted but the channels leading to Lancaster and Smith sounds are
relatively deep with sill depths extending to 490 and 720 ft respectively.

A gently sloping continental rise usually lies at the foot of the continental slope. North of Alaska, this rise is 25 to 50 mi wide. Widths of
150 to 250 mi occur off the Canadian Arctic Archipelago. Crossing the
Canadian continental rise is a system of deepsea channels with relief of 15
ft.

A marginal plateau is a level feature which borders the continental
shelf at a greater depth and several are known in the Arctic Ocean. The
Chukchi Rise is crowned at its outer end by the Chukchi Plateau which has
a flat summit with a diameter of about 50 mi at the 1,000-ft isobath (Fig.
15). The surface is marked by relief of 15 to 100 ft. Two submarine canyons indent the southwest side of the Plateau. Southeast of the Chukchi
Plateau is an area of rough topography which has been described as a continental borderland. Within this area is another plateau, the Northwind
Cap. Other marginal plateaus include the Beaufort Terrace, which on its
outermost edge is similarly elevated above the saddle which connects to
the continental shelf, and the Morris Jesup and the Yermak rises in the
Greenland-Svalbard area.

The central Arctic Basin is crossed by three submarine mountain ranges.
The ridges and rises are nearly parallel to one another and span the basin
from Eurasia to Canada. The Lomonosov Ridge, stretching 900 mi between
the Novosibirskiye Ostrova and the Greenland-Ellesmere shelf, was discovered by Soviet scientists in 1948. It is a single continuous feature 50

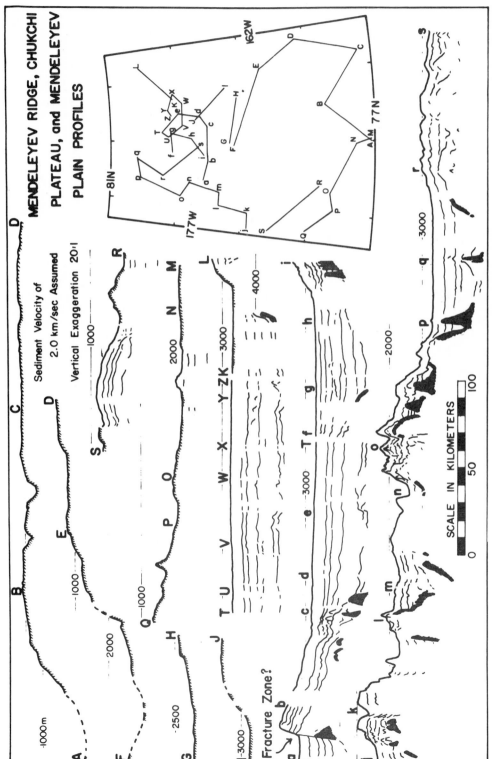

MENDELEYEV RIDGE, CHUKCHI
PLATEAU, and MENDELEYEV
PLAIN PROFILES

Sediment Velocity of
2.0 km/sec Assumed

Vertical Exaggeration 20:1

SCALE IN KILOMETERS

Figure 15

to 100 mi wide. Echograms show a steep-sided ridge with a rather smooth profile. Its minimum depth reported is 3,100 ft, and saddles along the crest have depths of 5,000 to 5,250 ft. A falt surface near the crest of the ridge has been noted on two different crossings. An offshoot of the Lomonosov Ridge is known as the Marvin Spur.

The Alpha Cordillera is about the same length as the Lomonosov Ridge but much broader, its width ranging from 125 to 400 mi. The crest of the Cordillera is 5,000 to 6,500 ft deep, and the topography is much rougher than that of the Lomonosov Ridge (Fig. 16). The magnetic fields over these two features also differ. The field over the Alpha Cordillera is disturbed with numerous anomalies, many of them exceeding 1,000 gammas, while over the Lomonosov Ridge there is little disturbance at all. Neithe₁ of these ranges is now seismically active.

The Nansen Cordillera is an extension of the Mid-Atlantic Ridge into the Arctic Ocean. Where the topography has been sampled, it is rough, as it is on the Mid-Atlantic Ridge. The most distinctive characteristic of the Nansen Cordillera is the narrow earthquake belt along its crest. The belt of earthquake epicenters crosses Iceland and then abruptly changes direction just north of the island, where a large east-west fracture zone intersects the mid-oceanic ridge near Jan Mayen. Between northeastern Greenland and northern Siberia the earthquake belt is narrow and straight for a distance of over 1,000 mi, while within Siberia the earthquake zone spreads out and disappears. In the Atlantic a similar earthquake belt coincides with a central rift valley at the crest of the mid-oceanic ridge. Although this relationship might be expected to hold in the Arctic, insufficient evidence has been collected for positive verification.

The abyssal plains are the repositories for sediments which have been transported across the continental shelves and down the continental slopes. In the deep basins the sediments collect to form some of the globe's most extensive level surfaces. Four of the abyssal plains in the Arctic Ocean are arranged in steplike pairs. Each pair is connected by an abyssal gap through which sediments are transported from the upper to the lower plain. The Canada and Chukchi abyssal plains are connected by the Charlie Gap. The complete route of sediment flow is from Herald Canyon to the Chukchi Abyssal Plain and then through Charlie Gap to the Canada Abyssal Plain. The Wrangel and Fletcher abyssal plains are connected through Arlis Gap.

Seismic reflection profiles show that a prominent sub-bottom basement ridge exists in the vicinity of the Arlis Gap. This ridge seems to have acted as a bedrock dam for the sediments of Wrangel Abyssal Plain, ponding them behind it until there was sufficient accumulation to spill over into Fletcher Abyssal Plain. Sediments move from the Siberian Shelf to Wrangel Abyssal Plain and then through Arlis Gap to Fletcher Abyssal Plain. A system of interplain channels funnels the flow across the plain and into the gap. The right (east) bank of these channels is higher than the left bank - a condition that is apparently due to the influence of the earth's rotation.

The most extensive of the plains in the Arctic Ocean is the Canada Abyssal Plain which covers an area of 80,000 sq mi. It is remarkably flat with depths ranging from about 12,400 ft in the north to 12,600 ft in the south. On its northern and western edges it is bounded by the scarps of the Alpha Cordillera and Chukchi Rise. The eastern and southern boundaries grade smoothly into the continental slope. The Pole Abyssal Plain in the

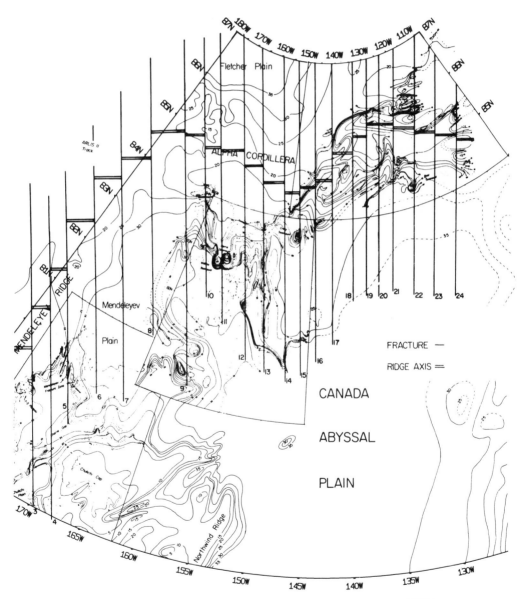

Figure 16.   INFERRED FRACTURE PATTERN OVER THE ALPHA
CORDILLERA AND THE MENDELEYEV RIDGE

Fram Basin, is deeper than the four plains mentioned previously. In the neighborhood of the North Pole it is flat and smooth with a depth of 13,400 ft, but away from the Pole the depth of the plain increases to 15,000 ft.

Water Masses

Data from the Arctic Ocean taken over many years and during all seasons of the year show a remarkable regularity in the distribution of temperature and salinity at depth throughout the year as well as a repeating seasonal regularity in the surface waters. This nearly steady state in the observed distribution of temperature and salinity is apparently a result of continuing processes within the Arctic Basin. For many purposes the importance of taking data synoptically is thus reduced, and much may be learned about the geographic distribution of properties by comparing data from different seasons and years.

The most important processes conditioning and modifying the Arctic Ocean water are:

(1) addition of fresh water from the land, primarily from the large Siberian rivers;
(2) addition of fresh water locally through melting of ice;
(3) heat gain through absorption of solar radiation in areas that are not ice-covered;
(4) concentration of salt, and hence increase of density, of surface water as a result of freezing; and
(5) heat loss to the atmosphere at any open water surface, including leads in the pack ice.

The first three processes lead to decreased density of the water affected, and they operate only from June to September. Consequently, the surface waters exhibit somewhat lower salt content in summer than in winter, and in ice-free areas (e.g. parts of Baffin Bay) surface temperatures may rise to a few degrees above freezing. In ice-covered areas the temperatures in summer remain near the freezing point because the heat is dissapated by melting the ice rather than warming the water.

The latter two processes lead to increases in density of the surface water. In some areas under certain conditions these modified waters sink to subsurface levels, 325 to 650 ft in depth, but in general in arctic waters these concentration mechanisms are not adequate to create water of sufficient density that it can replace waters lying deeper than 650 ft. Thus all deep arctic waters are advected into and out of the arctic seas from adjacent areas. As the connection with the Pacific Ocean through the Bering Strait is narrow (about 40 mi wide and about 165 ft deep), the deeper waters of the Arctic Ocean, and probably Baffin Bay, essentially originate in the North Atlantic.

The similarity in vertical structure at diverse locations throughout the Arctic Ocean (Fig. 17) reflects the common North Atlantic origin of water deeper than 650 ft and the similarity of local processes modifying the surface water, principally the arctic climate factors. On the basis of temperature, three water masses may be defined:

(1) The surface layer (Arctic water), from the surface down to about 650 ft, has varying characteristics. In ice-covered areas the water temper-

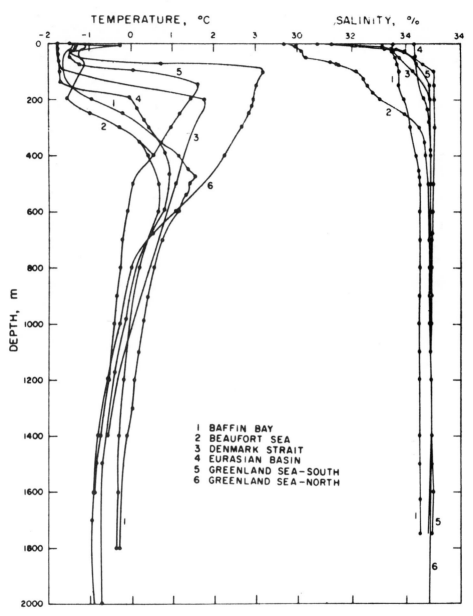

Figure 17.   VERTICAL DISTRIBUTIONS OF TEMPERATURE
AND SALINITY AT SIX LOCALITIES

ature is close to the freezing point for the salt content. In the usually
ice-free areas (eastern Greenland Sea; along West Greenland north through
Davis Strait) temperatures may be a few degrees above freezing as are
those in areas that are ice-free in summer (Chukchi Sea; nearshore areas
of other peripheral seas; most of Baffin Bay). Temperatures below the
surface are typically always cold, except in the Canada Basin of the
Arctic Ocean, where there may appear a small temperature maximum (-1.0°C)
in the 250- 325-ft layer. This is attributable to influx of Bering
Sea water, which is transported around the Beaufort Sea gyre. The
salinity of the surface layer may be uniform down to about 160 ft and
then increase until at 650 ft it is 34.5°/oo, or it may begin to increase
closer to the surface. The surface salinity values also exhibit spatial
variation.

(2) The layer below the Arctic water, from about 650 to 3,000 ft, is
known as the Atlantic layer. It has temperatures above 0°C, with a maximum (up to 3°C) at 1,000 to 1,600 ft. Salinities continue to increase
over the surface values until by 1,300 ft and in many instances shallower
depths, they attain in the Greenland Sea and Arctic Ocean nearly uniform
values in the range of 34.9 to 35.1°/oo.

(3) Beneath the Atlantic layer is bottom water with temperatures below
0°C and the same uniform salinities attained in the Atlantic layer (34.93
to 34.99°/oo). Deep temperatures vary slightly from basin to basin; in
the Canada Basin they are about -0.30 to -0.40°C, in the Eurasian Basin
-0.70 to -0.80°C, in the Greenland Sea -1.2°C, and in Baffin Bay -0.45°C.

The density of cold water is influenced much more by salinity than by
temperature - thus the vertical distribution of density closely parallels
that of salinity. On the basis of density, arctic waters show a two-layer
system, with a thin, less dense surface layer separated from the main body
of water of quite uniform density by a strong pycnocline. The pycnocline
restricts vertical motion and the vertical transfer of heat and salt, and
hence the surface layer acts as a lid over the large masses of warmer
water below.

There is little spatial variation of water surface temperature throughout the Arctic. Only those areas that are normally ice-free all year exhibit temperatures significantly above freezing. These areas are influenced
by currents carrying warmer water into the Arctic and remain ice-free for
that reason. Seasonal temperature fluctuations occur in areas that are
typically ice-free seasonally (July to September) including the coastal
sectors of the peripheral seas of the Arctic Ocean and around eastern and
northern Baffin Bay. Areas in which major currents carry Arctic water
toward the North Atlantic remain perennially ice-covered and have temperatures close to the freezing point at all times.

In nearly closed basins in higher latitudes (e.g. Arctic Ocean, Baffin
Bay) there is a surface outflow of relatively fresh water with some saline
water entrained with it and an inflow of more saline water at depth. In
such basins there is an increase in surface salinities from the head of the
basin, close to the source of fresh water, toward the mouth. This can be
attributed to progressive mixing between the surface layer and the underlying more saline water.

The general conditions for basins in high latitudes are present in the
Arctic Ocean and Baffin Bay. The surface salinity in summer is lowest

along the periphery of the Arctic Ocean from the Mackenzie River Delta to
the Kara Sea, because major rivers discharge throughout that area. Salinities are never much below about 27°/oo, except very close to a river
mouth, because the fresh water is efficiently mixed with more saline water
on the shallow continental shelf by the action of winds, tides, and currents. Salinities in general increase progressively in the direction of
flow of the surface water and attain maximum values in those areas where
currents are directly introducing North Atlantic surface water into the
Arctic Basin. The North Atlantic surface water is heavier and sinks within
the central basins to subsurface levels. Though no large rivers discharge
into Baffin Bay, the same general picture of the surface salinity holds.
The flux of Arctic Ocean water through the sounds has lower salinity and
hence is less dense and contributes primarily to the surface layer. Inten-
sive melting of ice in summer contributes significant amounts of fresh
water locally, and hence relatively low salinities (31°/oo) may be observed
in central Baffin Bay and along Baffin Island associated with the central
pack and the outflowing Canadian Current.

Surface salinities in winter can be higher by 0.5 to 1°/oo in the
Arctic Ocean and by 1 to 2°/oo in the peripheral seas, as at this season
melt and runoff are not contributing fresh water but mixing with more
saline waters is continuous. However, the general pattern of distribution
remains similar. In winter, (October to April), a process of considerable
importance in modifying the surface waters takes place. When ice grows
from seawater, the salt is largely excluded from the ice and results in a
local increase in salinity and hence density of the remaining water. However, the ice cover is not continuous and leads are continually opening
and closing. Heat loss to the atmosphere from the open water of leads
occurs perhaps 100 times faster than through ice; thus freezing is more
rapid and considerable salt will be concentrated in the waters of leads,
where also temperatures slightly below the freezing point may be observed.

Probably some sort of cellular convection is induced, with downward-
moving columns under the leads carrying excess salt and supercooled water.
This effect may reach as deep as 325 ft, the excess salt contributing to
the maintenance of the strong salinity (density) gradient present in the
lower part of the surface layer, while upward motion elsewhere slowly
transports the heat of the Atlantic layer toward the surface.

Currents

The surface circulation has been largely derived from the observed
drift of various manned ice islands, floe stations, and ships. Current
measurements show that on the average the drifting stations and the
surface water tend to move in similar directions at similar speeds, though
there may be considerable variations between them over short periods. The
mean pattern is depicted in Figure 18 in which the velocity vectors of the
various drifting stations are plotted together with the mean dynamic
topography calculated from over 300 oceonographic stations.

The circulation of the arctic water is in part created by density
differences and in part is wind-induced, which is confirmed by theoretical
studies. The net effect of tides is unknown, although there may be some
asymmetry in their action which would modify the circulations. The surface waters from the whole Eurasian side of the Arctic Ocean tend to move
toward the North Pole. This flow is on the average 0.04 to 0.06 knot; but

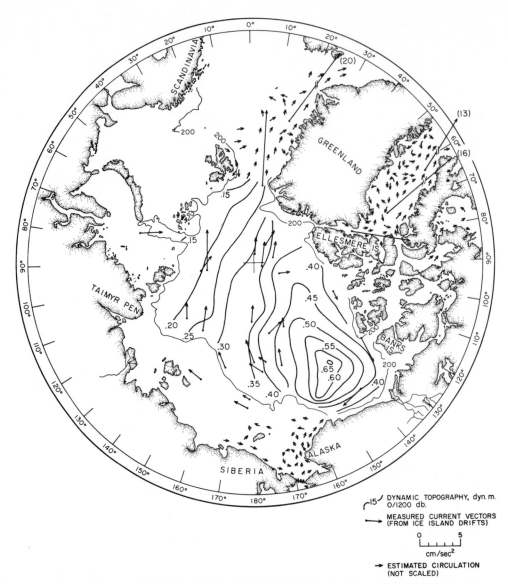

Figure 18.   COMPOSITE SURFACE CIRCULATION FROM DYNAMIC TOPOGRAPHY
and estimated from temperature and salinity distributions.   The station drift vectors are scaled to the
speed scale given, except for three that are labeled
"(16)".

after passing the region of the pole, the flow becomes more concentrated and then exits from the basin as the East Greenland Current. In the Beaufort Sea the surface waters have a clockwise movement, apparently a result of the general wind pattern, such that they tend to flow to the southwest along the shelf off the Canadian Arctic Archipelago and to the north in the area north of Bering Strait.

Around the Greenland Sea there is a large cyclonic circulation, with average speeds in the range of 0.2 to 0.4 knot. Inflow of North Atlantic water, both at the surface and at deep levels, occurs along the east side of the sea as the West Spitsbergen Current. The East Greenland Current is the major flow south on the west side; surface water from the Arctic Ocean contributes to the upper layers, while the deeper waters are largely from the West Spitsbergen Current, completing the cyclonic gyre. The current follows closely the continental slope, and over the wide continental shelf of the northern area (77 to 80°N) the currents tend to be weak and variable. The East Greenland Current seems to accelerate toward the south, attaining speeds of 0.3 to 0.8 knot near Denmark Strait.

The same general pattern of circulation is found in Baffin Bay. A cyclonic circulation dominates the bay; inflow of North Atlantic water occurs off western Greenland through Davis Strait, and inflow from the Arctic Ocean through Smith, Jones, and Lancaster sounds. The Canadian Current runs south along Baffin Island, and as it accumulates water from the various inflows it generally shows higher speeds toward the south.

Direct current measurements from Fletcher's Ice Island, T-3, in 1965 disclosed an unexpected phenomenon - a core of high-speed current (approximately 1 knot) located in the major pycnocline separating the Arctic water from that of the Atlantic layer at depths of 250 to 650 ft. This swift motion occurs only occasionally and has been observed to grow and then decay within a few days. Presumably this motion is associated with certain atmospheric phenomena and it is at present the subject of more intense study.

The circulation of the Atlantic layer has been deduced from the distributions of temperature and salinity. Direct current measurements of this layer from Soviet and U.S. drifting stations confirm the general pattern of motion (Fig. 19). On entering the Eurasia Basin from the Greenland Sea much of the water flows east along the edge of the Eurasian continental slope. The water enters the Amerasia Basin on a broad front across the Lomonosov Ridge. There appears to be a general cyclonic circulation in the Eurasia Basin and a smaller anticyclonic gyre in the Beaufort Sea. Variations between the mean flow pattern and the direct measurements are apparent, but observations are as yet so sparse that it is not known whether the deduced mean pattern is in error or whether periodic or aperiodic effects are significant in the motion.

Direct current measurements in the Atlantic layer of the East Greenland Current show there is little variation in velocity with depth. Thus the deep motion is similar to that of the surface water. Relatively few current measurements have been made in the Atlantic layer of Baffin Bay; however, deductions from the mass and temperature fields indicate a circulation similar to that of the Greenland Sea (without the loss of

Figure 19.   COMPOSITE CIRCULATION OF THE ATLANTIC LAYER

water into the Arctic Ocean). The speeds presumably would be of the same
order as those of the surface currents. Likewise, practically no current
measurements in the bottom water of the Arctic Ocean have been made.
Two measurements of bottom currents in over 10,000 ft of water from T-3
gave results similar in both speed and direction to that of the Atlantic
layer above. Thus, though the circulation of the bottom water is essentially unknown, it appears that it may be similar to that of the Atlantic
layer. The same situation may exist in the Greenland Sea and Baffin Bay
as well.

Advection Boundaries

The major advection boundaries are the Bering Strait, the Greenland-
Spitsbergen strait, and the straits through the Canadian Arctic Archipelago. Oceanographically, the best known of these is the Bering Strait,
through which, in summer, surface Bering Sea water flows north into the
Arctic Ocean. The volume transport is about 2.7×10^7 ft^3/sec. In the
east channel of the strait, speeds normally range between 1 and 2 knots,
although speeds over 3 knots have been measured. In the west channel,
speeds are lower by a factor of 2 to 3. The situation in winter is still
essentially unknown, though it has been suggested that the northward
flow may be only one-fourth that of summer or may even reverse on occasion.
Year-round monitoring of the flow in the strait has been started with a
nuclear-powered current meter and telemetry system in the eastern channel
near Fairway Rock.

The general flow through the passages of the Canadian archipelago
is from the Arctic Ocean toward Baffin Bay. Direct current measurements
are essentially nonexistent. Documentation of the drift of ice island
WH-5 through Nares Strait confirms the general flow out of the Arctic
Ocean through this strait. However, there was evidence of large pulsations in the southerly flow; the indicated periodicity of a few days
to weeks suggest that major atmospheric disturbances may be important
in significantly altering the flows through these channels.

The strait between Greenland and Spitsbergen provides the primary
connection between the waters of the North Atlantic and the Arctic Ocean;
water flows into the Arctic Ocean on the eastern side of the strait and
out of the Arctic Ocean on the western side as the East Greenland Current.
A new concept of the circulation in the Greenland Sea and of the East
Greenland Current resulted from an analysis of current measurements made
from ARLIS II during its drift along East Greenland during the winter
of 1965. The measurements showed the volume transport of the current
to be 1×10^8 ft^3/sec, an order of magnitude larger than previously estimated. This large transport is apparently a major circulation internal
to the Greenland-Norwegian seas; the outflow and inflow from the Arctic
Ocean represent only minor contributions and subtractions from a large
cyclonic circulation. The Arctic water portion of the current to a large
extent controls the ice distribution, and so its presence is manifested
out of all proportion to its small contribution to the total transport.

Peripheral Seas

Of the seven seas which constitute a portion of the Arctic Ocean six
are worthy of brief mention. The seventh, Beaufort Sea, is physically

and oceanographically a part of the Canada Basin. The suggestion has
even been made that the term be dropped but custom and habit will probably
secure its place in common usage.

The Barents Sea occupies nearly a half-million square miles on the
continental shelf of Eurasia. It has free contact with the Norwegian
Sea on the west and with the Arctic Ocean on the north; and it is deeper
than the other peripheral seas, much of it more than 650 ft deep.
The bottom is more like a continental borderland than a shelf, as it
has both exceptionally shallow and deep areas scattered through it. The
flat shelf areas are east and southeast of Svalbard and in the southeastern part of the sea. An east-west ridge at a depth of 650 ft connects
the shore areas around Zemlya Frantsa Iosifa with Svalbard, and a north-
south ridge at 1,000-ft depth separates the western Björnöya basin, with
depths of over 1,300 ft, from the eastern basin. The eastern depression
extends southwest between Zemlya Frantsa Iosifa and Novaya Zemlya with
general depths over 1,000 ft and occasional depths over 1,300 ft. In
the extreme north there is a third depression between Svalbard and Zemlya
Frantsa Iosifa.

The White Sea is a large extension of the Barents Sea that projects
more than 250 mi into the European mainland. The approach from the Barents
Sea is appropriately called Voronka (funnel), and is about 60 mi wide.
The entrance narrows to the southwest until between the Polvostrov
Kol'skiy and the mainland it becomes a strait, called Gorlo (throat),
25 mi wide, where ice obstructs navigation even when the western, inland,
and wider part of the White Sea is reasonably ice-free. The White Sea
is for the most part less than 330 ft deep, but the floor of Kandalakshskaya
Giba in the northwest descends to more than 1,000 ft below sea level.

The surface characteristics of both climate and sea ice in the
Barents Sea result primarily from an influx of warm water from the Norwegian Sea. This warm current flows north along the coast of Norway; a
southern branch enters the Barents Sea along the north coast of Norway and
Kol'skiy Polvostrov as the North Cape Current; the northern branch flows
north of Björnöya and then turns northwest, passing along the south and west
coasts of Svalbard as the Spitsbergen Current. Off Varanger Halvöya the
North Cape Current flows at 0.3 knot but the velocity decreases to the east.
The current splits at Varanger Fjord - one part flows in a belt 50 to 60 mi
wide to the entrance of the White Sea, the other curves northeastward across
the Barents Sea and passes north of Novaya Zemlya into the Kara Sea. This
branch is weak in the north and south of its course, but between 36 and
44°E it runs at approximately 0.75 knot.

The major inflow of cold water into the Barents Sea is between Novaya
Zemlya and Zemlya Frantsa Iosifa. This current also branches into two
parts - one part flows southwest of the archipelago and the other west
as the Bear Island Current. In the southeast the general movement of
water is toward the Kara Sea except for the Litke Current which has the
reverse direction. It moves west through the northern half of Proliv
Karskiye Vorota and then northwest along Novaya Zemlya joining the general
northerly movement there. In the White Sea there is a weak outward
current in spring and summer and an equally weak counterclockwise eddy
within the basin.

The Kara Sea is exceptionally shallow in the east but relatively deep
for its position on the continental shelf in the west. Off the east

coast of Novaya Zemlya there is a 40-mi wide basin that in some places
is 1,750 ft deep. A ridge in the north of the Kara Sea separates the
basin from the Arctic Ocean. Between Poluostrov Yamal and Novaya Zemlya
there is another trough of deeper water. There are two more basins in
the north of the sea which have maximum depths of about 1,700 ft and
are separated by a ridge. Ostrova Uyedineniya, Vize, and Ushakova
form the highest elevations of this ridge. In the southeast of the
Kara Sea depths average only 165 ft 50 to 120 mi from the shore. The
water adjacent to the mouths of the Ob' and the Yenisey rivers is
also exceptionally shallow.

The only important current in the Kara Sea forms a closed counter-
clockwise circulation in the western portion. The gyre begins in the
east with Ob' and Yenisey waters which spread as they leave the estuaries.
One branch flows to Novaya Zemlya where it turns southwest to Proliv
Karskiye Vorota. Within the main circulation are two small weak counter-
clockwise eddies. Water also enters the Kara Sea around the north of
Novaya Zemlya from the Barents Sea and eventually mixes with the Ob'-
Yenisey waters.

Tides in the Kara Sea are semidiurnal and relatively weak. They
come from the Barents Sea along eastern Novaya Zemlya and from the Arctic
Ocean along western Severnaya Zemlya. They merge at Ostrov Uyedineniya
and progress southwest. The average amplitude is 1.5 to 3 ft but winds
commonly increase the tidal range by 3 ft or more.

Both the Laptev and the East Siberian seas are shallow basins with
gentle shores. The edge of the continental shelf is up to 400 mi offshore. Only in the northeastern Laptev Sea, off Severnaya Zemlya, are
depths greater than 300 ft. The western sector of the East Siberian
Sea, south of the Ostrova Novosibirskiye and east to the Kolyma River,
is exceptionally shallow with many shoals. Between the Indigirka and
the Kolyma rivers an almost continuous shorebank, defined by the three-
fathom curve, extends about 23 mi out from the shore. From the Kolyma
east to Mys Shmidta, the coastal water is deeper. There are only a
few islands, and these, with the exception of Ostrova Medvezh'i, are
close to the shore. The sea deepens slowly to the northeast; maximum
depths are 150 to 180 ft.

The general flow of water in both the East Siberian and Laptev seas
is counterclockwise. There is a weak easterly coastal current which
is modified by water from the large rivers which forces it offshore
in a northeasterly direction at 1 knot; counterclockwise eddies develop
when it is caught in coastal indentations. The major current entering
the Laptev Sea comes through Proliv Vil'kitskogo between Mys Chelyuskin
and Severnaya Zemlya. It is joined by a cold current flowing southeastward along Severnya Zemlya at 0.2 knot, and the combined waters move
along the Taimyr coast into the shallow part of the Laptev Sea. At the
Lena Delta the current splits; and one part, flowing along the west
side of the Ostrova Novosibiriskiye at 0.5 to 1 knot, flows to the north
of the archipelago and joins the main arctic drift. The other part
flows through Proliv Dmitriya Lapteva and other straits into the East
Siberian Sea.

The waters that pass through the straits separating Ostrov Novosibirskiye
and the mainland spread out on reaching the East Siberian Sea. The main
branch near the coast flows at approximately 0.3 knot. A branch of this

current is believed to pass north and west of Ostrov Vrangelya.

North of the coastal currents in both the Laptev and the East Siberian seas, the water flows in large counterclockwise eddies. Farther north still is a west-northwest current which runs northwest at the Ostrova De-Longa and passes north of the Ostrova Novosibirskiye into the Laptev Sea. It continues northwest across the northern margin of the sea and flows north of Severnaya Zemlya.

Tidal progression is southward from the Arctic Ocean in both seas. Tides are semidiurnal and their range is 1 ft, although it may be raised to 10 to 12 ft with an onshore wind. Tidal currents flow from 0.5 to 0.8 knot in the Laptev Sea but are weaker in the East Siberian Sea.

The Chukchi Sea is nearly 600 mi across, north from Bering Strait toward the pole. Its floor is probably the flattest plain in the world and over extensive areas slopes are less than 12 in/mi. The greater part of the sea within 120 mi of the coast is from 50 to 100 ft deep. The overall mean depth is about 165 ft. Low swells rise from the plain, the best known being the Herald Shoal that comes to within 50 ft of the surface at about 70°30'N midway between Wrangel Island and Alaska. The bed of the sea is probably crossed by a network of valleys formed sub-aerially when the floor was dry land during the Pleistocene. One of the large landforms of this type is the Hope Submarine Valley which leads west from Cape Thompson and has relief of about 30 ft. Poorly formed terraces have been recognized below sea level and the remains of a former spit can be traced 25 mi north from Cape Prince of Wales.

The continental slope commences at about 650 ft and is crossed by several submarine valleys. Chukchi Cape, 125 mi across, and the smaller Northwind Seahigh are outliers of the continental shelf beyond the slope.

Water enters the Chukchi Sea through Bering Strait. This current appears as warm and low-salinity water that converges on Point Hope and there turns east toward Point Barrow. The waters on the Siberian coast (in the vicinity of Bering Strait) are cold and of high salinity. It was thought that this water passes south through Bering Strait, but it now appears that it is north-flowing and its properties derive from divergence and upwelling. A cold current passes east through Proliv Longa. There is consequently a tendency for a clockwise circulation in the Chukchi Sea.

Other Arctic Seas

Norwegian and Greenland Seas

The Norwegian and Greenland seas are bounded on the west by the Greenland continental shelf and on the east by the Norwegian, Barents, and Svalbard continental shelves. The depths of the edges of the shelves vary greatly. A large area of the shelves is deeper than 600 ft and frequently extends to 1,320 ft. Seaward of the shelves are the continental slopes with gradients of 1:15 to 1:40 leading down to the abyssal plains.

The Norwegian shelf is 50 to 140 mi wide in its southern and central parts but narrows to 10 mi off the Lofoten. It is more irregular than normal continental shelves and is crossed by a number of troughlike gullies.

These are associated with the major fiord systems of Norway, and their present form is mainly the result of erosion by the Quaternary ice sheets. The
glaciation also produced morainic ridges which are found out to the shelf
edge.

The Svalbard shelf is 10 to 40 mi wide. It is traversed by deep glacial
canyons originating in the fiords of Spitsbergen and also contains elongated
depressions parallel to the coast. This shelf extends to the banks south
of Björnöya, while eastward to the banks off northern Norway is the shelf
area of the western Barents Sea. The latter shelf is deeper and less irregular than the shelves off Norway and Svalbard.

The Greenland continental shelf north of the Denmark Strait is generally
broad (60 to 170 mi) but narrows to about 15 mi in the extreme north. It
is widest at the Belgica Bank. Typically the bottom is irregular and rough,
but local smooth areas are common and there are a number of shoal areas
less than 330 ft in depth. Troughs are present in the shelf and are both
parallel and normal to the shoreline. South from Denmark Strait the Greenland Shelf narrows from 170 mi in width to 25 mi at Kap Farvel. It is
crossed by extensions of the fiords of East Greenland. A rise of 165 to
330 ft - the terminal moraine of the Quaternary ice sheet - is found all
the way along the edge of the shelf, and it closes these channels against
the sea.

Around Iceland the continental shelf is up to 80 mi wide in the west
and north and 50 mi in the east, but off the south coast it narrows to 10
mi. In the north and west it is crossed by gullies that start in the
fiords and inlets of the Icelandic coastline; in the southeast pronounced
gullies seem to have no such link.

The dominant feature of the central parts of the Norwegian and Greenland
seas is the mid-oceanic mountain range forming the Iceland-Jan Mayen and
Mohn ridges. This is the continuation of the Mid-Atlantic Ridge which
rises above sea level in Iceland. The Mid-Atlantic Ridge is characterized
in its most elevated region by a central rift zone and by the fact that
earthquake epicenters tend to lie on or very near to its axis. These
features continue in the Iceland and Jan Mayen ridges. A narrow, deep rift
valley, 2 to 3 mi wide at the 10,800-ft isobath, extends along their axial
lines and has well-developed structural benches on its walls. It ends at
78°30'N where it meets the Spitsbergen block. The base of the ridges
extends about 35 mi from the rift, and their crests lie at depths less than
7,200 ft. On both flanks of the ridges are many seamounts. The mountains
of the ridge systems rise above the sea as the island of Jan Mayen. A
massive, almost unbroken feature, the south Jan Mayen Ridge runs south
from the island; its upper surface is levelled with least depths between
2,640 and 3,600 ft.

The Greenland Sea Basin was formerly considered to be separated from
the Arctic Basin by the Nansen Sill, but Soviet investigations have shown
that a continuous sill does not exist because it is cut through the middle
at about 1°E longitude by the deep Lena Trough, the minimum depth of which
is 10,200 to 11,200 ft. The mid-oceanic ridge turns in a northwesterly
direction from a region to the west of Prins Karls Forland and runs in what
is known as the Spitsbergen Fracture Zone to the northeastern tip of Greenland. This results in a bottom topography with a complicated ridge and
trench structure. To the east of this zone is the gently undulating Yermak
Plateau which extends for 130 mi from the northwestern corner of Spitsbergen

with crests at depths shallower than 3,000 ft.

The basin of the Norwegian Sea is separated from the abyssal plains of the northernmost Atlantic, which has depths as great as 10,000 ft, by the Scotland-Greenland Ridge. The eastern part, between Scotland and the Faroes, is known as the Wyville Thomson Ridge and most of it is less than 2,000 ft in depth; but between Faroe Bank and the Faroe Islands is a narrow channel through the ridge with a sill depth of about 2,700 ft and a least width, at the 650-ft isobath, of about 13 mi. The Faroes-Iceland Ridge lies mainly at a depth of 1,300 to 1,650 ft, but the central part is shallower than 1,300 ft and has several peaks. It is crossed by three saddle-like depressions with depths of 1,375 to 1,600 ft. The Iceland-Greenland Ridge lies at depths between 1,000 and 1,300 ft, but it is cut from northeast to southwest by a narrow channel which has a sill depth of 2,000 ft at about 26°30'W.

The deeper parts of the Norwegian Sea can be divided into three regions. The Iceland Basin lies between the Iceland-Jan Mayen and South Jan Mayen ridges and has depths of 6,500 to 8,200 ft. The Norwegian Abyssal Plain, to the east of the South Jan Mayen Ridge, is the most extensive of the three regions and has a considerable area deeper than 11,500 ft. A number of tall, isolated steep-flanked seamounts rise from this plain. To the east it is bounded by the Norwegian Plateau, a flat-topped feature generally shallower than 6,500 ft. An extension of this plateau to the northwest separates the Norwegian Abyssal Plain from the Lofoten Abyssal Plain. This third region is relatively extensive, and it has a large area greater than 10,500 ft in depth. It is bounded on the north by the Mohn Ridge.

Beyond the Mohn Ridge is the basin of the Greenland Sea. It consists in the south of the Greenland Abyssal Plain, at a depth of 12,000 to 12,500 ft, with the deepest parts toward the southeast and east. This is separated from the smaller Boreas Abyssal Plain by the Greenland Fracture Zone, which has a crest shallower than 9,000 ft and many individual peaks shallower than 6,000 ft and is a precipitous feature with gradients up to 1:10 on its steeper southern side. To its north is the Hovgaard Fracture Zone parallel to and slightly smaller than the Greenland Fracture Zone. The Hovgaard Fracture Zone separates the Boreas Abyssal Plain from a small basin which is probably not a true abyssal plain. This has a smaller irregular relief smoothed by a blanket of sediment and lies immediately to the south of the Spitsbergen Fracture Zone.

The water masses of the area together with their temperature and salinity characteristics are listed in Table 6.

TABLE 6

Temperature and Salinity Characteristics of the Water Masses
of the European and American Arctic and Subarctic Seas

Northeast Atlantic water	9.5°C; 35.35°/oo
Irminger-Atlantic water	4° to 6°C; 34.95 to 35.10°/oo
Arctic water	<0°C; <34.0°/oo
Labrador Sea water	3.4°C potential temperature; 34.89°/oo
Northeast Atlantic Deep water	3.0°C potential temperature; 34.95°/oo
Northwest Atlantic Bottom water	0.8° to 1.5°C; 34.91°/oo

Norwegian Sea Deep water	<0°C; 34.92P/oo
Arctic-Atlantic water	0° to 2°C; 34.8 to 35.9°/oo
North Icelandic Winter water	2° to 3°C; 34.85 to 34.9°/oo

The two dominant features are the warm currents which form the ends of the Gulf Stream system and the cold currents that derive from the Arctic Basin. The North Atlantic Drift divides at the Mid-Atlantic Ridge at about 51°N latitude. One arm moves northward parallel to the ridge toward Iceland where it becomes the Irminger Current. This latter carries the Irminger-Atlantic water and bifurcates to the west of Iceland, one branch proceeding northward and then turning east along the north coast of Iceland and the other turning first west and then south to flow along the East Greenland slope eventually to round Kap Farvel and flow northward along the West Greenland slope in the Davis Strait.

A second arm of the North Atlantic Drift carries warm northeast Atlantic water eastward toward the British Isles and passes through the Faroes-Shetlands Channel and to the west of the Faroe Islands into the Norwegian Sea where it is known as the Atlantic or Norwegian Current. This current moves northward along the Norwegian coast and gradually becomes cooler and less saline. Off northwest Norway it divides into the North Cape Current, which flows eastward into the Barents Sea, and the Spitsbergen Current, which continues northward past Spitsbergen to enter the Arctic Basin. Part of the Spitsbergen Current turns westward off the northern part of Spitsbergen and flows toward the Greenland Shelf. It then turns south and proceeds below the East Greenland Current as a warmer more saline intermediate layer at a 650- to 1,300-ft depth.

The main cold current of the region is the East Greenland Current. This carries ice and Arctic water, with subzero temperatures and low salinity, from the Arctic Basin along the whole length of the East Greenland shelf to round Kap Farvel and enter Davis Strait. There are two branches of the East Greenland Current. The first, the Jan Mayen Current, flows eastward to the north of Jan Mayen in the region of the Mohn Ridge. The second, the East Icelandic Current, flows southeastward past the northeast coast of Iceland sometimes reaching the north coast of the Faroe Islands or beyond. Lesser sources of Arctic water and ice are the Björnöya and East Spitsbergen currents. These originate in the northeastern part of the Barents Sea and move southwestward over the Svalbard Shelf, the former to reach Björnöya and the latter to round Sorkapp on Spitsbergen and flow northward between the Spitsbergen coast and the West Spitsbergen Current. The distribution of the sea ice is determined by the East Greenland Current and its two branches and to a lesser extent by the East Spitsbergen Current.

Between the East Greenland Current and its branches, on the one hand, and the Atlantic Current, on the other, an effective mixing takes place and wide areas in the Norwegian and Greenland seas are covered by mixed water. Similar mixing - though on a smaller scale - between warm and cold currents takes place on the Svalbard and Barents shelves and along the East Greenland slopes south of Denmark Strait. Where the warm and cold currents meet, extremely sharp temperature gradients can occur in the near-surface layers.

Coastal water of varied composition and temperature occurs along the coasts of Iceland and Norway. Those coastal waters mix along the edges of the Norwegian and Icelandic shelves with the warm currents that flow outside and beneath them.

The speeds of the various currents are not well established. There is
evidence to suggest that there are frequent changes because of the wind,
but the direct measurement of the Eulerian form of the motion over long
periods of time by means of moored recording current meters has only just
begun. Some estimates of the Lagrangian form of motion have been obtained
from the sets of ships and the drift of floating objects. These put the
speeds of the Atlantic Current and East Greenland Current at 0.5 to 1 knot.
Locally the East Greenland Current can reach very high speeds; for example,
it is 3 knots just south of the Denmark Strait.

The basins of the Norwegian and Greenland seas contain a very nearly
uniform deep water with a salinity of about 34.92°/oo and a temperature of
about -1°C. The mixed water in the upper layers, primarily in the Greenland
Sea and to a smaller extent in the Norwegian Sea, is cooled in winter; but
before it can freeze it reaches a higher density than that of water below
it and so sinks to form the deep water. In the region of the Iceland-Jan
Mayen and Mohn ridges Arctic Intermediate water appears above the Norwegian
Sea Deep water and below the Arctic water of the East Greenland Current
System. In the Icelandic coastal area, vertical mixing of Atlantic water
and Arctic water in winter results in a homogeneous water in the uppermost
650 to 1,000 ft. This water has a temperature of 2 to 3°C and a salinity
of 34.85 to 34.90°/oo and is called North Icelandic Winter water.

The Norwegian Sea Deep water flows into the North Atlantic Basin through
the channel between Faroe Bank and the Faroe Islands. It flows at the bottom of this channel at a speed in excess of 2 knots, and as it does so the
northeast Atlantic water which lies above it is entrained into the flow.
The resultant mixing produces the northeast Atlantic Deep water. This water
mass has minor constituents because at times the Arctic-Atlantic water flows
through the same channel. Also, the Norwegian Sea Deep water, Arctic-
Atlantic water, and North Icelandic Winter water - particularly near Iceland - overflow the Faroes-Iceland Ridge and proceed down its southern
flanks, entraining overlying northeast Atlantic water as they do so, to
eventually join the outflow from the Faroe Bank Channel as it flows westward
at the foot of the ridge.

The northeast Atlantic Deep water turns south when it meets the Reykjanes
Ridge; at about latitude 53°N it breaks through this ridge and flows northward along its western flanks to fill most of the Irminger Sea at a depth
of 5,700 to 8,200 ft. Above it, in the Irminger Sea, is Labrador Sea water
with its core at 1,700 to 4,300 ft. This water is formed as the result of
the vertical mixing from the surface down to 4,600 ft of low salinity water
in the Labrador Sea in winter. Below the northeast Atlantic Deep water in
the Irminger Sea is the northwest Atlantic Bottom water which originates
with the overflow of water from the Norwegian Sea across the Iceland-Greenland Ridge in the region of the narrow deep channel in the Denmark Strait.
The overflowing water is at times Norwegian Sea Deep water and at times
Arctic-Atlantic water. In both cases the overflow proceeds at high speed
down the East Greenland continental slope and entrains first overlying
Irminger Atlantic water and later Labrador Sea water and northeast Atlantic
Deep water to produce a water mass of high density which fills the bottom
parts of the basins of the Irminger and Labrador seas. Thus, in addition
to a counterclockwise horizontal circulation in the upper part of the water
column with the northeast Atlantic water entering this area and the East
Greenland Current leaving it, there is also a circulation in the vertical
plane with the inflow of the northeast Atlantic water being compensated for
by deeper outflows over the Scotland-Greenland Ridge of Norwegian Sea Deep

water and Arctic-Atlantic water.

Baffin Bay

The central parts of Baffin Bay and Davis Strait are occupied by the
Baffin Basin that is separated from the deep waters of the Labrador Sea
by a broad sill between Cumberland Peninsula and Greenland north of Godhaab.
The continental shelf on both sides of Baffin Bay is crossed by U-shaped
troughs that head into fiords and are believed to have been glacially
formed. The valleys end abruptly at the continental slope.

The narrow channel that separates Canada from northwest Greenland consists of two basins - Hall and Kane - joined by Robeson and Kennedy channels and Smith Sound. In the north, at the narrowest part, the two shores
are separated by only 10 mi. The surface of the floor is hummocky. The
shallowest part is in the north of Kane Basin where there is a submerged
watershed at 300 to 600 ft. In both directions the floor drops away to
1,300 to 1,600 ft near the Lincoln Sea and About 2,100 ft at the south end
of Smith Sound.

The bathymetry of Jones Sound is not well known. The central part
may have depths of about 2,300 ft, and this is joined by entrenched valleys
that cross the shallower sea floor on either side. Lancaster Sound has a
wide flat floor that drops eastward to 2,600 ft where it enters Baffin Bay.
As in Jones Sound, submerged valleys enter the main trough from the side
fiords and channels.

The surface circulation in Baffin Bay is counterclockwise. The West
Greenland Current flowing north along the coast is formed by the combination
of the Irminger and East Greenland currents near Kap Farvel and is relatively warm for the latitude. Its velocity probably decreses from about
1 knot in the south to less than half this amount in northern Baffin Bay
where complex gyrals develop as the current is deflected to flow south off
the Canadian coast as the cold Canadian Current. This current also receives
water from Kane Basin, Jones Sound, and Lancaster Sound, although the exact
quantities are not known and are probably variable. In both sounds it
appears as though there is a westerly setting surface current on the north
side and probably for the whole width of Lancaster Sound below 650 ft.
Icebergs in the Canadian Current may move on the average of 0.3 knot.

Three water masses have been recognized in central Baffin Bay. In the
upper 650 ft the temperature is about -1.5°C and the salinity 33.8°/oo; the
characteristics of this mass originate from a combination of the West Greenland Current, the arctic inflow through the channels, and local cooling.
Beneath the upper layer and down to 3,300 ft is a warmer mass with a temperature above -0.5°C and salinity of 34.2 to 34.5°/oo. In the deepest parts
of the basin there is cold water with a temperature below -0.5°C and salinity of 34.45°/oo. The upper two layers are also present in Lancaster and
Jones sounds.

Labrador Sea and Gulf of St. Lawrence

Off northern Labrador the mountainous coast is matched by a rapid deepening of the sea floor, and the 300-ft isobath is only a few miles offshore.
Deep, glaciated trenches lead from the fiords across the shelf. Many of

the fiords have sills at their mouth at depths of 65 to 200 ft, and the
waters behind reach depths in excess of 650 ft. South of Nain the continental shelf is generally wider and inshore depths are correspondingly less.
All of Newfoundland is surrounded by a wide continental shelf. Off the
Strait of Belle Isle and northeastern Newfoundland the shelf is 120 mi wide
and broadens to 160 mi at the Grand Banks.

The Labrador coast is washed by the Labrador Current. This great
stream of cold water pours south in a belt approximately 150 mi wide. The
inshore part is uniformly cold with surface temperatures not above 5°C in
late summer as far south as Hamilton Inlet; and off the Atlantic coast of
Newfoundland the surface temperature is lower than 10°C.

The Gulf of St. Lawrence is a shallow continental sea that is penetrated
by two deep channels. The larger, the Laurentian Channel, extends from the
continental shelf south of Newfoundland almost to the Saguenay River. For
much of its distance it is about 1,400 ft deep. A shorter and shallower
channel separates from the main trough and then divides again to pass north
of Anticostia Island and into the northeast corner of the Gulf; its average
depth is 850 ft.

In addition to the St. Lawrence water, water masses enter the Gulf
through Strait of Belle Isle and round the southwest corner of Newfoundland.
The outlet is mainly on the south side of Cabot Strait. The northern current carries cold water into the Gulf, and the whole of the Quebec north
shore has sea surface temperatures from 8 to 11°C in late summer. The
water entering on the north side of Cabot Strait is relatively warm and
temperatures of 15 to 16°C are only a degree or two colder than the shallow waters around Prince Edward Island.

Hudson Strait and Bay

Hudson Strait is deeper than most continental seas. At the southern
entrance maximum water depths are about 2,250 ft. In the central section
of the Strait, the sea floor is commonly below 900 ft and reaches 1,375 ft.
Comparable depths occur at the west end. Coastal waters are shallow in the
bight between Big Island and Foxe Peninsula.

The overall movement of water in Hudson Strait is from west to east and
the mean outflow for the whole Strait is about 0.18 knot. There is, however, an inflow of the Canadian Current along the north side of the Strait
which brings small icebergs into the Strait. Most of this water turns and
joins the outflow on the south side but part penetrates into southeastern
Foxe Basin.

The division between Hudson Strait and Ungava Bay is the 1,300-ft isobath. Water depths around Akpatok Island approach 300 ft and there is
probably a trench running south, east, and northeast around the island with
depths of 650 to 1,000 ft.

Tidal ranges in general in Hudson Strait are high (20 to 40 ft). On
the west side of Ungava Bay they are among the largest in the world and at
Leaf Basin can approach 60 ft.

Foxe Basin is exceptionally shallow. A large part of the southeast
and northeast sectors are less than 100 ft deep. In the absence of

soundings, it must be considered that all the western Baffin Island coast south of Air Force Island is too shallow for ships. Small boats have worked on these coasts but have experienced great difficulty with the wide tidal flats. Contrasting strongly with these conditions, depths of 600 to 1,500 ft occur in Foxe Channel where there is a broad submarine trough adjacent to Southampton Island. Surface currents in Foxe Basin are largely tidal. There is a general cyclonic movement which carries water that enters the Basin through Fury and Hecla Strait south at 0.3 to 1.1 knots. There is a smaller inflow of water along the west side of Foxe Peninsula.

Prince Regent Inlet, Gulf of Boothia, and Admiralty Sound have similar submarine topography. All are extremely shallow at the southern end. Depths increase northward in what are almost certainly submerged glacial troughs, becoming greater than 2,000 ft. Sills separate the sounds from Parry Channel.

Hydrographic surveys of Hudson Bay are incomplete but it is known that depths in excess of 900 ft occur and that the average depth is about 300 ft. Several of the main river valleys entering Hudson Bay can be traced sub-aerially for considerable distances and are part of an original drainage system that flowed northeast into Hudson Strait.

James Bay, with an area of about 20,000 sq mi, is even shallower than Hudson Bay; the deepest part is little more than 150 ft and occurs in an elongated sea-floor depression that trends north-south a little east of the center of the Bay. The west coast is very shallow with depths of 50 to 150 ft. The largest island in James Bay, Akimiski Island, is separated from the west coast by a shallow channel, passable only to small boats at high tide.

The James Bay trough extends northeast in a depression on the sea floor at about 150 ft; the depression then deepens to below 400 ft parallel to the arc-shaped central east coast of Hudson Bay. Westward, the bottom rises forming a plateau area less than 200 ft deep on which are located the Belcher Islands. Similar shallower zones surround the Ottawa Islands, Mansel and Coats islands, the south side of Southampton Island, and the Hudson Bay Lowland in northern Ontario and Manitoba. Between Mansel and Coats islands there is a narrow trench over 600 ft deep that connects with a channel in the west end of Hudson Strait.

An extensive shallow water zone borders the west coast of Hudson Bay south of Chesterfield Inlet. North of 61°N the coast is rocky with many islets and reefs; farther south an 8-ft tidal zone of mud and boulders widens to several miles.

The circulation in Hudson Bay is counterclockwise. Part of the circulation is closed but there is inflow through Roes Welcome Sound and Fisher Strait (between Coats and Southampton islands) and from rivers. Outflow is between Coats Island, Mansel Island, and the northwest corner of Quebec. Preliminary data suggest that the water mass has arctic characteristics with bottom water temperatures of -2°C.

Canadian Arctic Archipelago

The continental margin northwest of the Canadian Arctic Archipelago consists of a shelf that slopes seaward and drops in a series of shallow steps to depths of 1,300 to 1,500 ft, 40 to 60 mi offshore. The channels between the islands are interpreted as drowned river valleys. They have been much modified by glacial action and they characteristically have steep trough sides and a horizontal, although somewhat irregular, floor that is separated by sills into basins. The general depth in the channels is about 1,300 ft.

The virtual absence of ships from the ice-filled waters of the western Queen Elizabeth Islands has restricted the collection of oceanographic data. In the last decade, however, there has been successful sounding and sampling through the sea ice. The movement of ice islands in the channels and the distribution of driftwood suggests that there is a general south-easterly and southerly movement of surface water from the Arctic Basin through the Archipelago. Stronger local currents result from tides although the low tidal range must limit them except in narrow channels. The highest tides are found in the southeastern part of the area where at Resolute the maximum tidal range is about 6 ft. The range decreases westward through Parry Channel until along south Melville Island it is about 4 ft and on Prince Patrick Island 1.2 ft. Similar low ranges occur in the more northerly islands of the Sverdrup Basin.

Little is known of the oceanographic characteristics of the southwestern waters of the Archipelago. The submarine topography is interpreted most easily as a partly drowned land with today's channels representing major river valleys that were modified by Pleistocene ice. The main river in former times flowed from the east end of Queen Maud Gulf westward through Dease Strait, Coronation Gulf, and Dolphin and Union Strait to Amundsen Gulf. The lowland (now drowned) that it occupied deepens unevenly westward with local shallow sections notably at the east end of Dolphin and Union Strait where one section is probably no more than 60 ft deep. In Amundsen Gulf ice erosion has resulted in depths of between 200 and 1,500 ft. Farther east in Coronation Gulf depths are about 600 ft, and on the north side of Queen Maud Gulf they vary from 180 to 350 ft. The shallowest area is in the east at Simpson Strait where shoals are numerous and the deepest channel is possibly no deeper than 35 ft.

Few reliable data are available on depths in Victoria Strait or M'Clintock Channel, both of which have been almost continuously blocked by ice since their discovery by Europeans. Channels suitable for northern movement of ships toward Parry Channel are restricted to Prince of Wales Strait in the west and Franklin Strait and Peel Sound (or Bellot Strait) in the east. Prince of Wales Sound has a general depth of 120 to 180 ft and ships of any draft can pass through it. In the eastern channels depths apparently increase from the southern end of Franklin Strait, where they are of the order of 300 ft to about 1,400 ft opposite Bellot Strait. This depth is maintained northward, but at Prescott Island the floor of Peel Sound rises to form a sill at 800 ft.

There are few observations about currents in this area, although it is believed that the majority are the result of tides, changing barometric pressure, and winds. The tidal range everywhere is low - of the order of 2 to 3 ft for spring tides to 1 ft or less at neap tides. The spring tides show a semidiurnal form but at neap tides, at least locally, a diurnal solar tide appears. All larger fluctuations of sea level are a direct result of pressure and wind changes; and these, particularly the neaps, may completely override the normal tide.

The continental shelf between Point Barrow and Cape Prince Alfred varies in width from less than 50 mi in the west to nearly 100 mi in the center and northeast. Off Alaska the profile is characteristic of the continental oceanic margin in all parts of the world, consisting of the flat shelf and a steep upper continental slope that decreases as it reaches the Canada Basin at about 11,400 ft. East of the border the slope diverges from the mainland in a curving arc toward northwestern Banks Island, and the upper slope is gentler in this area than farther west. The continental shelf is crossed by several deep valleys. In the west is the Barrow Sea Valley which originates off Cape Franklin and deepens northeastward to become 20 mi wide and U-shaped north of Point Barrow. A second valley is 55 mi to the east. Northwest of Mackenzie Bay is the Mackenzie Sea Valley, a broad flat-bottomed valley apparently leading from a Pleistocene outlet of the Mackenzie River. One hundred forty miles to the northeast a smaller valley has been recognized. The largest of the shelf valleys is a broad asymmetrical feature, the Amundsen Trough, between Banks Island and the mainland. It has an average width of 24 mi and the floor is at about 1,400 ft. It is believed to mark the course of a major outlet glacier from the Pleistocene ice sheet.

Surface currents in the Beaufort Sea are light and probably irregular, depending largely on wind and pressure changes. The clockwise circulation of the Beaufort Gyre sets southwest and west at roughly 0.1 knot over the continental slope, but there is little evidence that it is found inshore. Along the Alaskan coast there is thought to be a reverse (eastward) current.

Bering and Okhotsk Seas

The submarine topography of the marginal seas of the north Pacific has unusual variety. The northern half of Bering Sea (from Unimak Island to Mys Navarin) is a continental sea with few areas deeper than 300 ft. The southern half, in contrast, is oceanic with depths in excess of 10,000 ft except close to the Aleutian arc where two submarine ridges project north from the islands. The more westerly reaches the Soviet mainland and separates a small basin from the main Bering Sea; the easterly ridge curves back toward the Aleutians about 160 mi north of the arc.

The Sea of Okhotsk also shows striking differences between the northern margins, including the Kamchatka and Okhotsk coasts, which are underlain by typical continental shelves with depths of less than 600 ft, and a broad central basin more than 3,300 ft deep. A wide underwater lowland leads into the basin from Zaliv Shelekhova in the northeast. The basin deepens rapidly to a trough parallel to the Kuril arc south of 48°N, and the deepest point is more than 11,000 ft below sea level.

The currents in the Bering Sea are not well known except for observations near Bering Strait. It is clear that a cold current flows southwestward along the Kamchatka coast and becomes strong off the Kuril Islands. Elsewhere there are several closed circulations and a net inflow to the sea between the Aleutian Islands. The general circulation in the Sea of Okhotsk is counterclockwise and runs strongest 20 to 40 mi offshore. A complex pattern of currents has been reported from the middle of the sea. The current moves north along western Kamchatka at 0.5 knot; in other sectors velocities up to 1 knot are recorded. The Sea of Okhotsk has one unusual feature which affects both the ice conditions and the climate. This consists of patches of substantially colder water (1 to 6°C) that are located at the

entrance of Guba Shelekhova and Ostrova Iony and between the Ostrov Shantar
and northern Sakhalin. These cold spots mark upwellings of colder deeper
water the cause of which is still in doubt. They are associated with continuous dense fogs in the summer and with concentrations of ice in the
winter. The exchange of water with the Pacific Ocean is not great due to
the shallow depths (usually less than 1,600 ft) of the channels between the
Kuril Islands. Pacific waters normally enter through the northeastern channels and Okhotsk water leaves by the southwestern channels.

Acoustics

The propagation of underwater sound in the Arctic Ocean differs in
several ways from that in nonpolar oceans. In the Atlantic and Pacific
oceans, the SOFAR channel lies at depths of 3,250 to 4,500 ft, but in the
Arctic it is at the surface. Low-frequency sound is propagated to great
distances in the Arctic SOFAR channel. Sound rays are alternately refracted
upward in the water and reflected downward from the base of the ice. At
great ranges signals consist predominantly of low frequencies, between 8
and 100 kHz. The roughness of the lower surface of the ice strongly atten-
uates the high frequencies but has a negligible effect on the low frequencies. Signals generated by small explosions have been recorded clearly at
distances from 40 mi up to 1,500 mi. Beyond a range of 300 mi, sounds above
100 Hz are very weak. The Arctic SOFAR signal is dispersed so that an
impulsive signal increases in duration as the range is increased. At a
range of 300 mi the duration of a signal from a small explosion is about
five seconds. At shorter ranges and over smooth bottoms such as abyssal
plains, bottom-reflected arrivals can be of importance. They are late
arrivals and increase still further the duration of the signal.

In the shallow water of the shelves, propagation characteristics depend
strongly on bottom parameters. In general, long-range transmission is much
more strongly attenuated along shallow-water paths than it is along deep-
water paths. Dispersion is even more pronounced in shallow-water transmission.

Transmission Loss

The stable positive sound velocity profile in the Arctic Ocean results
in a half-sound channel bounded at the interface of the water and ice. The
divergence loss in this situation can be calculated as a function of the
skip distance of the deepest traveling ray and the range, assuming spheri-
cal spreading to one-quarter of the distance traveled by the deepest limiting ray from the source to where it strikes the surface and then cylindri-
cal spreading thereafter.

In the Arctic the only other significant loss at low acoustic frequencies, where absorption can be neglected, is the loss suffered at each ray
reflection at the ice-water interface. For long-range propagation where
many reflections occur, this reflection loss can most simply be handled as
a loss per unit distance. This loss will be a function of frequency,
since the degree of roughness of the ice-reflecting surface - and hence its
scattering power - is a matter of the wavelength of the impinging sound.
Therefore the total transmission loss is equal to divergence loss plus
reflection loss.

Discrete frequency smoothed curves of transmission loss in the range from 20 to 3200 Hz are given in Figure 20. Also shown are the standard deviations of actual measurements from the smoothed curves. The deviations result from variations in the yield of explosive signals, reflection effects at the source and the receiver, variations at bottom depth, and measurement errors.

Since at the lower frequencies the wavelengths are comparable to the source and receiver depths of the loss measurements made in the Arctic, the Lloyd mirror effect must be considered. Figure 21 is a representation of this effect on transmission loss derived from the geometry of the arriving waves. Note the 6-db amplification of the signal at 40 Hz with a receiver at 200 ft. This amplification quickly becomes a loss as the receiver is moved toward the surface. The same holds true for the source depth of the sound. The curves in Figure 21 are idealized and represent observed results from the first minimum near the surface to the first maximum (or 6-db enhancement point) for any given frequency while below that there is considerable variation.

Figure 22 exemplifies the need to know the depth of the source to measure transmission loss. The two traces are for identical charge size and receiver depth with varied source depth. Note the greatly increased bottom bounce arrivals from the shallow shot. These arrivals comprise more than half of the total arriving energy, the rest being in the water-traveling rays. For the deep shot, the bottom bounce energy is a very small fraction of the total energy. The reason for this is that, for the shallow shot, reflections close to the source enhance the ray emanations which depart at the greater angles and which propagate as bottom-bounce rays. For the deep shot the small-angle, shallower-traveling rays that do not strike the bottom are enhanced and the deeper-traveling rays are not.

Bottom depth along the path plays an important role in determining the transmission loss. Figure 23 shows the typical explosive signal arrival over a deepwater path. The first energy to arrive (group A) is from deep-traveling rays that arrive as individual energy packets. The next group (B) is comprised of the shallow-traveling rays that arrive in phase addition, giving what is sometimes called the first normal mode arrival. The last group (C) are the bottom-bounce rays that arrive at ever-increasing intervals. If there is water shallower than about 1,800 ft along the transmission path, ray theory predicts that group A arrivals will not be present. This represents a considerable reduction in total signal strength. If the bottom is deep but the source depth is below about 1,800 ft there will be an A and a C group but no B, since those rays propagate shallower than 1,800 ft. For a source below 1,800 ft with water shallower than 1,800 ft anywhere along the path, both groups A and B will be absent, leaving only C. These conditions greatly affect the energy of the arriving signal and explain some of the deviations mentioned above.

Ambient Noise

Although there are undoubtedly contributions to ambient noise levels from biological sources, the background noise in deep arctic water is attributed largely to ice activity. At the low end of the frequency spectrum the background is, in all probability, due primarily to gross ice movement (pressure ridging) that originates from nearby out to extreme distances. In the mid-frequency range, local ice-fissure generation and distant gross ice

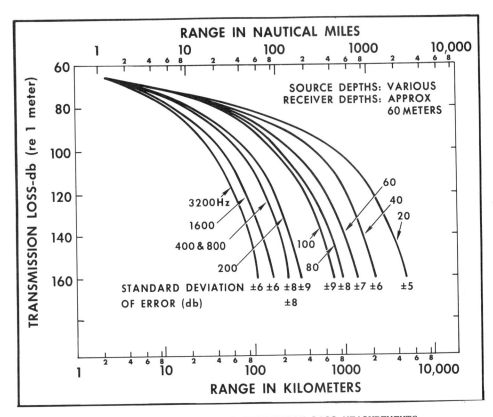

Figure 20.   BEST-FIT TO TRANSMISSION LOSS MEASUREMENTS
             IN THE ARCTIC OCEAN

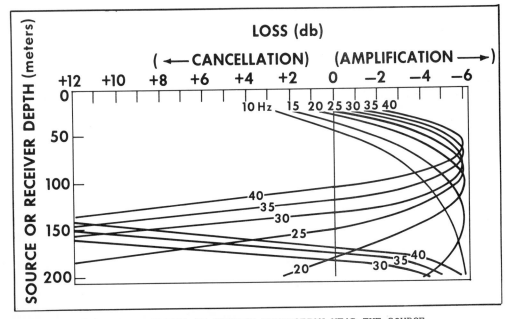

Figure 21.   EFFECT OF SURFACE REFLECTION NEAR THE SOURCE
             OR THE RECEIVER ON SIGNAL

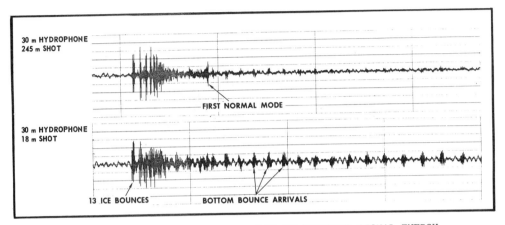

Figure 22. EFFECTS OF SOURCE DEPTH ON ARRIVING SIGNAL ENERGY

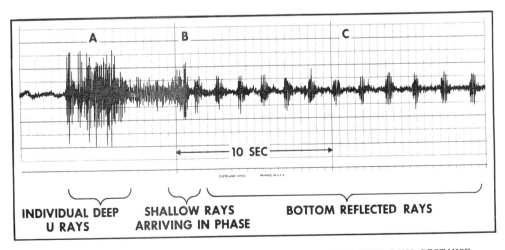

Figure 23. TYPICAL EXPLOSIVE SOURCE SIGNAL ARRIVING FROM LONG DISTANCE
OVER A DEEP-WATER PATH

movement probably contribute about equally to the noise. The high frequencies are dominated by local ice cracks, which are caused by thermal changes during periods of low wind, and by wind turbulence at the air-ice interface during periods of high wind.

The presumption that low-frequency noise is more dependent on remote ice activity than high-frequency noise has been shown to be true. However, there is a systematic decrease in the degree of correlation at lower frequencies, suggesting that the lower frequencies are more affected by distant ice movement. There is enough correlation, nevertheless, to indicate that both the low and the high ends of the range are influenced by nearby ice activity.

Marine Biology

Nansen believed that the phytoplankton were sparse in the Arctic Ocean, but later investigators found a considerable development, including an intense bloom of diatoms in the lower layers of sea ice. During the International Geophyical Year, chlorophyll a was used to determine the standing crop of phytoplankton, and carbon-14 uptake was used to estimate the amount of primary production. The annual productivity was found to be very low in comparison with that of other ocean areas. A net retained less than 10% of the chlorophyll a retained by the membrane filter, since many of the photosynthetic organisms in the arctic seas, perhaps the majority of the biomass, are minute, difficult to preserve, and often impossible to identify from preserved material. A relationship between cell counts, chlorophyll a concentration, and carbon-14 uptake has not been demonstrated.

The oceanographic variables affecting the magnitude of primary production are known, but the relative importance of each in the arctic situation must be assessed further. Many proposed mechanisms for the initiation of the annual phytoplankton bloom and the possible importance of production within the ice are based on ignorance of the arctic environment and the dynamics of primary production in the ocean. The surface water in the Arctic Ocean is not rich in dissolved inorganic nutrients and is not responsible for high nutrient concentrations encountered near the periphery of the permanent pack ice. The upper and lower limits of the Pacific water mass in the Canada Basin are regions of significant density change, and the layers near these limits are rich in detritus and nutrients. These limits form two scattering layers in the Beaufort Sea - one occurs at a depth of 150 ft coincident with the pycnocline between the surface Arctic and intermediate (Pacific) water masses. This layer (pycnocline scattering layer) is detectable at 100 kHz frequency and correlates with an accumulation of pteropods, *Spiratella helicina.* The second layer is a more typical deep scattering layer which appears seasonally in the northern part of the Beaufort gyral; it may be detected at 12 kHz and 100 kHz. Although no fishes have been captured within the layer due to the problem of trawling through pack ice, the appearance of the layer on the depth sounder implies a nektonic organism. The Arctic cod, *Arctogadus placialis,* is probably the responsible species.

A small ozygen-minimum layer is present at the interface of the intermediate (Pacific) water and the Atlantic water at 660 ft. There is no evidence to show any special biological cause for this depletion, therefore physical manifestation of circulation and vertical eddy diffusion are probably responsible.

Published studies on the zooplankton under the permanent pack ice are even more fragmentary than the information available for the phytoplankton. Faunal lists are available from several expeditions and recent work on drifting ice platforms; but the life histories, physiology, growth rates, reproduction, relative abundance, population dynamics, vertical distributions, and behavior of the animals are almost totally unstudied. The consequences of low primary production, very low temperatures, long light and dark seasons, and the "inverted bottom" formed by the pack ice are of enormous zoological interest and should be investigated extensively.

The nekton, including seals, are quite difficult to capture from the permanent pack ice. Most sampling devices for nekton and macroplankton depend upon a horizontal component of motion provided by a moving ship, and the drift of the ice is generally too slow for such a purpose. Of the fishes only the polar cod (*Boreogadus*) has been taken from the center of the Arctic Ocean, although bottom photographs have shown at least one other species of fish.

Bibliography

Aagaard, K. and L. K. Coachman, 1968. The East Greenland Current north of Denmark Strait. 2 pts. *Arctic* 21:181-200, 267-90.

Campbell, W. J., 1965. The wind-driven circulation of ice and water in a polar ocean. *J. Geophys. Research* 70:3279-3301.

Coachman, L. K., 1966. Production of supercooled water during sea ice formation. in *Proceedings of the Symposium on the Arctic Heat Budget and Atmospheric Circulation,* held Lake Arrowhead, Calif., 31 Jan.-4 Feb. 1966. Santa Monica: The Rand Corp. Memor. RM-5233-NSF. pp. 497-529.

Coachman, L. K. and K. Aagaard, 1966. On the water exchange through Bering Strait. *Limnol. Oceanogr.* 11:44-59.

Coachman, L. K. and C. A. Barnes, 1962. Surface water in the Eurasian Basin of the Arctic Ocean. *Arctic* 15:251-77.

_____, 1963. The movement of Atlantic water in the Arctic Ocean. *Arctic* 16:9-16.

Collin, A. E., 1963. Waters of the Canadian Arctic Archipelago. in *Proceedings of the Arctic Basin Symposium, October 1962.* Washington, D. C.: Arctic Institute of No. Amer. pp. 128-36.

Dunbar, M. J., 1951. Eastern arctic waters. Fisheries Research Board of Canada *Bulletin* 88:1-131.

Hall, J. K., 1970. *Arctic Ocean Geophysical Studies: The Alpha Cordillera and Mendeleyev Ridge.* Palisades, N. Y.: Lamont - Doherty Geological Observatory of Columbia University. AD-715 026. 125 pp.

Hunkins, K., 1966. Ekman drift currents in the Arctic Ocean. *Deep-Sea Research* 13:607-20.

Hunkins, K. L., 1971. Sound Scattering Layers in the Arctic Ocean. U. S. Navy *Journal of Underwater Acoustics,* 21:83-9.

Hunkins, K. L., H. W. Kutschale and J. K. Hall, 1969. *Studies in Marine Geophysics and Underwater Sound from Drifting Ice Stations*. Palisades, N. Y.: Lamont-Doherty Geological Observatory. Final report of contract Nonr 266(82). 102 pp.

Johnson, G. L. and O. B. Eckhoff, 1966. Bathymetry of the north Greenland Sea. *Deep-Sea Research* 13:1170.

Leeuw, M. M. de, 1967. *New Canadian Bathymetric Chart of the Western Arctic Ocean, North of 72°*. Ottawa: Marine Sciences Branch, Dept. of Energy, Mines and Resources.

Malloy, A. E. and M. A. Beal, 1971. *New Bathymetric Chart of the Arctic Ocean* Presented at the Second International Symposium on Arctic Geology, San Francisco. (Abstract)

Marine Sciences Centre, 1971. *Annual Report 1970*. Montreal: McGill University. 32 pp.

Milne, A. R. 1967. *Sound Propagation and Ambient Noise Under Sea Ice*. Victoria, B. C.: Defence Research Establishment Pacific. Reprint 67-4. 36 pp.

Monson, A. P. B. and J. E. Sater, 1969. *Proceedings of the Naval Arctic Research Laboratory Dedication Symposium*. *Arctic* 22:174-364.

U. S. Navy, 1958. *Oceanographic Atlas of the Polar Seas: II, Arctic*. Washington, D. C.: Hydrographic Office Publ. 705. 143 pp.

_____, 1965. *Oceanography and Underwater Sound for Naval Applications*. Washington, D. C.: Oceanographic Office Special Publ. 84. 134 pp.

Climate

Four aspects of the northern climate may be said to characterize the Arctic. The first is a distinctive regime of daylight and darkness together with low solar elevation which give rise to a prolonged period of radiational loss from the earth's surface. Second are the surface weather systems associated with the large-scale, cold-cored circumpolar vortex present in the free atmosphere over the area. This is a function of the differential heating between the equator and pole and of the earth's rotation. These upper air flow patterns are apparent at 5,000 ft (850 mb) but reach their greatest intensity near 33,000 ft (200 mb). The surface cyclones and anticyclones responsible for much of the weather are embedded in and steered by this flow, so that changes in the shape and position of the vortex can radically affect regional conditions.

The third aspect is a surface cover of snow or ice for at least a significant part of the year. In cold regions the nature of the surface is largely a question of whether or not there is a snow or ice cover. The difference in the percentage of absorbed solar radiaiton is as great as 60% (up to 20% absorption with a fresh snow surface compared with greater than 80% in most snow-free regions). The immediate effect of changes in this cover on the heat exchange at the surface is so great that the region can be said to have two seasons only, with a swift transition of a week or two each at the spring thaw and the fall freeze-up. Over the permanent ice caps and the polar pack ice during the brief summer, the ice maintains the air temperature at about 32°F, while temperatures in snow - or ice-free areas can reach 70 to 85°F. Toward mid-latitudes in the periglacial zone, as the length of the snow-free period increases, variations from winter to winter in the timing and continuity of the snow cover become more important, and the number of freeze-thaw cycles in the year increases rapidly. The continental subarctic can experience minimum temperatures lower than the central Arctic Basin; but with the approach of total winter darkness at the pole, the persistence of low temperatures increases.

The presence of a snow or ice cover plays an important role in the modification of air masses crossing the region. Cyclones depend on temperature contrast, and generally speaking their intensity and frequency are closely allied to the sharp gradients at the margins of the snow or ice cover and open water. Over the central Arctic Basin cyclones oftentimes stagnate and fill. The distribution of precipitation is largely related to the passage of cyclones over open water; and, as large areas of open water are conspicuously lacking, the occasional open leads in winter become important heat and moisture sources. However, the cooling of the air masses over the snow and ice reduces the water-holding capacity of the air to such an extent that the greater part of the Arctic is virtually a desert. The coldness of the air causes precipitaiton to characteristically take the form of small, dry, hard snow particles which are easily redistributed by the wind to produce blowing-snow storms. Middle and high clouds are also associated with cyclonic activity; but, owing to the dryness of the air, the clouds tend to be less dense over the central Arctic. Low cloud and fog, characteristic of coastal areas and the broken pack ice in summer, are essentially linked with the distribution of snow

or ice and open water. The combination of overcast sky and an unbroken
snow or ice surface produces the optical phenomenon of whiteout.

It is characteristic of snow and ice masses that once a certain critical
growth is reached, they tend to be self-perpetuating. However, where there
is a snow- or ice-free period, the relationship between the earth's surface
and the atmosphere is finely balanced and any induced changes resulting
in a crossing of the freeze-thaw threshold can significantly alter the
complex association. Animal and human destruction of the natural cover
and additions to the heat and moisture sources can initiate virtually
irreversible chain reactions.

The fourth distinctive aspect of the arctic climate is a strong temperature inversion above the snow or ice surface resulting from strong radiational cooling. In winter, the average depth of this inversion layer is
4,000 to 5,000 ft (850 mb). Its development is most intense under calm,
clear anticyclonic conditions, when outgoing radiation is unhindered and
extremely low temperatures can occur. Inherently a stable feature under
conditions of negative radiation balance at the surface in winter, it is
only temporarily or partially cleared by the strong winds, cloud cover, or
precipitation associated with cyclonic activity; and it rapidly reforms.
In summer this type of inversion is confined to the pack ice and ice cap
surfaces. It is less intense at this season and is frequently lifted off
the surface by the presence of a shallow mixing layer over the ice itself.
The configuration of the surface plays an important role in the local
intensity and persistence of the inversion. Where the dense cold air is
trapped in hollows and valleys, as for example in the Yukon and northeastern
Siberia, the lowest temperatures have been recorded. Over the convex surfaces of the ice caps, the dense cold air appears to drain off in surges
under gravitational flow.

Atmospheric Circulation

Considering both the descriptive and predictive aspects of climate at
high latitudes, the dominant factor is the presence of the cold-cored
westerly vortex in the middle and upper atmosphere. Its north-south
temperature gradient is generally steepest in mid-latitudes, where it
increases with height to a maximum near 33,000 ft and is associated with
a zone of strong westerly flow. The westerly jet streams at the periphery
of the vortex play a vital role in the development and steering of the
surface cyclones and anticyclones, so that variations in weather (and
individual meteorological elements) from day to day, season to season, and
year to year, and from one region to another, are closely linked with
deformations of this upper vortex. Those areas below the periphery of
the vortex are generally characterized by a succession of eastward-moving
frontal cyclones, whereas regions under the sluggish cold core of the
vortex experience persistent cold lows - cold, non-frontal systems resulting
from the occlusion of the frontal storms. The majority of the storms are
occluded before they reach the Arctic. Aloft, the cold low centers of the
circumpolar vortex appear to be related to the upward growth of these
occluded systems in which adiabatic cooling occurs. The movements of these
cold lows are slow, erratic, and difficult to predict.

Anticyclones are typically large irregular areas of high pressure
without distinct centers and characterized by subsidence and stability.
In the Arctic, they are frequently shallow surface systems; but when they
are associated above with the northward ridging of the circumpolar vortex

and are capped by warmer air of subtropical origin, they become deep and persistent. From time to time smaller migratory anticyclones move out of the Arctic directed by the upper flow toward the southeast, but more characteristically these systems are very slow-moving and tend to oscillate around preferred positions or to change shape rather than to follow clearly defined paths.

Figure 24 shows the mean situation for January, April, July, and October at approximately 10,000 ft above sea level. The vortex shows a marked three- to four-wave pattern which appears to reflect the influence of the earth's major topography and the differential heating of the continents and oceans.

In winter (Fig. 24a) the vortex shows three centers - one each over the Canadian Arctic Archipelago, Kamchatka, and Novaya Zemlya. Two major troughs occur over eastern North America and off the east coast of Asia, and there is a third weaker trough over eastern Europe. The main ridges lie over the eastern Pacific and the Rocky Mountains and over the eastern Atlantic and Scandinavia, with the third weaker ridge over the Urals and western Siberia. The well-developed ridge over the longitudinal barrier of the Rocky Mountains and the deep trough downstream over eastern North America are quasi-permanent features of the general circulation throughout the year. In winter, however, they are most firmly established as the equator-to-pole temperature gradient is greatest, the vortex most intense, and the westerly flow strongest. As the gradient builds up during the fall, the vortex expands and the belt of strongest westerlies shifts southward.

Owing to the strong southerly and northerly components of the main westerly current, cold dry arctic air is carried far to the south especially over central and eastern North America and eastern Asia, while warm moist air over the oceans of lower latitudes is drawn northward over the Atlantic and Pacific oceans toward the Arctic. In the troughs over eastern North America and Asia, temperature gradients between continental and oceanic air are strongest, and here are located the major cyclogenetic regions of the hemisphere at this season. The surface cyclonic disturbances, steered in the direction of the upper air flow, move northeast toward polar latitudes and frequently spiral in toward the upper vortex centers. As they approach high latitudes, they generally lose much of their temperature contrast, and the warm air is undercut and lifted off the ground by the colder air (i.e. the cyclone becomes occluded). Over the north Pacific and Atlantic there are the two main graveyards where many storms stagnate and fill. Occasionally cyclones are regenerated at the ice-water margin, and storms continue toward the central Arctic Basin. Anticyclogenesis occurs just east of the major ridges, the Yukon showing a particularly high frequency; while occasionally systems move out to the southeast, they can remain stationary for many days at a time.

Through the spring and in summer (Figs. 24b and c), as the north-south temperature gradient diminishes, the vortex weakens and contracts to a single mean center near the pole. The mean location of the belt of strongest westerly flow and the corresponding tracks of surface cyclones now lie over higher latitudes. With the lessening of the energy in the vortex and its contraction to the north of the Tibetan plateau, the wave pattern is weaker and the circulation tends to be more zonal (i.e. from west to east). With the heating of the snow-free land surfaces at this season, cyclogenesis is frequent inland over the subarctic and at the ice-water-land margin of the Arctic Ocean. The mean surface pressure chart for July shows a weak circulation pattern, hiding the considerable

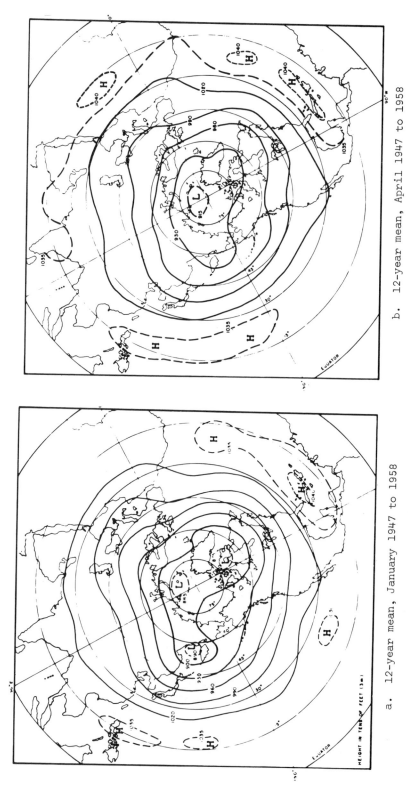

a. 12-year mean, January 1947 to 1958

b. 12-year mean, April 1947 to 1958

Figure 24.   MEAN HEIGHT OF THE 700-MB SURFACE

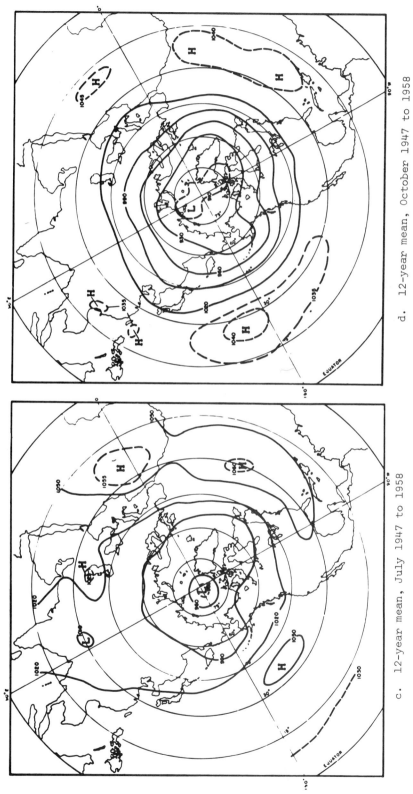

c. 12-year mean, July 1947 to 1958

d. 12-year mean, October 1947 to 1958

Figure 24 (cont'd).   MEAN HEIGHT OF THE 700-MB SURFACE

small-scale fluctuations that can occur from day to day. Small-scale variations include the successions of weak, rapidly moving cyclones and the
oscillating cold lows that persist below upper-level vortices over the
central Arctic. In summer, cyclones predominate over the Arctic and
subarctic, except within the zone from 70 to 75°N where anticyclones are
more frequent.

With the exception of the Pacific trough, the autumn patterns both
aloft (Fig. 24d) and at the surface already closely resemble those of midwinter.

The change from a well-developed wave pattern with strong northerly
and southerly components (a meridional situation) of easterly flow to a
more zonal (east-west) flow pattern, already recognized in the seasonal
means, is one of the most significant features of the northern circumpolar
vortex with respect to arctic and subarctic climates. It is especially
remarkable in the colder season, when the patterns are more strongly
developed, that the vortex appears to undergo a cycle of deformation of a
period of roughly a month from more zonal flow to strongly meridional
conditions, when the long-wave pattern intensifies. The major cold troughs
over the continents extend rapidly toward the equator, while the warm
ridges over the Pacific and Atlantic reach northward, frequently as far
as the inner Arctic Basin. One sector may experience a more zonal flow
while meridional conditions exist at other longitudes, but the sequence and
mechanism of these changes has still not been fully explored. During
zonal flow, however, a slow progression of the long waves toward the east
is characteristic; as the zonal flow breaks down, the situation frequently
becomes quasi-stationary and then shows an apparent slow retrogression
toward the west.

The effect on arctic and subarctic climate of these major changes in
general circulation is best described with the aid of synoptic examples.
Figures 25a and b illustrate a well-developed meridional circulation on
January 6, 1959. At approximately 18,000 ft (500-mb surface), the pattern
is dominated by a warm ridge extending northwestward from the Atlantic to
the pole, with other major ridges over the Pacific and western Siberia
and a weaker ridge over North America. The cold vortex has four main
centers located in the troughs over subpolar latitudes. The strongest
westerly flow is associated with the strongest temperature gradient.

The sea-level pressure chart reflects these circumstances. Strong anticyclonic conditions exist over the Arctic Basin and south over North
America and Siberia; it is essentially a cap of very cold, dense, dry
arctic air. These polar outbreaks over the continental masses temporarily
extend the arctic climate into middle latitudes. Frontal cyclones below
the strong westerly currents are being steered around the troughs into
graveyard areas - on this occasion over the Gulf of Alaska, Labrador, and
Scandinavia. The upper ridge over the Atlantic-Davis Strait region successfully blocks the main line of entry of storms into the Arctic Basin,
but over northeastern Siberia weak cyclonic disturbances are being guided
around the upper vortex from the Sea of Okhotsk northward to the Arctic
Ocean where they soon fill and disappear. Similarly, storms moving toward
the Barents Sea around the European trough rapidly weaken and fill in the
vicinity of the upper low center over Novaya Zemlya.

Figure 25a also shows spot temperature reports and regions of falling
snow. In general the anticyclonic areas with clear, calm conditions are
the coldest with continental temperatures lower than those over the Arctic

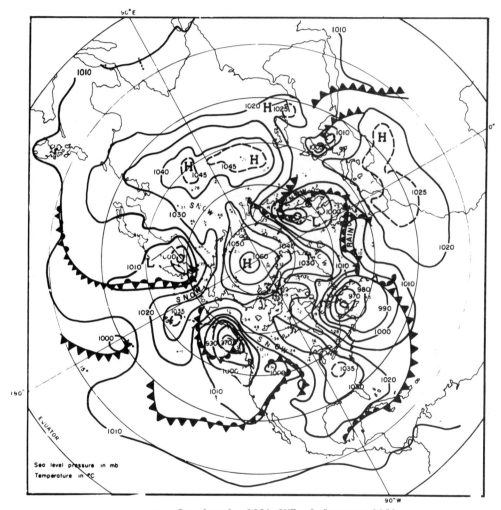

a. Sea level, 1230 GMT, 6 January 1959

Figure 25.   SELECTED DAILY SYNOPTIC CHARTS FOR SEA LEVEL AND THE 500-MB
SURFACE

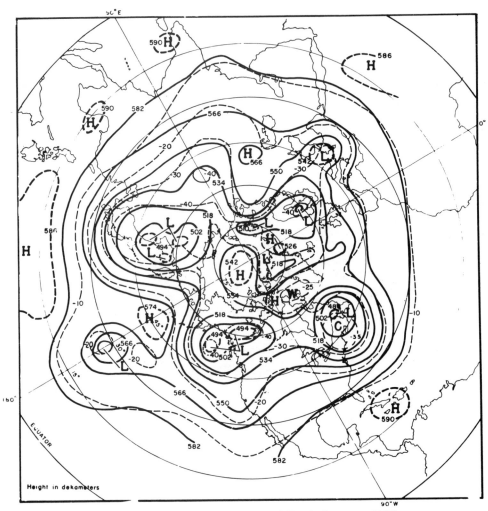

b.   500-mb level, 1200 GMT, 6 January 1959

Figure 25 (cont'd).   SELECTED DAILY SYNOPTIC CHARTS FOR SEA LEVEL AND
                      THE 500-MB SURFACE

Basin. The lowest values (below -58°F) are recorded in the valleys of the Yukon, Alaska, and northeastern Siberia; and local fog (probably ice fog) is frequent where temperatures are below -40°F. Blowing snow is reported where pressure gradients are particularly steep - over the northern Canadian Arctic Archipelago, for example, where strong winds and a temperature of -27°F combine to give a severe wind-chill effect.

Higher temperatures and storms are associated with the four cyclonic centers of activity and with open water where the strongest temperature and humidity contrasts and pressure gradients exist. Over northeastern Siberia and the Gulf of Alaska these gradients are emphasized by the strong relief barriers which cut off the interior from the full effect of the open ocean. The 32°F recorded on the western shore of Greenland near the open water of Davis Strait contrasts with the -58°F at the same latitude in western Canada. Over northern Eurasia in general, the temperature distribution is a mirror image of that over North America, with temperatures near 32°F at the Pacific coast falling rapidly to -58°F in northeastern Siberia and then varying between -22°F and -40°F over the central section with a rapid rise to -4°F over the White Sea and north Scandinavian coasts. Snow, cloud cover, blowing snow, high winds, and high wind-chill are generally associated with these strong cyclonic centers.

Figures 26c and d illustrate a more zonal circulation on February 26, 1959. At the 500-mb level the vortex shows a single major cell and is more nearly circumpolar with a characteristic tendency toward asymmetry. The jet streams and associated storm tracks cross more northerly latitudes over northwestern Europe and west-central Siberia.

At sea level cyclonic circulation dominates the Arctic and subarctic except for the northeastern extension of the Siberian anticyclone linked by a narrow weak ridge to a small high-pressure center south of Hudson Bay. Trains of frontal cyclones move eastward with the westerlies, spiraling in toward the upper vortex center. In general, circulation patterns are weaker over northern latitudes below the central vortex with less striking regional contrasts in weather than on January 6. The major difference lies in the weak ridge development over the Pacific and Atlantic; instead there is a ridge of high pressure over central Europe and Scandinavia, and a series of Atlantic storms is being steered through the North Atlantic gateway and into the central Arctic under the vortex center.

The cold low center at the surface near the pole is giving neither cloud nor precipitation and winds are light, so that surface cooling is unhindered and temperatures as low as -35 and -42°F are reported on ice islands near the pole. However, the active storms entering the Barents Sea are associated with cloud, snow, and temperatures around the freezing point; and 48 hours later the temperature on one of the ice islands had risen to -2°F as a storm approached the pole. An overcast sky with continuous light snow and 22-knot winds were also reported. The Atlantic gulf of warmth shows up well on this chart. It is the major source of warmth and humidity in the central Arctic at this season and is reflected in almost every climatic distribution.

Over North America the eastern areas are now under the influence of northwesterly flow from the Arctic; and the cold, dry conditions of northern Quebec and Labrador contrast sharply with the abnormal warmth and heavy snowfall of January 6. On the other hand, western North America reports temperatures 35 to 55°F higher than on the previous occasion as Pacific storms cross the mountain barrier, reappear as weaker centers, and

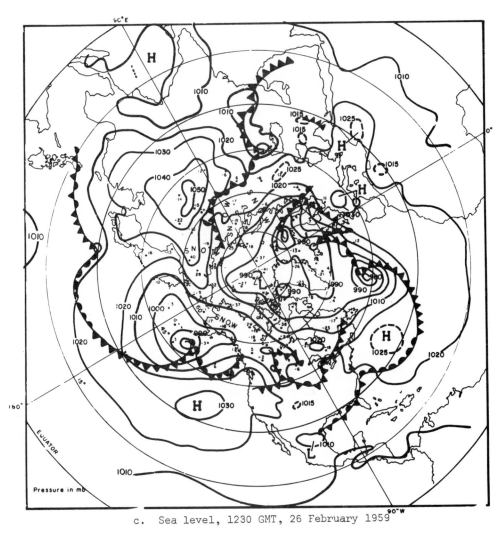

c.   Sea level, 1230 GMT, 26 February 1959

Figure 25 (cont'd).   SELECTED DAILY SYNOPTIC CHARTS FOR SEA LEVEL AND
THE 500-MB SURFACE

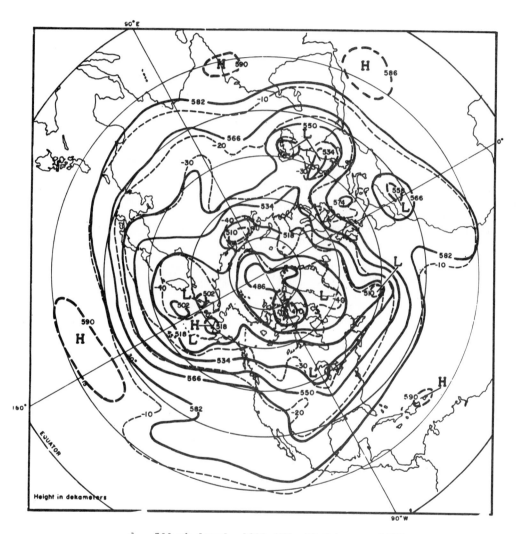

d.   500-mb level, 1200 GMT, 26 February 1959

Figure 25 (cont'd).   SELECTED DAILY SYNOPTIC CHARTS FOR SEA LEVEL
AND THE 500-MB SURFACE

approach the plains. Over Eurasia surface storms are moving across central
Siberia to the arctic coast while the weakening anticyclone is now confined
to eastern Siberia. As a result of this southerly flow, the snow, and the
clouds, temperatures here are also 35 to 55°F higher over much of the
region compared with January 6, while the eastern coast of Asia is expe-
riencing colder weather under the cold northerly flow around the anticyclone
cell. Northwestern Europe, in the warm southwesterly airstream, reports
temperatures that are, almost without exception, above freezing.

Figures 25e and f, charts for July 2, 1959, illustrate a summer situation. Here the 500-mb map shows the weaker, contracted vortex of the
summer season; at the surface the broad-scale patterns are less well-
defined and the cyclonic and anticyclonic systems comparatively weak and
shifting. Over Siberia the strongest upper westerly flow and steepest
temperature gradient are over the northern coastal region while on the
North American side this belt lies farther south. A succession of small
surface cyclones is moving eastward in this flow to fill-in (eventually)
below the shallow vortex centers aloft. At the surface a very great
temperature contrast exists between the Arctic Ocean or coastal stations,
where temperatures are close to 32°F, and the inland stations. Even at
sheltered locations near the coast, temperatures soon rise to over 50°F and
some 250 mi inland reach values as high as 77 or even 86°F. The high
frequency of frontal storms along this belt in summer may be associated
with these strong temperature gradients.

Over North America the 500-mb chart shows weak ridge development over
the Davis Strait-Greenland area and the northwest, almost cutting off the
cold vortex center over Keewatin. At the surface weak high-pressure systems
and a cold low center reflect this upper pattern, while weak frontal systems
are beginning to move down over Alaska and the Yukon as the upper flow
strengthens in the next 48 hours and the cold low gradually fills. The
reported temperatures over this sector are notably lower than those over
Eurasia. This is largely a result of the complex interrelation of land,
ice, and open water (with Hudson Bay extending almost to 50°N), together
with the fact that a fair proportion of these stations have coastal
locations. A further factor of influence in the more southerly regions
is the difference in the local time of observation. At 1230 at the
Greenwich meridian it is late afternoon near 90°E but only early morning
at 90°W.

The main Atlantic storm track at this season typically crosses southern
Scandinavia, while higher pressure is predominant over the Barents Sea.
On July 2 temperatures as high as 54°F were recorded on the north coast
of Scandinavia, with 52°F on Novaya Zemlya. This results not only from
the warm southerly airstream on this occasion but also from the generally
northward drift of relatively warm Atlantic waters. In turn, the coolness
of the east coast of Greenland is also due to a large extent to the southward drift of the Greenland Current. Over the northeastern Pacific the
configuration of the coastline is not so favorable to the northward
penetration of the warm surface waters into the central Arctic, and temperatures on the north Alaskan coast remain near 32°F.

Drizzle and light rain are reported from place to place in the vicinity
of fronts; over the Beaufort Sea and Zemlya Frantsa Iosifa there is continuous snowfall. Overcast skies and fog are widespread over northern
coastal areas as a result primarily of the cooling effect on the air of the
ice and cold northern waters. Here the local factors of station situation

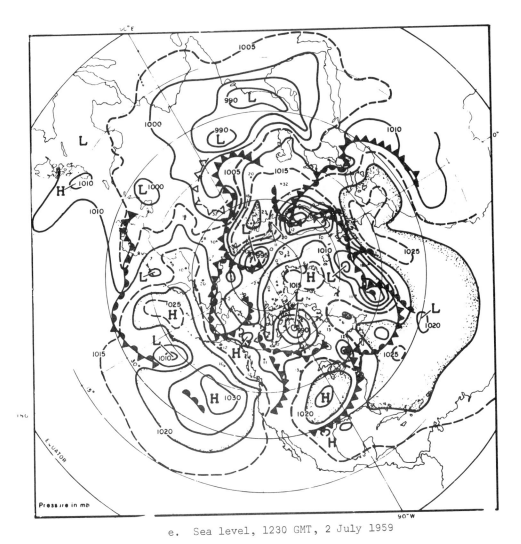

e.   Sea level, 1230 GMT, 2 July 1959

Figure 25 (cont'd).   SELECTED DAILY SYNOPTIC CHARTS FOR SEA LEVEL AND
THE 500-MB SURFACE

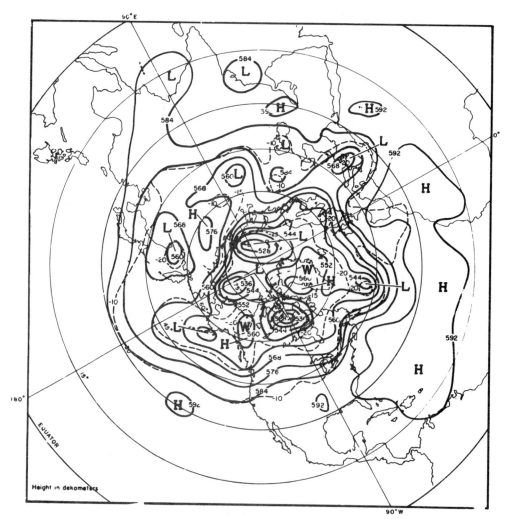

f.   500-mb level, 1200 GMT, 2 July 1959

Figure 25 (cont'd).   SELECTED DAILY SYNOPTIC CHARTS FOR SEA LEVEL AND
THE 500-MB SURFACE

and wind direction play an important role.

Several basic considerations concerning the variability of northern climates are illustrated in the following three examples:

(1) Large-scale patterns tend to persist. The stalled large-scale circulation patterns on January 6, 1959 are characteristic of well-developed meridional situations which can be highly persistent. Over the western hemisphere the broad pattern remained essentially unchanged from early January, with the extension of the Atlantic ridge, to January 24, when there was a shift to the east and storms once again traveled northward over the Atlantic. Regionally these stalled situations can result in extended periods of abnormally cold or mild temperatures, drought or heavier-than-normal snowfall, high winds, or other extreme conditions. Over the eastern hemisphere there was a change to more zonal flow over Eurasia in the second half of the month, and this pattern tended to persist well into February.

(2) The modification of the tracks and frequency of surface cyclones and anticyclones is importantly influenced not only by relief barriers but also by the dynamic barriers formed by persistent well-developed upper ridges and high centers. Areas of most frequent blocking are Scandinavia, Alaska, the Ural region, and the Davis Strait-Greenland sector. Blocking is characteristic of the spring (March) when anticyclonic conditions are most frequent over the continental areas of the high Arctic. At this season the snow and ice cover is still intact, the air is stable, and visibility is good so that flying conditions are generally at their best.

(3) The degree of expansion or contraction of the vortex can have serious effects on arctic operations by causing abnormal displacement of the upper westerlies. In the summer this becomes a major factor over the Arctic and subarctic. In August 1955 the strongest westerly flow lay over the rim of the Arctic Basin and was associated with an unusually high frequency and intensity of cyclones. This had repercussions on the distribution of ice and open water and seriously jeopardized the success of the supply mission to the Distant Early Warning Line sites under construction between Point Barrow, Alaska and Shepherd Bay, Canada. It was not until the polar vortex began to break down about September 5 and storms took a more southerly track across the Bering Sea and Alaska that an offshore lead was created permitting supply operations to continue along the coast of north Alaska. Here the steady offshore flow of cold moist air slowed down the disintegration of the pack ice in August and caused refreezing of the leads by thermal action.

In brief, since the tracks of surface disturbances are so closely related to the upper westerlies, the climate of any season or year, decade or epoch, over the Arctic and subarctic depends to a large extent on the relative frequency of either zonal or meridional conditions, on the most favored location of blocking, and on the degree of contraction or expansion of the vortex. The southern limit of the Arctic fluctuates accordingly. On a regional scale, the local shape, orientation, and intensity of the vortex; the location of individual cells; and the changes in its morphology are basic considerations. There appears to be a tendency for a particular type of large-scale circulation pattern to recur persistently in the same season after only a brief interruption. The nature of the pattern may differ considerably from one season to the same season of another year. Thus the average or normal conditions conceal several well-defined modes of general circulation, each remarkably stable over the Arctic.

The distribution of mean sea level pressure for January (Fig. 26a) summarizes the winter situation. The major semi-permanent features are the
Icelandic and Aleutian lows and the Siberian and northwestern Canadian
highs linked by a ridge across the Arctic Ocean. The mean isobars give
some indication of the general direction of flow. Figures 26b and c
supplement the mean map by indicating the most frequent areas of formation
and stagnation of cyclones and anticyclones and their major tracks.

Over North America most anticyclones form over Alaska and northwest
Canada. Cyclogenesis occurs over Alberta where systems from the Pacific
produce closed surface lows on the eastern (lee) slope of the Rockies.
These cyclones generally move east-southeast to a center of maximum
frequency over the Great Lakes region where tracks converge from the
southwest and south. Most of these disturbances are then steered northeast
to Newfoundland. Here they are joined by cyclones from the east coast,
an area which favors cyclogenesis because of thermal contrasts between the
cold continental and warmer maritime air masses. From Newfoundland storms
generally migrate either toward Iceland (their high frequency resulting
in the semi-permanent Iceland low) or along the west or east coasts of
Greenland. A few disturbances also enter Davis Strait by way of Hudson
Bay or drift in erratically from western Canada below the cold upper
vortex center; and an area of high cyclonic frequency is located west of
Greenland.

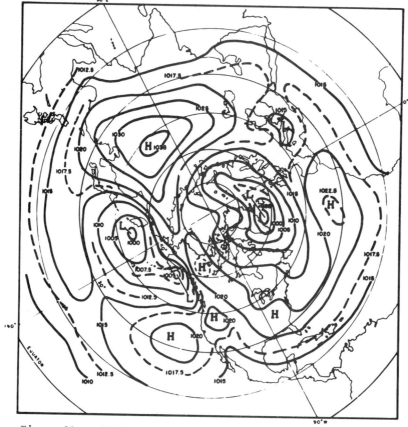

Figure 26a. SEA LEVEL PRESSURE (MB), JANUARY (12-YEAR MEAN)

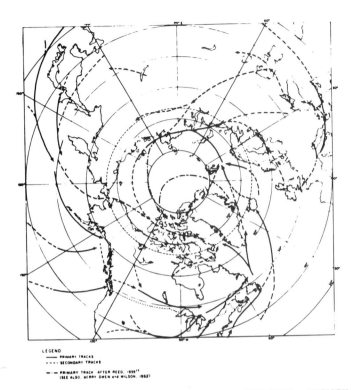

Figure 26b. PRINCIPAL TRACKS OF CYCLONES, JANUARY

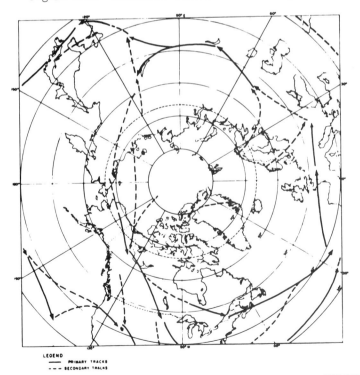

Figure 26c. PRINCIPAL TRACKS OF ANTICYCLONES, JANUARY

Over Eurasia the westerly jet stream is split into northern and southern branches by the Himalayan massif. To the north of these mountains there is no cyclonic development comparable with that over continental North America, and the winter anticyclone over Siberia is persistent. Cyclones moving eastward over western Siberia are often old occluded storms and rapidly lose their intensity, although secondary cyclones occasionally form near Lake Baikal and deepen rapidly on moving toward the Pacific coast.

Major anticyclonic activity over western Siberia is related to the development and persistence of the strong upper ridge over the Urals. With the collapse of this blocking, the surface centers move to the southeast causing outbreaks of intensely cold air over China and Mongolia. These outbreaks are associated with strong cyclogenesis off the east Asian coast. The majority of these east coast storms are steered northeastward toward the semi-permanent Aleutian low to then stagnate or curve south. Occasionally storms enter the Arctic Ocean over northeastern Siberia or the Bering Strait; those that cross the Alaskan mountains appear to stagnate in less than 48 hours. From time to time new storms develop on the north side of these mountains after primary storms have stagnated to the south. In general, storms over the Beaufort Sea appear to be largely of the cold low type which is characterized by colder air near its center rather than around its periphery.

The daily charts of more recent years indicate that over the Arctic Basin many cyclones spiral in toward the pole and that cyclones outnumber anticyclones by 2 to 1. Storms breaking away from the Icelandic low usually move northeast to the Norwegian-Barents Sea area, and a primary track continues along latitude 75°N where polynyas or leads appear to exist in the Kara and Laptev seas. These frequent storms play an important role in the climate of the north European and Siberian coastlands. This primary track is joined by tracks from the Baltic, Black, and Caspian seas. Some storms stagnate near Novaya Zemlya, others regenerate and curve toward the pole. However, intense anticyclones occur to the north of the Beaufort and Chukchi seas, frequently in association with the extreme northward extension of the upper Pacific ridge. It is in March, at the time of the greatest frequency of blocking situations, that anticyclonic conditions are most frequent over the Arctic Basin.

The most striking pattern to emerge north of 60°N is the predominance of cyclonic activity over the Atlantic hemisphere and of anticyclonic activity over the Pacific hemisphere (the Aleutian low center lies to the south of 60°N). Regions of highest cyclonic frequency extend:

(1) From a maximum south of Greenland northeastward to the north of Norway and Novaya Zemlya, thence spiraling into the central Arctic. It has been suggested that the frequency over the Arctic Basin would be greater if the observation network were closer. These Atlantic storms are responsible for most of the weather and variation in the climatic elements over the Arctic Basin.

(2) Over Davis Strait and Baffin Bay. The role played by the 8,000- to 10,000-ft barrier of the Greenland ice sheet is an important element. There is evidence that the upper manifestations (700 mb) of the surface disturbances and fronts frequently cross the Greenland ice sheet with significant effect on the weather. These upper-level features can often be identified with renewed surface systems on the eastern side of Greenland. Again, when deep lows lie near southern Greenland or Iceland and there is easterly flow across the ice sheet, rapid development or intensification

occurs to the west (in the lee) over Baffin Bay. The cyclonic activity of this region is the dominating factor in the weather of much of the Canadian Arctic Archipelago.

Regions of highest anticyclonic frequency extend:

(1) In an arc from eastern Siberia over the East Siberian and Beaufort seas to Alaska and northwest Canada, a reflection of blocking associated with the upper Pacific ridge. The maxima are over the Yukon, the Arctic Ocean, and northeastern Siberia.

(2) Over Greenland. More than a third of the ice sheet surface is above 850 mb (5,000 ft) and the crest over 700 mb (10,000 ft). The mean charts at 700 mb show no sign of such centers at any season, although there is always a ridge due to the topographic barrier. However, the frequency maximum is real. It is composed of both small shallow systems lying between predominantly cyclonic regions to the east and west and large systems related to the extension of the main upper Atlantic ridge over Greenland during blocking situations. An analysis over this region of the 12 years from 1947 through 1958 shows a tendency toward more frequent blocking than is evident for past years.

(3) Over southern Scandinavia. This is a favored location of the northward extensions of the Atlantic ridge.

(4) Near 90°E at a northern extension of the main west Siberian anticyclone, which generally lies to the south of 60°N. This maximum is linked with the frequent upper-ridge development in the vicinity of the Urals.

A comparison of the mean pressure charts for January and April (Figs. 26a and 27a) shows the general weakening of the mean systems in spring, the northeast shift in the mean center of the Icelandic low, and the new high-pressure centers which are the dominant feature of the central Arctic at this season. In April the mean 700-mb chart shows a single circumpolar cell, although the axis of the main westerly belt is still far to the south (Fig. 24b); during May and June, however, it shifts rapidly to the north.

During spring there is a reduction in frequency of the anticyclone tracks over western Canada (Fig. 27c), while there is a shifting eastward of the primary track toward Hudson Bay. These Hudson Bay highs are characteristic of this season when there is more anticyclonic activity in eastern than in western Canada. Over the arctic portions of North America and Siberia there is a maximum intensification of anticyclonic conditions, while cyclonic activity is at a minimum.

An effect of the increasing insolation is a shifting of the areas of cyclogenesis from water to land regions. In Siberia spring is marked by increasing cyclonic activity which reaches a maximum in May; secondary cyclonic developments over Lake Baikal and northeastern China reach maximum frequency and intensity at this season. The cyclone track over the Arctic Ocean becomes a secondary feature in May, and primary tracks shift inland over the northeastern part of Eurasia. Over North America the cyclone paths shift poleward, to the north of the Great Lakes; and by June cyclonic frequency in Alberta reaches a maximum for the hemisphere.

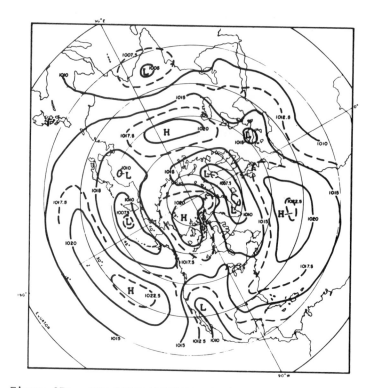

Figure 27a. SEA LEVEL PRESSURE (MB), APRIL (12-YEAR MEAN)

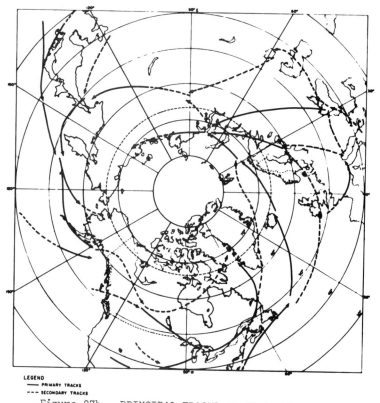

LEGEND
— PRIMARY TRACKS
--- SECONDARY TRACKS

Figure 27b. PRINCIPAL TRACKS OF CYCLONES, APRIL

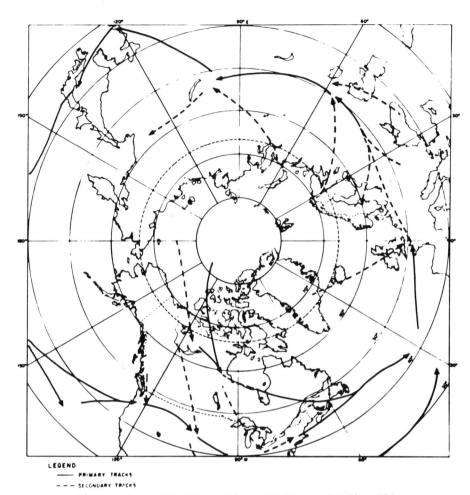

LEGEND
——— PRIMARY TRACKS
– – – SECONDARY TRACKS

Figure 27c. PRINCIPAL TRACKS OF ANTICYCLONES, APRIL

    The mean sea level pressure chart for July (Fig. 28) shows the remark-
able fall in mean pressure in summer and the rather amorphous mean pattern
which results from the relatively weak, shifting systems over the central
Arctic. There appears to be considerable variation in the mean summer pressure from year to year, depending on the frequency and intensity of cyclonic
activity. The main characteristics of the mean July pressure chart are the
marked east-west extension of the Pacific and Atlantic ridges, the absence
of a low center over the Gulf of Alaska, the westward shift of the weak
Icelandic center, and the major low center over the heart of Siberia.

    A comparison of the January and July mean height charts at 700 mb (Figs.
24a and c) shows the weakening of the upper westerly circulation in summer
and the contraction of the vortex to a single major center over the Arctic
Ocean. In July and August the peripheral zone of strong westerlies and the
associated surface disturbances are farthest north (Fig. 28b), and over Asia
this zone now lies to the north of the Himalayan massif. The primary
cyclone tracks are at approximately 60°N, and a further zone of high frequency occurs between 70 and 80°N.

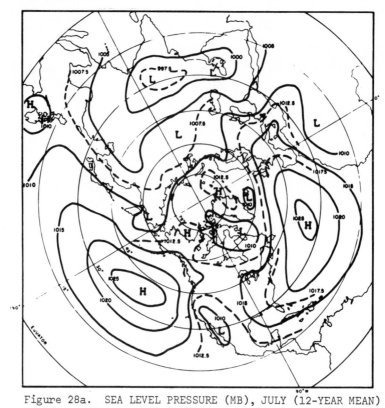

Figure 28a.   SEA LEVEL PRESSURE (MB), JULY (12-YEAR MEAN)

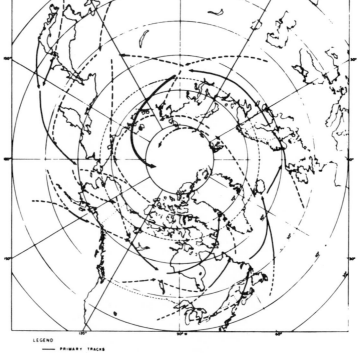

LEGEND

——— PRIMARY TRACKS

- - - SECONDARY TRACKS

▬▬▬ PRIMARY TRACK (REED, 1958²³)

Figure 28b.   PRINCIPAL TRACKS OF CYCLONES, JULY

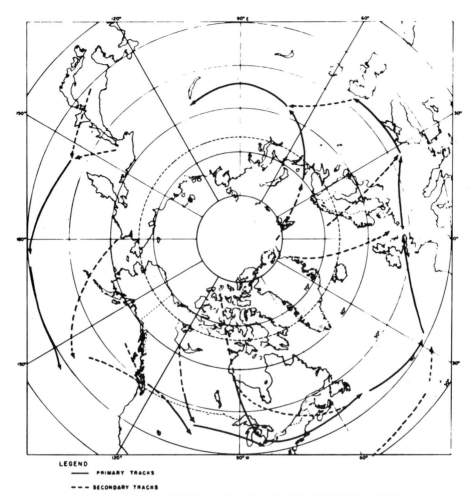

Figure 28c. PRINCIPAL TRACKS OF ANTICYCLONES, JULY

Over North America the most marked change at this season is the northern displacement of the track of the Alberta low. In summer the Prairie
Provinces have one of the highest frequencies of cyclonic activity in the
northern hemisphere; most of the storms cross Hudson Bay to the Davis
Strait-Baffin Bay area where they stagnate. Over the Atlantic, to the east
of the Icelandic graveyard, the primary track is more zonal in July with a
drop in the frequency of storms entering the Arctic Basin. A well-defined
path now extends from the eastern Atlantic into Siberia at about 60°N.

In the Pacific sector the main track is well to the north of the
Aleutians in summer, with storminess reaching an annual maximum over the
Bering Sea and Bering Strait. Fewer Atlantic storms enter the Arctic Basin
at this season; but when the circulation is more meridional, storms from
the Atlantic and the Pacific may penetrate well into the Arctic. There is
a high frequency of traveling disturbances along the northern coastal
regions of Siberia which appear to be related at least in part to the strong
temperature gradients at the margin of the heated land and the melting
arctic ice. The storms move mainly to the northeast, spiraling into the

central Arctic where they stagnate. Approximately one-third of the lows
that enter the Beaufort Sea are from northern Siberia.

The primary anticyclone tracks lie mostly to the south of the subarctic
in summer (Fig. 28c). Anticyclones form to the west of Hudson Bay and move
southeast to a region of maximum frequency over the Great Lakes. In August,
however, this major track of polar highs shifts westward to the Beaufort
Sea-Mackenzie valley area, although some centers still form in Manitoba.
Another important primary track in summer extends from the Barents Sea
southeast into central Siberia. Anticyclone frequency reaches an annual
minimum in eastern Siberia at this time.

The whole region is the scene of considerable cyclonic activity, but
maximum cyclonic frequency occurs:

(1) From southern Greenland to Iceland and to the north of Baffin
Bay - the graveyards for both continental and east coast storms. The center
west of Greenland is partially explained by the presence of the Greenland
ice sheet as a barrier to progress, although the summer records from over
the ice sheet reveal that frequent upper air disturbances (700 mb) cross the
plateau during the summer as in winter.

(2) Over the Arctic Basin where the high frequency reflects slow-
moving, stagnating systems.

Anticyclonic frequency maxima occur over Greenland, the western
Canadian Arctic Archipelago, and Poluostrov Taimyr - in general, a belt
between 70 and 75°N. The decreased frequency of cyclonic centers in this
belt is not only due to the tendency for quasi-stable anticyclones to
develop, especially over Greenland and near the Beaufort Sea, but also because of the greater mobility of the traveling cyclones in this zone.

The autumn is marked by the intensification and southward expansion of
the upper circumpolar vortex, and the mean October maps both for the 700-mb
(Fig. 24d) and surface levels (Fig. 29a) already show many of the major
features of winter. Following this southern shift in the zone of maximum
upper westerlies, the primary storm tracks move south. By November the
belt of strongest westerly flow is again in the latitude of the Himalayan
massif and the major winter features of the circulation are set up and held
during the following 5 or 6 months.

A second feature of autumn is the relative warmth of open water bodies
compared with the rapidly cooling land. The October track charts (Figs.
29b and c) show areas of maximum cyclonic activity over the Sea of Okhotsk,
the Barents Sea, the Gulf of Alaska, James Bay, and the Kara Sea. Primary
cyclones enter the Arctic Basin from the Atlantic and the Baltic Sea, and
the frequency reaches an annual maximum over the Kara Sea from which a primary track follows the coastal margin. In November primary storm tracks
from Alberta and Colorado again merge in a center of maximum frequency over
the Great Lakes. Over the Atlantic the primary track shifts from the east
to the west side of Iceland, and the southern Davis Strait track reappears
and intensifies.

During this season anticyclonic frequency increases over eastern Asia,
and centers of high pressure appear at sea level over Siberia. Over North
America the trajectory of polar highs over western Canada becomes of
primary importance by November and remains so until March.

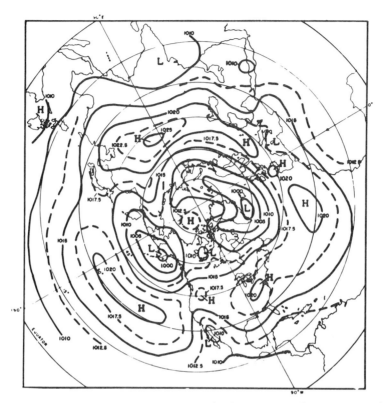

Figure 29a. SEA LEVEL PRESSURE (MB), OCTOBER (12-YEAR MEAN)

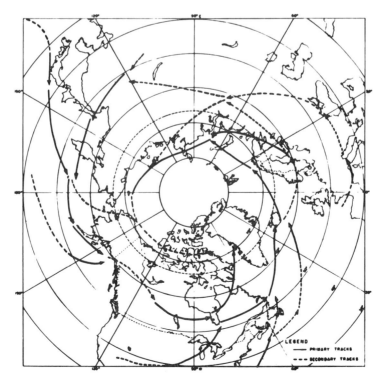

Figure 29b. PRINCIPAL TRACKS OF CYCLONES, OCTOBER

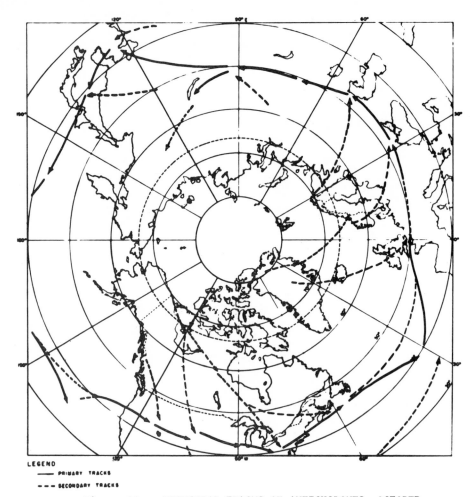

Figure 29c. PRINCIPAL TRACKS OF ANTICYCLONES, OCTOBER

Surface Weather

The surface weather associated with anticyclones and cyclones is profoundly affected by the high degree of static stability of the lowest layer
of the atmosphere, caused by the radiational cooling over the snow and ice
cover. The surface weather over much of the Arctic and subarctic depends on
the local effectiveness of anticyclonic and cyclonic activity in either intensifying or breaking down this very cold stable layer.

In general, the calm clear conditions of the central regions of large
persistent anticyclones favor the intensification of the inversion, both by
heating and drying the free atmosphere through subsidence, which characterizes these systems, and by not hindering outgoing radiation from the surface. Consequently very low surface temperatures occur and are maintained.
The normally excellent visibility can be marred by local ice fog around settlements if supersaturated air at about -40°F is present; and the sharp
density gradient in the inversion layer is often responsible for such optical
phenomena as mirages. Where leads exist in the ice, the cold air spreading
over the warm surface of the water gives rise to arctic smoke or steam fog.

Most of the various surface weather factors - cloud cover, precipitation, winds, and temperature change - are associated with the presence and passage of cyclonic disturbances. Besides the strong winds that frequently accompany the passage of cyclones, the cloud cover and precipitation effect a rise in the surface temperature through longwave radiation. This rise tends to be slow, but persistently overcast skies together with warm air advection can lead to extended periods of above-normal surface temperatures.

The weather associated with these cyclonic systems is modified, especially in winter, by the fact that air temperatures are generally so low that the moisture content even at saturation point is too little to give a dense cloud cover and heavy precipitation. Locally the weather resulting from these storms is influenced by their recent passage over land, water, or ice surfaces. Most of the cyclones originate in more southerly latitudes and by the time they reach the Arctic have lost most of their strong temperature contrast and their frontal structure at the surface with the associated high, middle, and low cloud sequences. They are generally weaker and occluded with the warm air lifted to considerable heights. When fronts do exist they are often ill-defined with no extensive cloud systems or precipitation. Although the cyclonic circulation at the surface may be weak or absent, the sky is generally overcast and occasionally ice needles or traces of snow are formed.

With the general breakup of the ice and the disappearance of the snow cover, the surface inversion weakens and is confined to a shallow layer over the pack ice and ice caps. At this season, the differential heating of the land, water, and ice and the local modification of the temperature profile and moisture content of the moving air masses become a prime factor affecting surface weather over the arctic and subarctic regions.

Over the arctic pack and coastal waters, where the presence of ice holds the surface temperatures near 32°F, the high frequency of fogs and heavy low stratus cloud in the 0- to 5,000-ft layer is closely linked with the inversion itself and to a large extent independent of the type of circulation system. Condensation occurs when warmer air flows over and is cooled by the cold waters or watery ice surface. If the wind speed is low, fog forms close to the surface; if the wind is blowing strongly enough, the fog is lifted to form a low ceiling of stratus cloud. When the wind direction is favorable the fog and cloud drift in over the coastal regions, and hence conditions over coastal airstrips can change rapidly. Drizzle and snow frequently fall from the stratus layer, and temperatures remain low beneath this layer of cloud. Wherever cloud is present within the temperature range of -22 to 32°F there is the possibility of aircraft icing. Moderate to heavy icing has been encountered where cold air passes over open water forming cloud with a large concentration of supercooled droplets; usually this type of cloud does not extend above about 4,000 ft. Inland the inversion and the stratus layer soon disappear over the heated land surfaces.

It is the frequent cyclonic activity over the central Arctic Basin in summer which is responsible for the middle and high clouds, the storms, and much of the precipitation. Cyclones with very great temperature contrasts, strong winds, well-defined frontal zones, extensive cloud systems, and precipitation zones occurred over North Pole IV during the summer of 1955. The vigor of these storms is partly related to the strong thermal contrasts that exist near the arctic coast at this season. In frontal cyclones over the Arctic Basin, the relationship between cloud amount and type is probably similar to that in mid-latitudes, where the large-scale upgliding motion of the warm air produces the sequences of cirrus and cirrostratus, lowering to altostratus and altocumulus, and finally to nimbostratus with

the onset of precipitation. However, the different cloud types often lie
in discrete overlapping strata rather than in a single sloping layer. The
largest amount of cloud occurs in the vicinity of the occlusion, which
may extend to over 20,000 ft. Strong cumulus development and thunderstorms
are rare over the central Arctic.

Once the snow and ice have cleared from the continental subarctic,
surface temperatures generally rise rapidly; however, heavy cloud cover
and increased precipitation in areas of high cyclonic frequency can do
much to delay the temperature rise and the drying out of the surface.
Labrador, for example, has a lower cyclone frequency and a correspondingly
higher number of sunshine hours. The amount of weather associated with
cyclonic activity over the subarctic will again vary according to the
temperature contrasts and moisture content of the air masses involved.
These in turn are influenced by surface conditions, from the strong contrasts over land and ocean to the lesser variations over local water bodies
such as the lakes in the Mackenzie valley.

Under an anticyclonic regime the long hours of daylight can produce
warm clear weather with inland temperatures north of the Arctic Circle
rising above 70 or even 85°F. With continued heating of the surface,
convection leads to cumulus development and thunderstorms.

Over both the central Arctic and much of the continental subarctic
the precipitation maximum occurs in the warmer half of the year and is
associated with the passage of frontal cyclones. The low stratus give
some additional precipitation over the basin, and convective showers occur
south of 75°N where continental heating is strong. The amount and type of
precipitation depend on the temperature and moisture content of the air.
Rain can fall anywhere in the Arctic in summer, and it has been suggested
that nearly 50% of the annual total precipitation over the Canadian Arctic
Archipelago may fall as rain. Where temperatures are in the vicinity of
32°F, it is not easy to predict a type of precipitation without a
detailed knowledge of local conditions which are often unknown. Furthermore, since the greater part of the Arctic is virtually a desert, a
single storm can represent a high precentage of the total annual precipitation. At Thule on July 22, 1957, 1.9 inches - almost the whole season's
rainfall - fell in one day. There is, therefore, considerable variability
in the amount from year to year. Local terrain also ensures considerable
variation from place to place in the amount of precipitation received
from any one storm.

Over coastal regions, the bulk of the precipitation frequently falls
at the end of the warm season when the land surfaces are cooling more
rapidly than the open water. The latter serves as a heat, as well as
moisture, source in modifying the air masses.

Wind

Surface wind velocities usually are not very high over the Arctic
Ocean. On the average the force is between 8 and 10 knots. When an
inversion is present the surface layer is effectively isolated from the
faster-moving air above. It is this fact, in combination with the lack
of topographic effects, which results in the low number of occurrences of
strong winds.

The annual mean wind speeds are greatest at exposed coastal stations near cyclone tracks, and it is in these same locations that storms are most frequent (Jan Mayen, northern Norway to Dikson Island, Bering Strait). A study of wind conditions over the central Arctic Ocean showed that the layer of the atmosphere from the surface to 1,600 ft is characterized by a minimum interdiurnal variability of the wind speed near the ice surface (4 to 6 knots), and that the seasonal variability of wind speed is slight.

The interdiurnal variability of wind direction was found to be greatest near the ice surface (50 to 70 ft) and less at greater heights. This is explained by the low surface wind speed and the consequent instability of the wind direction. Observations from drifting ice stations have been used to prepare the following table of surface wind speed.

TABLE 7

Frequency Distribution of Wind Speed Over Central
Arctic Ocean (Percent)

Knots	0	2	4	6	8	10	12	14	16	18	20-28	29-37	38	No. of obs.
J	11	7	8	10	13	12	8	8	6	4	10	2	1	564
F	10	6	11	15	17	15	9	5	5	1	6	0	0	548
M	6	6	8	18	22	15	7	6	4	2	5	1	0	585
A	6	5	15	15	17	15	8	7	5	4	3	0	0	479
M	7	5	11	16	16	15	11	7	6	3	3	0	0	744
J	5	5	9	15	13	15	11	9	6	4	7	1	0	669
J	4	3	9	12	13	16	10	9	9	6	8	1	0	609
A	4	4	7	11	11	15	11	11	8	5	11	2	0	570
S	8	4	9	13	15	15	8	10	5	4	7	2	0	545
O	7	5	9	12	12	12	10	9	7	4	11	2	0	586
N	9	7	10	13	16	15	7	6	6	4	6	1	0	607
D	11	10	14	14	17	12	6	5	4	3	4	0	0	607

There are certain regional characteristics in the arctic wind systems over land. Eastern Siberia, beyond the Verkhoyansk Khribet, experiences a monsoonal change in wind direction. During winter southerly winds prevail, being strongest over the coast and light or calm in the interior. At Verkhoyansk there is practically no surface wind from February to May. The frequency of storms there is greatest during the months of June, July, and August, with an average of two or three per month. During these months, the thermal low-pressure system shows greatest development over the interior. Along the coast the frequency of storms is least during the same summer months, Tiksi Bay having an average of one per month from April through September. During the colder months, when the anticyclone is well developed over the continent, there are no gales in the interior at Verkhoyansk; but during these same months at Tiksi Bay the frequency is greatest. From October through May there is an average of four storms each month.

The Bering Strait and the land areas immediately to the east and west of it, being low in elevation, present no obstacle to the free interchange of air between the Arctic Basin and the region of the Bering Sea. During the winter the prevailing wind through this region is northerly, and this flow of cold air replenishes the air moving from the Bering Sea into the Pacific

TABLE 8

Mean Wind Speed (mph) and Direction, Northern Hemisphere

	J	F	M	A	M	J	J	A	S	O	N	D	Year
Canada (1951-60)[11] [160]													
Aklavik													
mean speed	6.0	5.6	6.5	7.4	7.3	7.8	7.0	7.0	7.0	6.2	5.2	5.7	6.6
prevailing direction	S	S	NW	N	N	N	NW	NW	NW	NW	NW	NW	
Alert													
Mean speed	5.0	5.1	4.6	4.9	5.1	6.5	7.6	6.0	6.4	6.9	5.8	4.6	5.7
prevailing direction	W	W	W	W	WNW	NE	NE	NE	W	W	W	W	
Baker Lake													
mean speed	14.6	14.1	13.5	14.1	14.2	12.0	11.3	12.7	13.6	15.0	14.6	14.8	13.7
prevailing direction	NW	NW	N	N	N	N	N	N	NW	N	N	N	
Cambridge Bay													
mean speed	12.3	10.7	10.6	12.3	12.7	12.9	12.9	12.8	13.4	14.0	12.0	10.8	12.3
prevailing direction	W	W	W	N,NW	NW	N	N	E	E,NW	NW	W	W	
Chesterfield													
mean speed	15.3	14.2	12.9	13.2	14.9	11.8	11.7	13.0	15.2	17.1	14.9	15.6	14.2
prevailing direction	N	N	N	N	N	N	N	N	N	N	NW	N	
Clyde*													
mean speed	4.6	7.4	4.9	4.7	6.4	8.0	8.5	6.4	8.1	10.3	7.0	3.8	6.7
prevailing direction	NW	NW	NW	NW	NW	NW	NW	NW	NW	NW	NW	NW	
Coppermine													
mean speed	12.2	10:5	9.2	8.7	8.5	8.5	9.6	10.0	11.0	12.0	11.0	10.3	10.1
prevailing direction	SW	W	SW	W	W	N	NE	NE	N	SW	W	SW	
Coral Harbour													
mean speed	12.1	12.3	10.5	13.1	13.2	12.3	12.2	12.9	13.3	13.3	13.2	13.3	12.6
prevailing direction	NW	N	N	N	NW	N	N	N	N	NW	N	N	
Eureka													
mean speed	7.2	6.6	5.4	5.8	8.4	10.9	11.3	9.6	7.8	6.6	6.2	5.4	7.6
prevailing direction	E	E	E	E	NW	NW	NW	NW	NE	E	E	E	
Frobisher Bay													
mean speed	9.1	9.5	9.7	11.0	13.4	11.7	9.7	8.9	11.5	14.6	12.3	11.0	11.0
prevailing direction	NW	NW	NW	NW	NW	SE	SE	SE	NW	NW	NW	NW	
Holman													
mean speed	9.1	7.9	9.5	11.5	10.3	9.5	8.7	8.9	11.7	13.1	11.6	11.2	10.3
prevailing direction	E	E	E	E	E	E	W	E	E	E	E	E	
Isachsen													
mean speed	10.6	7.9	7.0	7.5	10.3	9.9	10.9	10.0	9.9	11.0	9.0	9.7	9.5
prevailing direction	N	N	N	N	N	N	NW	N,SW	N	N	N	N,NW	
Mould Bay													
mean speed	10.5	8.6	7.9	8.4	11.7	13.0	12.2	11.2	11.6	11.3	9.9	8.5	12.5
prevailing direction	NW	NW	N	N,NW	NW	NW	NW	S,NE	NW	NW	NW	NW	
Nottingham I.													
mean speed	10.9	11.5	9.9	11.5	11.2	10.7	9.8	11.1	10.9	14.5	13.0	11.6	11.4
prevailing direction	NW	NW	NW	NE	NE	NE	W	NE	NW	NW	N	N	

* 2 years only.

TABLE 8 (cont'd)

	J	F	M	A	M	J	J	A	S	O	N	D	Year

Canada (cont'd)

Resolute

	J	F	M	A	M	J	J	A	S	O	N	D	Year
mean speed	11.9	11.5	10.4	10.9	11.6	12.6	12.1	12.3	12.5	12.5	11.0	10.4	11.6
prevailing direction	NW	E	NW	NW	NW	NW	NW	NW	NW	NW	NW	NW	

Resolution I.

	J	F	M	A	M	J	J	A	S	O	N	D	Year
mean spead	20.5	20.5	16.1	16.2	14.4	13.2	12.5	13.5	13.9	18.2	17.9	20.4	16.4
prevailing direction	W	SW	W	NE	W	NE	E	E	W	W	W	W	

Sachs Harbour

	J	F	M	A	M	J	J	A	S	O	N	D	Year
mean speed	13.2	11.6	10.7	13.2	12.8	12.8	13.1	13.6	14.7	15.2	13.0	12.0	13.0
prevailing direction	N	E	SE	E,SE	E	N.E	NW	SE	E	E	E	E	

Knob Lake*

	J	F	M	A	M	J	J	A	S	O	N	D	Year
mean speed	10.1	10.6	10.6	10.0	10.6	10.3	10.2	10.7	12.7	12.5	12.1	11.8	11.0
prevailing direction	NW	NW	NW	NW	NW	SE	NW	NW	NW	NW	NW	NW	

Churchill†

	J	F	M	A	M	J	J	A	S	O	N	D	Year
mean speed	14.0	14.2	13.9	14.4	13.1	12.0	12.3	12.6	14.8	16.1	15.1	16.0	14.0
prevailing direction	NW	NW	NW	NW	N	N	N	NW	N	NW	NW	NW	

Fort Simpson†

	J	F	M	A	M	J	J	A	S	O	N	D	Year
mean speed	6.6	7.8	7.9	8.1	8.0	7.5	7.1	6.8	8.1	7.2	7.8	6.6	7.5
prevailing direction	NW	NW	NW	NW	NW	NW	NW	SE	SE	SE	NW	NW	

Yellowknife†

	J	F	M	A	M	J	J	A	S	O	N	D	Year
mean speed	8.0	9.2	10.7	11.6	10.5	10.4	10.5	10.2	10·4	11.7	9.3	8.6	10.1
prevailing direction	N	E	E	N	E	NE	N	SE	N	E	E	E	

Fort Nelson†

	J	F	M	A	M	J	J	A	S	O	N	D	Year
mean speed	3.9	4.7	5.6	6.5	6.4	6.1	5.6	5.4	5.2	4.8	4.0	3.5	5.1
prevailing direction	S	N	N	N	N	N	S	S	S	S	S	S	

Whitehorse†

	J	F	M	A	M	J	J	A	S	O	N	D	Year
mean speed	8.6	8.8	9.1	8.7	8.7	8.0	7.4	7.8	9.1	10.4	9.0	8.7	8.7
prevailing direction	S	S	S	S	SE	SE	SE	SE	S,SE	S	S	S	

Alaska[152]

Anchorage

	J	F	M	A	M	J	J	A	S	O	N	D	Year
mean speed (31)**	5.2	5.9	5.8	5.7	6.4	6.2	5.6	5.2	5.2	5.3	5.1	4.9	5.5
prevailing direction (8)	NE	N	N	N	S	S	S	NW	NNE	N	N	NE	N
fastest mile (10)	60	62	49	66	31	33	32	45	49	59	66	56	66
direction (10)	NE	S	N	S	S	S	S	S	SE	S	NE	SW	NE

Barrow

	J	F	M	A	M	J	J	A	S	O	N	D	Year
mean speed (30)	11.0	11.3	10.9	11.5	11.8	11.4	11.8	12.7	13.7	14.0	12.5	10.9	12.0
prevailing direction (7)	ESE	ENE	NE	E	NE	E	SW	E	ENE	NE	NE	ENE	NE
fastest mile (30)	56	51	48	52	43	38	41	47	56	51	63	70	70
direction (9)	E	SW			SW	W		E	W		W	W	W

Barter I.

	J	F	M	A	M	J	J	A	S	O	N	D	Year
mean speed (7)	14.7	15.2	11.7	12.7	11.9	11.0	10.3	11.0	12.8	14.7	14.9	11.9	12.7
prevailing direction (7)	W	W	W	ENE	E	ENE	ENE	E	E	E	ENE	ENE	ENE

* Average values 1954-62;[127] prevailing direction.[6]

† Periods prior to 1951-60.[6]

** Number of years of record.

TABLE 8 (cont'd)

	J	F	M	A	M	J	J	A	S	O	N	D	Year
					Alaska (cont'd)								
Fairbanks													
mean speed (27)	3.2	3.8	4.7	5.9	6.8	6.4	5.8	5.7	5.5	4.9	3.7	3.0	5.0
prevailing direction (8)	N	N	N	N	N	SW	SW	N	N	N	N	N	N
fastest mile (11)	41	57	60	35	42	40	50	34	49	50	50	34	60
direction (11)	SW	W	SW	SW	SE	SW	SW	W	SW	SW	SW	E	SW
Kotzebue													
mean speed (13)	15.3	14.3	13.2	13.4	10.3	12.2	12.9	13.9	13.0	13.6	13.9	12.9	13.3
prevailing direction (14)	E	E	E	ESE	W	W	W	W	ESE	NE	ESE	NE	W
McGrath													
mean speed (8)	2.7	3.5	4.0	5.0	5.6	5.7	5.4	5.1	4.9	3.8	2.5	2.4	4.2
prevailing direction (9)	NW	NW	NW	N	E	S	S	S	N	N	ESE	NW	NW
Nome													
mean speed (10)	12.0	11.1	11.2	10.9	10.0	9.5	9.9	10.7	11.4	10.9	11.6	9.8	10.8
prevailing direction (9)	E	ENE	E	ENE	NE	SW	WSW	SW	N	NE	N	E	E
fastest mile (10)	75	74	72	53	68	40	38	50	57	57	73	72	75
direction (10)	E	W	NE	S	NE	E	SE	SW	E	SE	SW	E	E
					Greenland								
Thule													
mean speed (11)	9	9	7	7	7	7	7	6	8	10	9	8	8
prevailing direction (11)	E	E	E	E	E.W	W	W	W	E	E	E	E	E
Eismitte													
mean speed (2)	11	9	13	12	9	9	9	8	11	10	9	14	10
Angmagssalik													
mean speed (30)	6	6	5	3	3	3	3	3	3	4	5	5	4
Scoresbysund													
mean speed (12)	5	5	4	4	3	3	3	3	3	4	4	4	4
Nanortalik													
mean speed (41)	12	11	11	10	7	10	7	6	8	9	10	10	10
					Eurasia								
Jan Mayen													
mean speed (mph)	21	21	18	17	13	14	12	14	16	18	19	18	17
no. of days with gales*													
Vardo													
mean speed (28)	22	21	21	19	16	16	13	14	17	19	21	21	18
no. of days with gales*(28)	5	5	4	3	2	1	1	2	2	3	5	5	38
Ostrov Diksona													
mean speed (19)	19	19	16	17	16	16	15	16	17	16	18	17	17
no. of days with gales*(19)	11	19	8	7	5	3	1	3	5	6	9	8	75
Bukhta Tikhaya													
mean speed (10)	16	15	12	12	11	10	8	9	13	15	15	17	13
no. of days with gales*(10)	10	9	7	5	3	3	2	2	4	6	8	11	69

* Gale defined as: windspeed $\geq$ 32 mph.

TABLE 8 (cont'd)

	J	F	M	A	M	J	J	A	S	O	N	D	Year
Eurasia (cont'd)													
Russkoye Ust'ye													
mean speed (9)	8	8	9	9	9	12	12	12	11	9	9	9	10
no. of days with gales*(9)	<0.5	<0.5	2	1	.1	2	2	2	1	2	1	1	15
Mys Shmidta													
mean speed (3)	13	11	12	11	11	11	10	13	14	17	14	12	12
no. of days with gales*(3)	10	6	8	5	5	4	2	4	5	7	4	8	68
Anadyr'													
mean speed (14)	13	14	12	11	9	10	11	11	11	12	13	13	12
no. of days with gales*(14)	4	4	4	2	1	<0.5	2	1	2	2	4	3	29
Verkhoyansk													
mean speed (21)	1	2	2	4	6	7	6	5	4	3	2	1	3
no. of days with gales*(21)	<0.5	<0.5	<0.5	<0.5	2	2	1	1	<0.5	<0.5	0	7	17
Yakutsk													
mean speed (21)	3	3	3	5	6	5	5	5	4	4	3	3	4
no. of days with gales*(21)	<0.5	<0.5	1	1	2	2	1	1	1	1	<0.5	<0.5	10
Polar Ocean													
"Sedov"													
mean speed (1)	11	9	10	11	13	14	12	11	13	14	14		
"Fram"													
mean speed (1)	11	9	8	8	11	12	12	11	11	10	9	10	10

Ice Caps[59]
(summer)

	Upper Ice I 1960	Penny Ice Cap 1953	Barnes Ice Cap 1950	Frøya Glacier 1939	Isachsen Plateau 1934
Height above surface (cm)	200	183	213	200	200
Mean speed (m/sec)†	5.1 (11.2)	4.4 (9.8)	4.3 (9.6)	2.8 (6.2)	2.7 (6.0)
Maximum speed (m/sec)†	20.0 (44.5)	16.1 (35.9)	16.5 (36.8)	6.2 (13.8)	8.1 (18.0)

* Gale defined as windspeed $\geq$ 32 mph.

† Mph in parentheses.

Ocean. During this season the Aleutian low is well pronounced, and the surface winds and upper winds at Nome, Alaska confirm this. Sixty percent of the surface winds at Nome are from the north to northeast at about 9 knots, and continue from that quadrant up to heights of 6,000 ft.

The wind regimen of Alaska, like that of eastern Siberia, is to some extent monsoonal in character. In the warmest months, a thermal low develops over the interior of Alaska whereas, in winter, high pressures are prevalent. As a result, winter winds at Fairbanks are regulated by the polar high-pressure ridge and by the proximity of the Aleutian low-pressure system to the south. Surface winds at Fairbanks itself are light because the town is located in a sheltered valley in which the average winter surface wind speed is about 4 knots. Immediately above the surface 71% of the winds are east-northeast to east-southeast; but with increasing height the wind veers, and at 10,000 ft 43% are from the south to the west-southwest. In summer the air pressure increases over the Gulf of Alaska, and a local thermal low is established over the interior. The prevailing winds at Fairbanks are southwesterly at about 5 knots.

The frequency of storms in Alaska is similar to that of eastern Siberia. In the interior the season of greatest frequency is during the summer, whereas along the coast it is during the winter. Point Barrow, on the north coast, has an average of 19 storms per year whereas Fairbanks in the interior has only 1. Wrangel Island has an annual average of 50 storms, and from May through August there is an average of 2 each month. Summer is the season of low storm average at Wrangel Island, at which time the Aleutian low is dissipated. During the colder months, between September and April, the average monthly frequency is between 5 and 6. At this season the Aleutian low is well developed.

The maps of air pressure show that a north and northwesterly air flow is directed over the Canadian Arctic Archipelago throughout most of the year. The flow is strongest during winter. Winds across the Hudson Bay region are northwesterly in winter and only disturbed in summer by the passage of individual storms. Such cyclones invade the region and give frequent summer storms.

In central Greenland, unlike the interior of Eurasia and North America, winter winds are strongest. The temperature inversion persists through the year in Greenland, and the pressure gradient controls the annual wind cycle.

At several arctic sites, the high surface winds associated with strong pressure gradients are often enhanced by local effects. Many stations show locally preferred wind directions due to topography, and surface wind data from arctic land stations must not be taken as typical of the wind speed and direction over a larger area. Certain locations in Greenland are good examples of this - Thule in the northwest and Narssarssuak in the southwest both have local strong winds partly associated with descent of the air from the inland ice sheet. Alert, Barter Island, and Juneau all experience local strong winds. Almost any fiord in the Arctic may have peculiar local wind conditions.

Windchill

It must be remembered that in cold climates the combination of temperature and wind produces the greatest heat loss and discomfort (Fig. 30 and

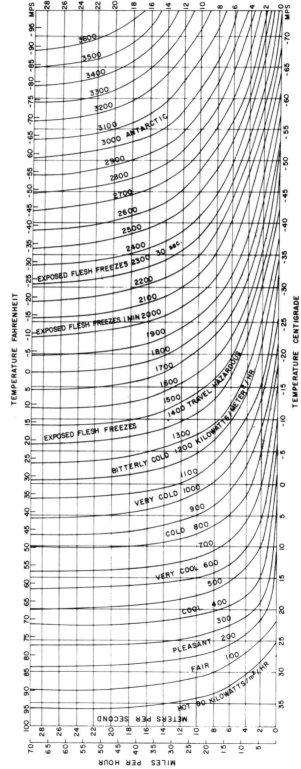

Figure 30.   WINDCHILL NOMOGRAM AND/OR T-W-P-R FACTOR WINDCHILL EXPRESSED IN
KILOWATTS PER METER SQUARED PER HOUR

Table 9). With a wind speed of 17 knots, a temperature of 5°F is just as effective in chilling a man as a temperature of -40°F with a very slight wind of less than 2 knots. In the system shown, exposed flesh freezes at a windchill value of 1,400 kilogram calories an hour per square meter; however, it should be noted that the windchill concept has not yet been rigorously defined by physiologists, and its usage and usefulness in terms of absolutes are consequently still open to consider-able controversy. Nevertheless it is a useful concept which should be taken into account prior to and during an arctic operation (Fig. 31). Some mean monthly windchill values for the extreme month (physiologically coldest) for several locations are:

Baker Lake, Canada	2,030	Resolute, Canada	1,940
Barrow, Alaska	1,705	Thule, Greenland	1,605
Churchill, Canada	1,820	Verhkoyansk, Siberia	1,471

Although the Siberian Arctic has low mean and extreme temperatures, the Alaskan-Canadian Arctic, particularly in the barren lands northwest of Hudson Bay, has higher winter wind speeds. Combined with low temperatures, these produce greater physiological stress. But physiologically the coldest place in the Arctic is probably the interior of the Greenland ice sheet.

Temperature

The most common misconception of the Arctic is that the land areas are perennially covered with ice and snow and that winter is continuous and in-tensely cold. A large part of Greenland is a striking example of an ice-covered land possessing these qualities, and from it the rest of the north has been pictured by analogy. The high average elevation of Green-land and the precipitation it receives are two factors which strongly favor glaciation. In general, however, other arctic lands posses neither of these characteristics, and over a large portion of the Arctic the scanty snows melt rapidly with the approach of summer. Most of the little snow that does fall is soon swept by the wind into gullies and the lee of hills or structures, so that more than three-quarters of the arctic lands are comparatively snow-free at all seasons. With respect to the intense cold: at the North Pole the lowest temperatures generally do not fall below -65°F, a figure that is reached equally often in some parts of the North American prairies. The coldest observed temperature on the surface of the earth before 1957 was recorded at Verkhoyansk, near the Arctic Circle in eastern Siberia and well over 1,200 mi from the geographic pole. However the temperatures recorded at Oimyakon, about 300 mi south-east of Verkhoyansk, have consistently averaged lower than those recorded at the same time at Verkhoyansk. The official minimum at Oimyakon is -90°F. Only the Antarctic, occupied since 1957, is colder (-128°F).

A great variety of climatic conditions are encountered in the arctic regions (Fig. 32). Areas adjacent to one another are found to have widely differing climatic characteristics determined by latitude, marine influence, and topography. A study of annual temperature curves reveals three well-defined types - maritime, coastal, and continental:

(1) The Arctic Ocean has a flat temperature curve during June, July, and August with small deviations from the freezing point. The winter curve is again flat, but at this time the temperatures stay around -29°F.

TABLE 9

Descriptive Terms With Windchill Values Appropriate to Different Temperatures and Windspeeds

Windspeed (mph)	(m/sec)	Temp (°F)	(°C)	Windchill	In sunshine	Light cloud	Thick cloud
5	2.5	90	32	18	Unbearably hot	Unbearably hot	Very warm
		80	27	146	Unbearably hot	Very warm	Warm
		70	21	269	Hot	Warm	Pleasant
		60	15.5	398	Warm	Pleasant	Pleasant
		50	10	528	Pleasant	Cool	Cool
		40	4.5	658	Cool	Cool	Very cool
		30	-1	788	Cool	Very cool	Cold
15	7	90	32	23	Unbearably hot	Very warm	Very warm
		80	27	187	Hot	Warm	Pleasant
		70	21	343	Warm	Pleasant	Cool
		60	15.5	508	Pleasant	Cool	Cool
		50	10	674	Cool	Very cool	Very cool
		40	4.5	840	Very cool	Cold	Cold
		30	-1	1005	Cold	Very cold	Very cold
25	11	90	32	25	Unbearably hot	Very warm	Warm
		80	27	206	Very warm	Pleasant	Pleasant
		70	21	378	Pleasant	Cool	Cool
		60	15.5	561	Cool	Very cool	Very cool
		50	10	744	Very cool	Cold	Cold
		40	4.5	927	Cold	Very cold	Very cold
		30	-1	1109	Very cold	Bitterly cold	Bitterly cold

EXPLANATION ON USE OF CHART

BY A SIMPLE TECHNIQUE, IT IS POSSIBLE TO ESTIMATE THE PROBABILITY OF A SPECIFIED LEVEL OF WINDCHILL. DATA REQUIRED (MEAN MONTHLY AIR TEMPERATURE AND WINDSPEED) ARE ENTERED IN THE SIPLE WINDCHILL NOMOGRAM AT THE LEFT AND A WINDCHILL INDEX OBTAINED. THIS INDEX IS TRANSFERRED TO THE PREDICTION CHART AT THE RIGHT AND FOLLOWED TO THE PREDETERMINED LEVEL DESIRED (READ ON ACTUAL WINDCHILL SCALE AT THE EXTREME RIGHT). PERCENTAGE FREQUENCY CAN BE READ ON THE PROBABILITY SCALE AT EITHER TOP OR BOTTOM OF THE PREDICITION CHART.

EXAMPLE AT FORT CHURCHILL, JANUARY MEAN TEMPERATURE (-18°F) AND WINDSPEED (14.9 MPH) ENTERED IN THE NOMOGRAPH AT THE LEFT GIVE AN 1,800 WINDCHILL INDEX. THIS 1,800 INDEX INTERSECTS THE 1,400 ACTUAL WINDCHILL (CONDITION AT WHICH EXPOSED FLESH FREEZES) AT 72 PERCENT ON THE UPPER SCALE OR 28 PERCENT ON THE LOWER SCALE, INDICATING THAT DANGER OF FREEZING IS A PROBABILITY 72 PERCENT OF THE TIME AT CHURCHILL DURING JANUARY. SAFETY FROM FREEZING IS A PROBABILITY 28 PERCENT OF THE TIME. THE POSSIBILITY OF THE SITUATION BECOMING DANGEROUS FOR TRAVEL OR LIVING IN TEMPORARY SHELTERS (2,000 ACTUAL WINDCHILL) IS A PROBABILITY 16 PERCENT OF THE TIME.

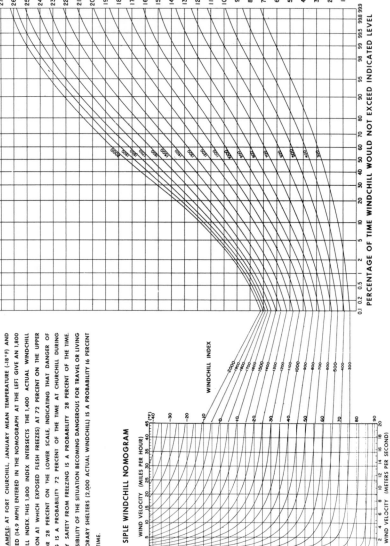

Figure 31.   WINDCHILL PREDICTION CHART

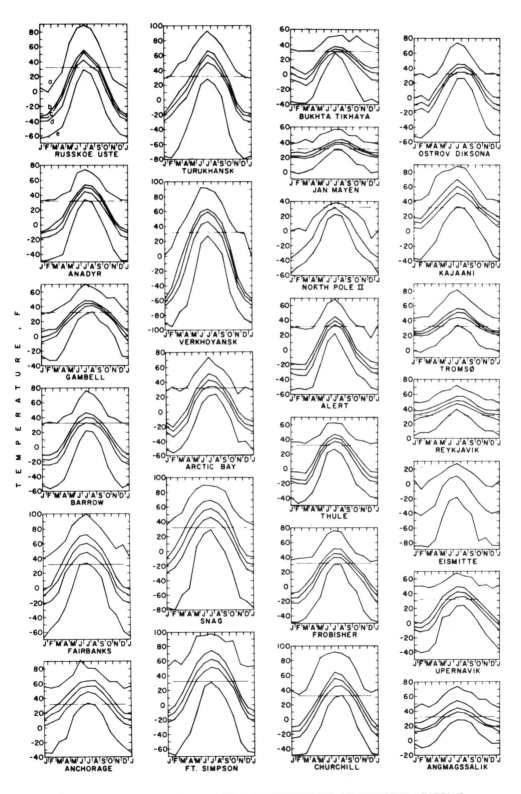

Figure 32.   MONTHLY TEMPERATURE DISTRIBUTIONS AT SELECTED STATIONS
a) Absolute maximum; b) Mean maximum; c) Mean;
d) Mean minimum; e) Absolute minimum.

(2) The coastal climate is quite similar to the maritime one. The year consists of a long cold winter and a short cool summer similar to the spring or autumn experienced on the continent. The annual temperature curve has the same winter characteristics as that of the Arctic Ocean but there is a seasonal maximum in July. The mean summer temperature, however, remains below 50°F.

(3) The arctic continental climate is characterized by very low winter temperatures with a pronounced winter minimum and high summer temperatures with a very pronounced summer maximum. Here the annual range of mean temperature may be as much as 130°F.

In Eurasia, winter temperatures (Fig. 33a) show a marked decrease from the warm coastal areas of Scandinavia to northeastern Siberia and the region around Verkhoyansk where the January mean is -54°F. The reason this area has the most extreme winters in the northern hemisphere is readily understood from its geographic location. Heat from the North Atlantic cannot penetrate into or over the frozen continent: the Pacific Ocean has no appreciable effect, since ranges of mountains intervene and the winds are prevailingly offshore; the ice-covered Arctic Ocean cannot modify the conditions; and the ranges of central Asia check any influence from the warm Indian Ocean far to the south. The characteristic lag of seasons, so highly pronounced on the arctic coasts and conspicuous at any locality with maritime influence, is almost totally absent. The temperature curve follows more nearly that of insolation and April (Fig. 33c) is as warm as October (Fig. 33f). In the interior of Canada the same characteristics are evident, but since the area is not comparable to the vastness of the Siberian land mass, the feature is less pronounced. The Siberian winter is by no means as unpleasant as its extreme temperatures might suggest - the air is often calm and the skies clear. Danger to man and beast occurs only when the bitter buran blows. Similar blizzards also occur in the interior of Canada. The probable occurence of extremely low temperatures in the North has recently been computed and is presented in Figures 34a through d. The most conspicuous element of these calculations is the rapid diminution of the likelihood of extremely low readings in North America as the temperature decreases.

The irregularities of the winter isotherms over the Arctic Ocean are produced by the influence of the Atlantic and Pacific oceans. In the North Atlantic the isotherms are pushed far northward, and the greatest positive anomaly of temperature (the greatest departure from latitudinal average) in the world occurs here. The winter temperatures in the vicinity of Bering Strait are influenced by the open waters of the Bering Sea. North of the Strait the influence is limited to a small area in which large local differences occur with different wind directions. Large and rapid temperature fluctuations are otherwise not a common feature over the Arctic Ocean. The air temperature near the surface is primarily dependent on the temperature of the ice surface itself. On occasion, however, warm air from the Atlantic may raise the winter temperature near the North Pole by as much as 54°F. After the warm air import has ceased, radiation control again dominates the surface temperature which will show an equally drastic drop. Strong winds may also cause higher surface temperatures by breaking down the temperature inversion and mixing the warmer air from above with that near the surface. Renewed cooling follows every slackening of wind.

The winter temperatures over the pack ice remain nearly constant for a considerable time. This flat minimum represents the temperature at which

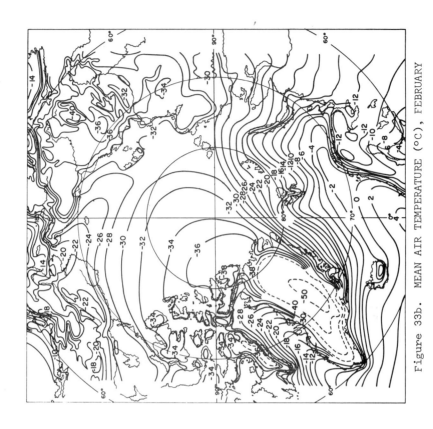

Figure 33b. MEAN AIR TEMPERATURE (°C), FEBRUARY

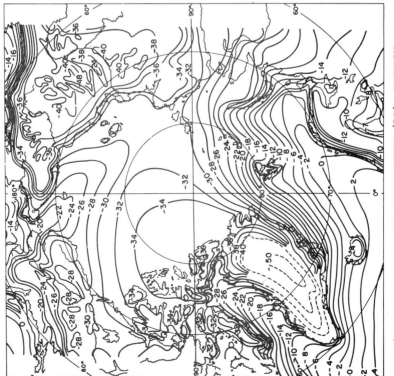

Figure 33a. MEAN AIR TEMPERATURE (°C), JANUARY

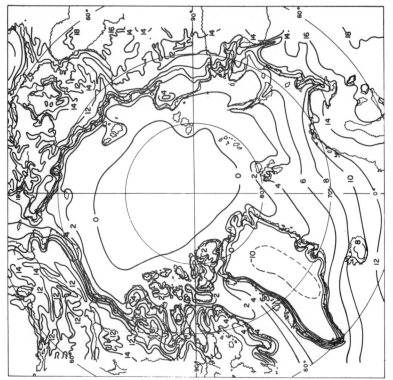

Figure 33d.   MEAN AIR TEMPERATURE (°C), JULY

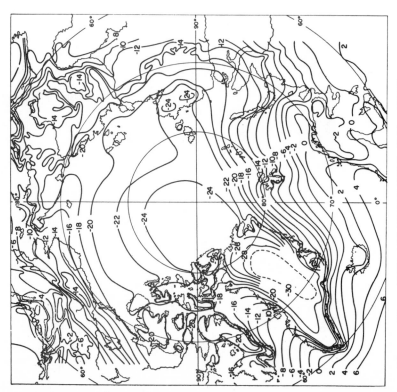

Figure 33c.   MEAN AIR TEMPERATURE (°C), APRIL

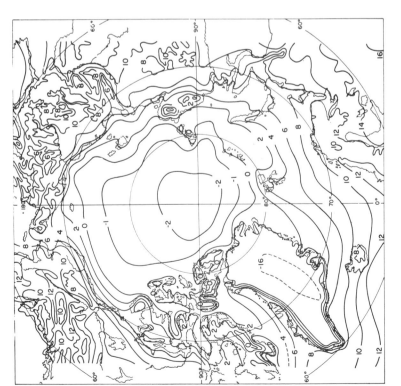

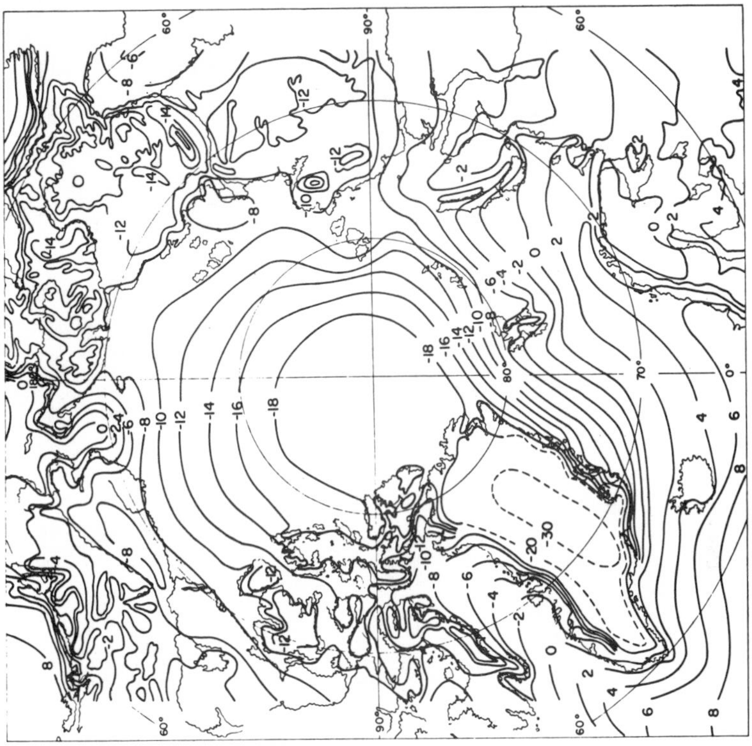

Figure 33f.   MEAN AIR TEMPERATURE (°C), OCTOBER

Figure 33e.   MEAN AIR TEMPERATURE (°C), AUGUST

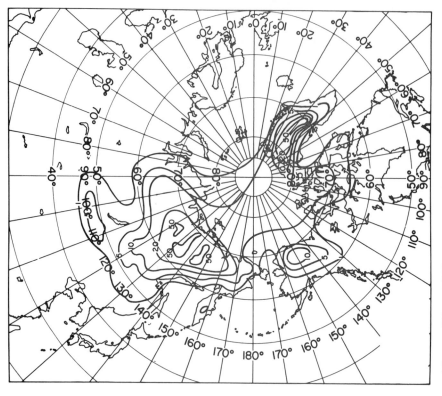

Figure 34b.   ESTIMATED RISK (PERCENT OF COLDEST MONTH)
TEMPERATURE BELOW −50°F

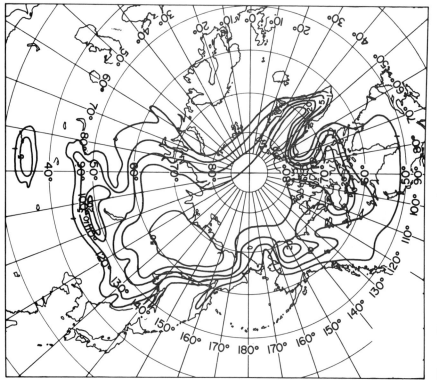

Figure 34a.   ESTIMATED RISK (PERCENT OF COLDEST MONTH)
TEMPERATURE BELOW −40°F

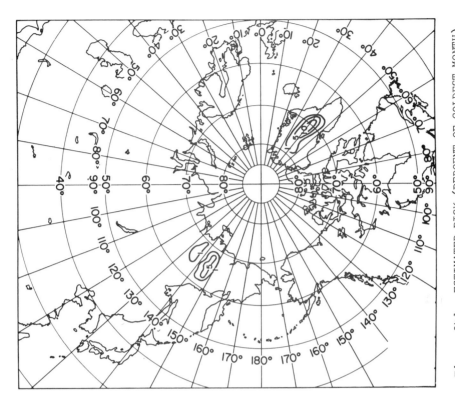

Figure 34d.   ESTIMATED RISK (PERCENT OF COLDEST MONTH)
               TEMPERATURE BELOW -70°F

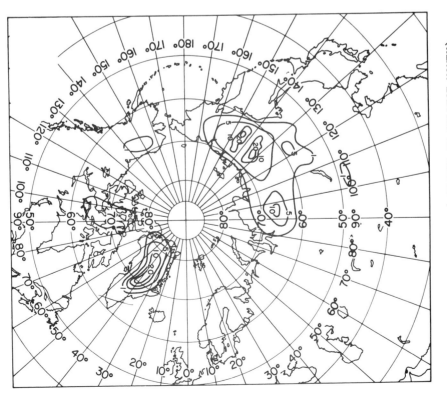

Figure 34c.   ESTIMATED RISK (PERCENT OF COLDEST MONTH)
               TEMPERATURE BELOW -60°F

the loss of heat by radiation from the snow and ice surface balances the heat which is conducted to the surface from the water under the ice plus the heat transported into the Arctic by intense warm air advected in cyclones. In periods of little cyclonic activity, heat transfer to the surface from the atmosphere is small since the eddy conductivity is very small in the inversion layer. The winter air over the Arctic Ocean is, as a rule, nearly saturated with water vapor. Surface temperatures are mainly governed by net radiation and conduction of heat to the surface from below.

Minimum air temperatures (Fig. 35) must occur when the net radiation loss is least balanced by transport of heat from the water. This will give a minimum temperature at the surface of about -40°F down to -58°F over thick ice. The maximum temperature in overcast calm weather is reached at about -13°F. The extreme maximum temperatures are nearly linear functions of the wind speed, increasing with increasing wind speed due to the transport of heat from above the inversion.

The presence, or nearness, of open water is seen in the temperature distribution in the winter half of the year when broad tongues of mild temperatures extend into Barents Sea and Baffin Bay and across Bering Strait. The strongest influx of heat by cyclonic activity occurs in the Atlantic section of the Arctic Ocean in January and February; and, as a consequence, the lowest temperatures are observed in that section in March. In the other regions the lowest winter temperatures usually appear in January or February. From April until June the temperature rises quite rapidly until the ice begins to melt. The mean summer surface temperatures (Figs. 33d and e) remain fairly constant, conforming to the nature of the underlying surface. Almost all regions are warmest in July. Temperatures close to the melting point prevail over the pack ice and along the fringes of the Greenland ice sheet. Cool temperatures dip southward across Bering Strait and Baffin Bay. Maximum temperatures in the Arctic Basin do not exceed 41°F. An examination of large departures of monthly mean temperatures from normal values for 20 coastal or island stations, from 20 or more years of observations, showed that the greatest departures are found in winter (from November to April) and small departures are most probable in July. Of the departures in winter, the greatest were observed in the Kara Sea and the smallest were noted in the East Siberian Sea. In summer the greatest observed departures from normal temperatures were on the coasts of the peripheral seas and decreased toward the north.

The temperature inversions observed in all arctic regions are especially prominent over the pack ice. As would be expected, the diurnal variation is somewhat irregular and the maximum occurs during the night hours and the minimum during the middle of the day. Again, the wind accounts for the irregularity; any slight increase in wind, regardless of direction, produces a considerable rise in temperature by the process of mixing.

In summer the melting of snow and ice keeps the surface temperature close to the freezing point. The number of days with a maximum temperature slightly above the freezing point is very nearly the same all along the latitude of 75°N - about 40 days. Nearer the pole, positive temperatures are usually observed in the second half of July on some 10 to 15 days.

The small temperature variability in summer is a characteristic common to all stations on the central Arctic Ocean. The temperatures over the pack ice never deviate far from the freezing point. The diurnal ranges are smaller and the interdiurnal changes are less in summer than in any other

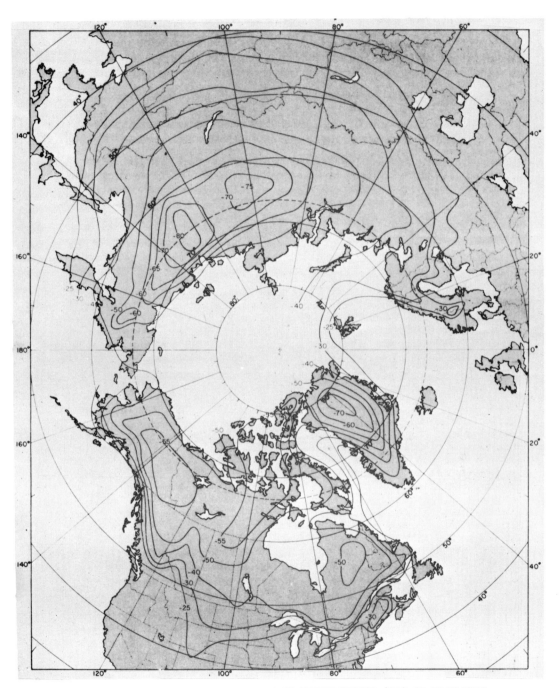

Figure 35. AVERAGE OF THE LOWEST TEMPERATURES (°F) OF EACH YEAR

season. Warm air from inland is often transported a considerable distance
from the coast; but, in passing over the ice-filled waters, it is cooled
so effectively by contact with the ice that a sharp inversion is formed.
Hence, the warm air current flows at some distance above the ground and
has practically no influence on the surface temperature. Considerably
higher temperatures are found on the coast and the change from coastal to
maritime conditions takes place within a very short distance. However,
this characteristic holds good for the surface layer only and does not
apply at higher levels. The discontinuity, therefore, represents only
a quasi-front and is of no consequence to the circulation of the atmosphere.

Humidity

The relative humidity of the air over the Arctic Ocean in the winter
always remains near 100%. During this period it should be calculated as
the relative humidity over ice, i.e. with respect to the saturation vapor
pressure over ice, which is lower than over water. This permits the air
to be slightly supersaturated with respect to ice, while it is not saturated with respect to water. It will cause water droplets to evaporate
while water vapor condenses on ice crystals. Supersaturation occurs
frequently near the surface in winter, as long as no condensation takes
place. Normally, however, hoarfrost formation begins when a value slightly
over 100% has been reached. The relative humidity over ice has a maximum
in midwinter (103%) and a minimum in June (95%), while the relative
humidity over water has a maximum in August (96%) and a minimum in midwinter
(73%). The actual pressure of the water vapor is very small in midwinter
(0.2 mb), and it has a maximum in July-August (6 mb).

The amount of hoarfrost which is deposited is proportional to the wind
speed and to the difference between actual pressure of the water vapor and
the saturation vapor pressure over ice. Hoarfrost is formed only when the
relative humidity over ice is greater than 100%. The amount of frost deposition is greatest at a temperature of around -20°F while the probability
of hoarfrost has a maximum at about -26°F. In July and August there is
relatively little hoarfrost since air temperatures usually are around
freezing point. Otherwise, the smallest amounts occur in April and the
greatest in September. In the latter month there is, over the entire
Arctic Ocean, a surplus of water in the air since open leads in the sea ice
are frequent. Hoarfrost is considerable on the vertical surfaces and may
amount to 0.8 inches - about 15% of the annual total precipitation.
However the deposition is less on a horizontal surface, and hoarfrost is
of small importance to the total snow cover in winter.

Visibility

The melting of the pack ice in summer leads to formation of persistent
fog and low cloud. Arctic Ocean stations experience fog more than 100 days
per year, most frequently in summer and least in winter. The summer fog
is generally caused by advection of relatively warm and moist air over
the melting ice or cold water. It is patchy and of fairly short duration.
Advection fog is particularly prevalent from June to September, occurring
on 10% of all observations in June, 15% in July, 25% in August, and 7% in
September. The fog does not occur at wind speeds above 20 knots. During
the cold season, small patches of steam fog form over open water leads in
the pack ice. This type of fog, sometimes called arctic sea smoke,

develops when cold air blows over open water causing rapid discharge of moisture and heat to the air.

The types mentioned above are water fogs. There also occurs during the arctic winter a phenomenon called ice fog. This may form where large quantities of water vapor are added to very cold air, preferably about -22°F. Lightweight ice particles, with a slight fall velocity, remain suspended in the stagnant air near the surface for a considerable period. Such fog occurs locally in the vicinity of human habitation. The second type that has major importance in the Arctic is the radiation fog of winter. These fogs form readily under an inversion in very cold weather and are caused by the cooling of the lowest layer of air by contact with the surface. Cooling by radiation takes place most rapidly over the land areas and least rapidly over open water. The fogs that are formed are generally thin and shallow; they occur most frequently along river bottoms where the air drainage is poor and the air movement sluggish. The locale of most frequent occurrence appears to be in the lower Lena River valley and the lower Mackenzie River valley. They are also quite frequent in the Yukon valley and the valleys of the principal northward-flowing rivers of central and eastern Siberia. Radiation fogs are also common over the pack ice. These fogs may be expected from 8 to 12 days per month during the winter, and in adverse years the number of days of radiation fogs may be doubled. In a few localities, such as the lower Mackenzie in the vicinity of Aklavik, early morning radiation fogs may be expected on 20 to 25 days monthly during the coldest months. It is stressed that these frost fogs do not present as serious an obstacle to aviation as do water fogs. They are generally thin fogs, so that con-trasting objects can be distinguished on the surface directly beneath the aircraft. It is only in the brief interval during which the aircraft is passing through the thin fog layer that visibility is seriously reduced. With experience, landings and takeoffs can be made with safety through the shallow frost fogs.

As a rule, fogs are not to be expected in summer with offshore winds. The offshore winds are relatively dry and are not cooled sufficiently to cause the formation of fog. Summer fogs are most frequent with light winds but under favorable conditions they may occur with high winds. Since they are advection fogs, they do not form readily in calm weather. The opposite is true of the mists or frost fogs of the winter season. The latter are radiation fogs and form most readily in calm weather or with very light winds. High winds are very unfavorable for the formation or continuation of fog in the colder months of the year.

Fogs in the Arctic are more frequent in the late-night and the early-morning hours than at any other time. In the Kara Sea region the maximum frequency of fogs occurs at midnight or in the hours immediately following and the minimum frequency occurs at noon or in the early afternoon. These observations agree closely with experience in the East Siberian Sea. Data on the diurnal distribution of mists or frost fogs elsewhere are not so conclusive but indicate a similar distribution for the summer advection fogs. Frost fogs are more frequent in the early morning than at noon or in the evening.

It will be noted from the figures shown in Table 10 that the summer fogs are less frequent over the Barents and Norwegian seas. This is due to the more turbulent nature of the lower atmosphere over these seas, resulting in less fog and more low clouds.

TABLE 10

Average Number of Days With Fog

PLACE	JAN.	MAR.	MAY	JULY	SEPT.	NOV.	ANNUAL
Dikson Island	5.5	7.9	4.9	22.9	10.5	5.2	152.2
Kola	0.7	0.2	1.0	3.1	1.9	1.6	16.1
Tiksi Bay	3.7	4.4	5.3	9.0	4.6	1.0	66.1
Verkhoyansk	3.4	0.6	0.6	1.5	4.1	1.8	25.9
Wrangel	1.6	4.6	12.2	21.4	10.8	3.8	113.5
Yugor Strait	4.5	6.2	9.1	19.6	14.1	4.5	123.8
Aklavik	19.6	27.6	2.0	2.2	21.2	15.6	165.6
Tromsø	1.0	0.8	1.0	2.0	2.0	1.0	14.0
Vardo	0.0	0.0	1.0	6.0	1.0	0.0	18.0
Green Harbor	0.1	0.1	0.4	4.0	1.0	0.0	13.0
Bear Island	1.1	2.7	6.7	18.7	12.0	3.3	82.0
Jan Mayen	1.9	3.2	3.3	12.8	5.9	1.8	58.3
Angmagssalik	1.0	1.0	7.0	9.0	4.0	2.0	48.0
Godhavn	9.0	11.0	15.0	17.0	8.0	3.0	127.0
Godthaab	1.0	1.0	7.0	13.0	7.0	1.0	61.0
Ivigtut	0.2	0.4	2.0	6.0	3.0	1.0	26.0
Upernavik	2.0	2.0	5.0	11.0	2.0	1.0	47.0
Churchill	1.0	*	1.0	2.0	1.0	*	13.0
Craig Harbour	*	1.0	0.0	2.0	1.0	*	9.0
Lake Harbour	2.0	1.0	2.0	5.0	2.0	3.0	30.0
Pond Inlet	1.0	*	*	*	*	2.0	9.0
Dutch Harbor	0.9	0.9	2.5	3.5	1.8	0.0	18.4
Fairbanks	17.2	11.6	0.8	2.4	3.2	6.1	68.0
Nome	5.3	5.2	5.0	8.1	4.4	3.2	67.2
Point Barrow	5.0	2.3	7.5	15.0	5.4	2.7	82.6
St. Paul's Island	1.7	2.8	6.9	7.0	2.8	1.5	52.2

*Less than one day

The matter of visibility in the Arctic is a complex one due to the extreme clarity of the air. The records contain many accounts of the extreme range of visibility - it is not uncommon to see dark mountains 80 mi distant. On the other hand, the lack of contrast, particularly where all surface objects are covered with new snow, results in the inability to distinguish some objects close at hand. As the arctic atmosphere is fairly uncontaminated by impurities, the visibility will be reduced only, apart from fog, by precipitation or blowing snow.

Wind speeds of about 5 knots will cause unconsolidated snow to drift along the surface. At speeds of 10 to 15 knots the snow is lifted into the air, and when it reaches a height of 6 ft the term 'blowing snow' is used. Coastal stations around the Arctic Ocean may experience more than 100 days of blowing snow per year - in winter on more than half the days.

In late autumn and winter, falling ice crystals may be observed when the moisture of advected air condenses over the cold ocean. Fine ice needles form a slight haze as they settle slowly from an otherwise-clear sky. Such falls of ice crystals add little to the snow cover, however.

The frequent well-marked temperature inversions of the Arctic explain the many accounts of mirages. Objects that are known, beyond any doubt, to be below the horizon are not infrequently visible as mirages and the periods of daytime and twilight are lengthened as the normal index of refraction is altered. The inversions may also interfere with the identification of landmarks through distortion while estimation of vertical distances is made much more difficult.

Whiteout is a very simple phenomenon with easily understood causes and only one direct effect: the loss of depth perception. This results in quite unexpected and sometimes disastrous consequences. The only recourse on the surface is to shuffle along at a slow pace. In the air, the only safe procedure is instrument flying rules, making landing difficult, if not impossible, at many arctic airfields.

Only two conditions are necessary to produce a whiteout: (1) a diffuse, shadowless illumination; and (2) a uniformly monocolored, white surface. In polar regions these conditions occur frequently. Large unbroken expanses of snow are illuminated by a sky overcast with dense, low, stratus clouds that blot out all traces of surface texture or shadow and merge bumps and hollows and snow-covered objects into a flattened, white background. Those who have not been exposed to whiteout are often skeptical about the inability of those who have experienced it to estimate distances under these conditions. In the normal environment there are so many direct and indirect clues to depth that it is hard to understand how one who can see clearly can still fail to guage distances accurately.

The primary clues are those that result directly and without the intervention of thought or logic in a "feeling" of depth. These are unaffected by whiteout. The remaining clues to depth - and they are of the greatest importance in everyday life - are secondary - that is, the mental estimate is not directly in terms of distance but of appearance relative to some standard. Normally, there is a continuous succession of familiar objects, starting from somewhere well within the range of binocular depth perception (where primary clues are effective) and extending out to and beyond the object of attention. Both foreground and background combine to furnish

many clues to the distance of any object, even objects of unknown size.
This is the crux of the matter, because the entire visual continuum is
erased by whiteout, and in such an unfamiliar situation all vestiges of
depth perception may be lost without one's even being aware of impairment.
Naturally, this frequently leads to extreme confusion and even disorienta-
tion.

Most concern about whiteout is in relation to flying safety. Whiteout
is generally a problem to the pilot in landing, takeoff, and taxiing.
However, low flying, at altitudes less than 1,000 ft above the terrain,
is particularly hazardous under these conditions and has resulted in
numerous wrecks that are strewn across the entire Arctic.

Ground operations are also impaired, whether they involve walking or
the use of vehicles. On an overcast morning following a new snow, the
roadsides may be littered with vehicles, frequently including the snow-
removal machinery. Often roads are closed - not because of snow depth,
but because of whiteout; and the whiteout need not be total.

Solutions may result from an approach involving 2 possible avenues -
the physical and the psychological. Physically, the point in question is
whether the quality of light reflected from snow-covered objects may vary
in some subtle way with the angle presented by the surface or from the
incident sky-light, so that contrast might be enhanced by the use of
appropriate filters. Yellow nickel-coated glasses seem to be helpful to
pilots. While the use of intense directional artificial light would
provide adequate shadows and contrast, it is not a solution of general
value because of its impracticability during normal daylight hours. The
use of smoke bombs on landing strips has been suggested, particularly
if there is a little wind to move the smoke across the snow in such a
fashion as to create stained "shadows." However, many objects are required
in the visual field to provide adequate clues to depth, and some 250 to
500 points are required for good motion parallax. The most suitable
method yet found in the latter connection is to line each side of the
airstrip with empty fuel barrels.

In addition to the clear air whiteout, there is an increasing tendency
to speak of obscuration-type whiteouts which may be caused by water fog,
ice fog, blowing snow, and/or precipitation. In these instances vision
is not only impaired by loss of depth perception but also by the presence
of hydrometeors that limit the seeing range. Although considerable study
has been made of these conditions, standard weather stations report weather
and obstructions to vision in terms of the causal agent while climatic
tabulations group all the conditions together (Fig. 36 and Table 11).

In blowing or falling snow, fog, or sea smoke - conditions that may be
concomitant with whiteout - and in arctic twilight with freshly fallen
or blowing snow, in all probability nothing will help the aviator; but men
on the surface can follow well-flagged trails. The training of pilots to
cope with the whiteout phenomenon presents difficulties, for whiteout is
not always available and hence establishing a training program would be
rather haphazard; but the ability of bush pilots to operate with relative
impunity in whiteout shows that experience in flying under these conditions
is useful.

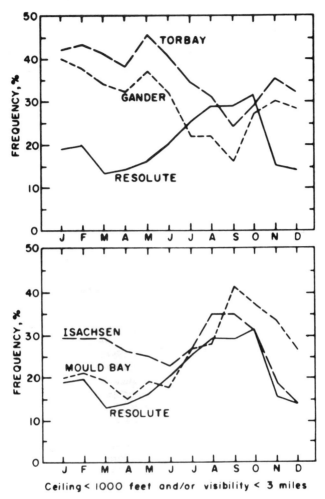

Ceiling < 1000 feet and/or visibility < 3 miles

Figure 36.   FREQUENCY OF BELOW-VFR CONDITIONS
AT FIVE ARCTIC STATIONS, 1954-1960

TABLE 11

Percentage of Below-VFR Conditions in Various Windspeed Groups
at Resolute, N.W.T., 1954 to 1960

	0-9 mph (0-4 m/sec)	10-19 mph (4½-8½ m/sec)	20-29 mph (9-13 m/sec)	≧30 mph (≧14 m/sec)
Jan	1	8	39	87
Feb	5	18	39	80
Mar	4	8	40	87
Apr	4	12	29	67
May	14	13	20	42
June	22	21	13	15
July	28	26	15	12
Aug	33	30	18	20
Sept	32	28	26	13
Oct	20	25	41	72
Nov	5	10	36	80
Dec	2	7	38	79

<u>Clouds</u>

Causes and Types

Two basically different causes for clouds and their distribution can be distinguished:

(1) Dynamic causes. The vertical motion associated with pressure systems favors cloudiness under cyclonic conditions and clear sky under anticyclonic conditions.

(2) Geographic causes. These usually work through the water or radiation balance. Moist surfaces with high evaporation rates favor cloud formation due to the high moisture content of the air, even under anti-cyclonic conditions. The opposite holds for dry surfaces. A strong positive radiation balance favors cumulus development independent, to a large degree, of the dynamic conditions.

A variety of cloud patterns will be caused by the interaction of these 2 influences. The main Arctic types are described below.

1. *Norwegian Sea Type* - In the zone of westerlies over the ocean all influences favor cloud formation. The cloudiness is high all through the year with a slight maximum in summer. It is noteworthy that, even in this area which is so clearly governed by cyclones, the maximum cloudiness is experienced in summer, the season with the lowest cyclone frequency (Fig. 37b). The cloud types of this area also show peculiar behavior. In winter cumulus cover reaches a frequency of 30 to 40% - more than that observed in any season anywhere else in the Arctic (Figs. 38 and 39). Observations from the Norwegian coast indicate that the most important cloud in this group is cumulonibus. In summer this dominance disappears mainly in favor of altocumulus and altostratus (Figs. 40 and 41).

The reason for this development is the frequent outbreaks in winter of arctic air masses over this area containing the warm water of the North Atlantic Drift. Extreme instability is created with a consequent development of convection cloud. As convectional clouds produce less cloudiness than do stratiform clouds, the cloudiness tends to diminish. Warm water and cold air masses combine to reduce the winter cloudiness below the conditions typical for the west wind zone.

In summer, with the water much colder in relation to its surroundings and with no extremely cold air available, the cumulus frequency and cloudi-ness approach the more normal patterns for the west wind zone - around 80% cloud cover. Due to reduced cyclonic activity, however, a relatively great proportion of the clouds is found in the medium cloud layers.

2. *East Siberian Type* - The whole of Siberia is dominated in winter by anticyclonic influences. The region of especially clear skies is found, not at 100°E, the zone of highest anticyclonic frequency, but nearer 140°E. The distance from sources of moisture must be responsible. Therefore, the characteristic stratus or stratocumulus formations under an inversion are conspicuously absent in this area. The clouds which exist are over-whelmingly cirrus (nearly 60%). Even at the height of middle clouds the moisture content drops to low values, and only the infrequent cyclone is able to cause condensation.

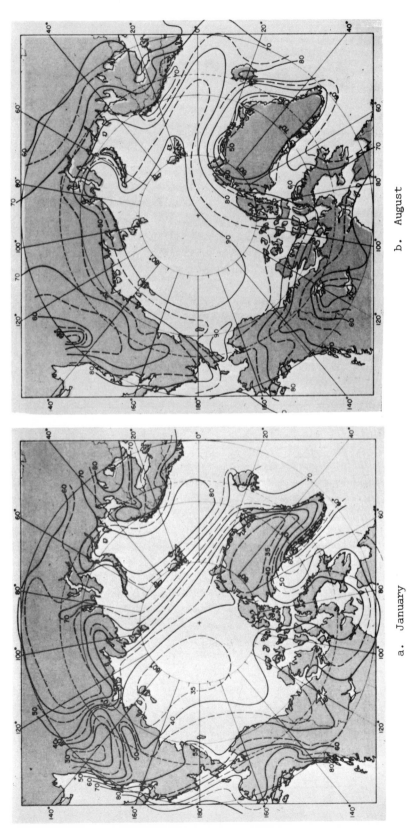

a. January

b. August

Figure 37.   CLOUD COVER (PERCENT)

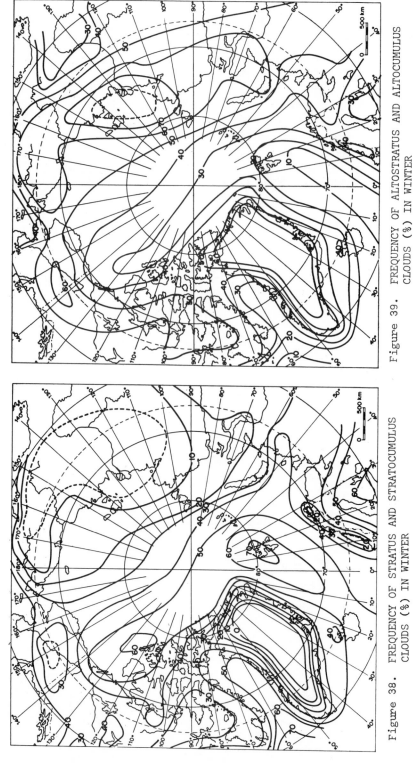

Figure 39.   FREQUENCY OF ALTOSTRATUS AND ALTOCUMULUS
             CLOUDS (%) IN WINTER

Figure 38.   FREQUENCY OF STRATUS AND STRATOCUMULUS
             CLOUDS (%) IN WINTER

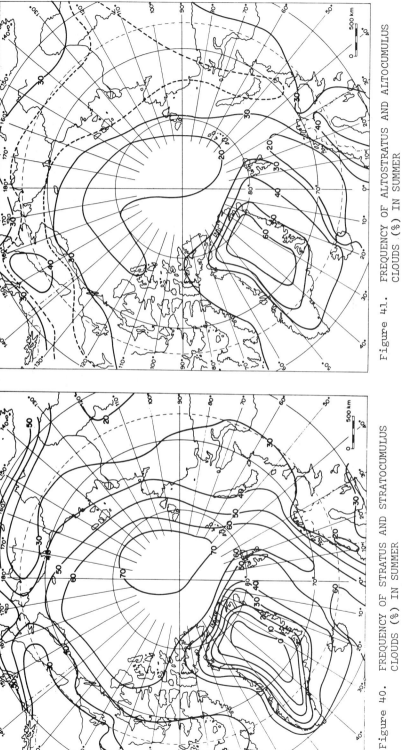

Figure 41. FREQUENCY OF ALTOSTRATUS AND ALTOCUMULUS
CLOUDS (%) IN SUMMER

Figure 40. FREQUENCY OF STRATUS AND STRATOCUMULUS
CLOUDS (%) IN SUMMER

The maximum cloudiness in the East Siberian type is reached in summer. Anticyclonic conditions are then much less frequent, and the Arctic Ocean has stretches of open water which serve as a moisture source. The frequency distribution of cloud types is rather uniform with a predominance of the convective types in the low and medium layers - a development characteristic of all continental arctic areas in summer.

The change from winter to summer conditions is gradual, while the decrease in autumn is abrupt. This difference between spring and autumn has little to do with the pressure distribution. The pressure curve (and also the temperature curve) is symmetrical in spring and autumn. The reason must be the availability of moisture. Because the snow cover is very slight in this area, the main moisture source during the spring and summer is the Arctic Ocean. Melting of the ice along the coast and the formation of puddles on the remaining ice is a gradual process, and accordingly the cloud amount increases gradually in eastern Siberia. In autumn the freeze-over is quick, and a sharp decrease in moisture supply occurs rapidly.

It is noteworthy that this type is not as clearly developed in Canada. In spite of the large land area and the sheltering effect of the Rocky Mountains, the winter minimum is not as pronounced as in eastern Siberia. Contrary to the Siberian conditions, however, the increase during spring is quite rapid. This is not caused by extensive stratus layers as over the Arctic Ocean but by clouds of the medium types, which would indicate a dynamic reason for this development.

3. *Polar Ocean Type* - Over the Arctic Ocean the cloud amount is least in winter and spring and greatest in summer. Dynamic factors have least influence in this area. The polar frontal zone is, in fact, best developed in winter when the cloud amount in this area is low. During winter, the water content of the very cold air is too low for cloud formation, irrespective of the dynamic conditions. The most outstanding feature of the Arctic Ocean zone is the high frequency of stratus and stratocumulus in summer. It rises to 80% and stratus predominates in the majority of cases. The reason is the continuous cooling of air to the freezing point over the pack ice. These summer clouds are extremely uniform, extending as vast sheets over much wider areas than other clouds. The mean thickness of these cloud layers is 1,150 to 1,700 ft, a high value when the manner of their formation is considered. The water content of these clouds shows a pronounced decrease from the coast toward the pole. A further characteristic of this area is that the seasonal change in cloudiness is restricted to a very short transitional period, while rather constant cloudiness prevails during the rest of the year. Similar abrupt changes are found only in monsoon areas with their complete changeover in circulation pattern.

Occurence

Winter is the season with the greatest mean deviation from latitudinal average. An outstanding winter feature is the zone of high cloudiness in the Norwegian Sea. It extends along the Eurasian coast far into the Arctic Ocean, until it gradually loses its identity. From its center line - Thorshavn south of Bear Island - where the described phenomena of the zone are most conspicuous, it changes its characteristics toward the east in the Arctic Ocean. Cumulus clouds disappear in the Barents Sea, and stratus and stratocumulus become less frequent. From the Laptev Sea eastward, middle cloud layers are most important with altostratus being

especially frequent. With practically no moisture supplied from the
frozen ground, cyclones penetrating to the east are only able to cause
condensation in the higher levels. From the Norwegian Sea northwestward
to the sea ice margin cumulus is replaced by stratus and stratocumulus
as the water becomes colder and the time available to create unstable
air becomes shorter.

Scandinavia and the western RSFSR show very high cloud amounts, with
low clouds dominant. Medium clouds become dominant in western Siberia,
much farther west than over the Arctic Ocean. They are replaced by cirrus
from central Siberia eastward. The reason for this rapid thinning of
clouds over the continent is the position of the Siberian anticyclones
which divert the disturbances toward the Arctic Ocean.

Across the mountains of northeastern Siberia toward the Pacific, the
clear skies are replaced by very great cloud amounts with a dominance of
low cloud types as the Bering and Okhotsk seas are reached. No such clear
pattern develops over the American continent where, apart from minor
irregularities, the main feature is the gradual decrease in cloudiness
to the north. There is a zone with few low clouds along the 65°N parallel,
with a minimum in the interior Yukon valley. Mountain ranges there hinder
free flow of air in the meridional direction. Another minimum occurs
over the Canadian Arctic Archipelago where the lowest cloud amounts are
observed. This same zone is characterized by a maximum of the medium-type
clouds and has a much higher frequency of altocumulus than in the eastern
hemisphere.

The influence of the Aleutian low and the Pacific frontal zone is hardly
noticed in the Arctic. The mountain ranges form an effective barrier;
and over the frozen surfaces of northern Canada the air does not pick up
sufficient moisture, after the descent to the plains, to show another
increase in cloud amount.

With the approach of summer, the Atlantic zone loses much of its
individuality. It appears merely as an extension of the large area of
cloud now covering the whole Arctic Ocean. It can be distinguished from
the latter region only by the higher frequency of cumulus-type clouds.
Although the reasons for the formation of these zones are different, in
appearance there is little on which to base a distinction between the two,
both having extremely dull and monotonous skies. At the continental
shores both influences come to a rapid end. The farther south the location,
the less cloudy are the skies and the more are the stratus and stratocumulus
replaced by cumulus. As over the Arctic Ocean, the maximum cloudiness over
the continent is reached in summer; but mean cloud amount remains lower,
and a much greater diversity of cloud types exists.

The cloud maximum in summer is a peculiarity of the Arctic and contrary to that found in mid-latitudes. The reason does not lie so much in
the different dynamic conditions as in the ground influences. In the
Arctic winter the ground is frozen everywhere; and, because of the
absence of sufficient incoming radiation for evaporation, the supply of
moisture to the atmosphere is limited. In summer the incoming energy and
the extensive moist surfaces permit high evaporation and cloud formation.
In middle latitudes solar energy is received also in winter and so evaporation is not suppressed to the same extent. In summer the incoming energy
is high, and the evaporation will dry the soil causing the relative
humidity of the air to be lower than in winter and the cloud amount to be

less.

The seasonal variability of cloudiness increases from south to north. This is a result of the increasing influences of the peculiar cloud regime of the Arctic Ocean. Latitudinal means of cloud-type frequency show that the North also has the highest seasonable variability of cloud type. The farther north, the greater the cloudiness in summer and the more frequent the low and dense cloud types. In winter, on the other hand, the cloudiness diminishes northward and the frequency distribution of types is more uniform.

A complete changeover of the north-south gradient in cloudiness is produced by this high variability in the north and the rather stable conditions in the south. During the winter there is a continuous decrease to the north, while an increase is found in summer. The changeover takes place very rapidly with the result that only during the short transition periods in spring (May) and in autumn (October) is there but little difference in the average cloud amount over the whole arctic sector.

Precipitation

Snowfall is light in the Arctic, and stations in continental areas have maximum precipitation in late summer, i.e. a large part of the annual total falls as rain. The main precipitation over the Arctic Ocean is frontal in nature. Partly for this reason the annual amounts decrease northward (Fig. 42). Along the margins of the Arctic Ocean the winter accumulation is, for the most part, less than 10 inches; the Siberian and Canadian arctic coasts receive as little as 5.5 inches per year (including rain and the water equivalent of snow). The annual precipitation over the Arctic Ocean is meagre - about 5 inches. It is mainly in the form of snow and falls during autumn and late spring. The minimum precipitation occurs in winter. The cycle, and the paucity of precipitation, is caused partly by the low moisture-holding capacity of cold air.

Although the amount of precipitation along the arctic coasts is small, the ground remains saturated for a long period in summer. Underground drainage is prevented by the permanently frozen subsoil. Even though somewhat larger amounts of precipitation are received farther south at inland stations, the summer temperatures there are so much higher that drought conditions are manifested.

The characteristics of the snow cover, such as thickness and duration, have important climatic effects on the heat and moisture exchange at the surface. Over the central Arctic Ocean the snow cover becomes established in late August. The thickness may be about 14 to 16 inches by late spring. Steady snow melt - caused by solar radiation - usually begins by the middle of June; and, while there are marked differences from year to year, the ice is usually snow-free by the middle of July.

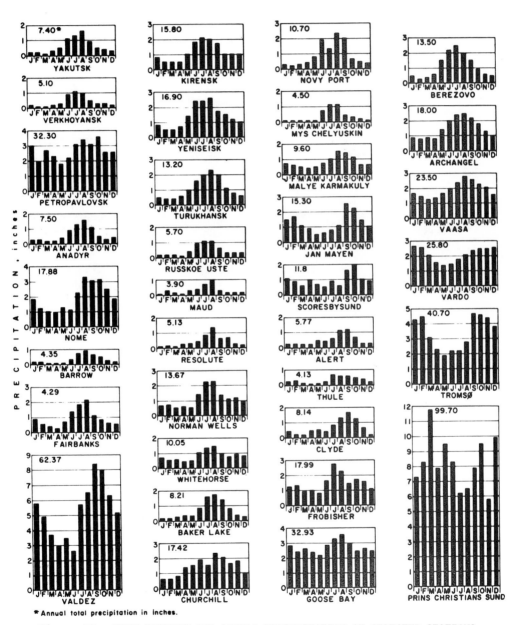

Figure 42.   MEAN MONTHLY AND ANNUAL PRECIPITATION AT SELECTED STATIONS
Snowfall has been reduced to water equivalent, 10 in.
snow = 1 in. water.

Bibliography

Anapolskaya, L. E. and I. N. Zavyalova, 1969. Some wind characteristics
    in the Arctic. in A. F. Treshnikov, ed., *Problems of the Arctic and
    Antarctic,* 32:440-47. Translated by Israel Program for Scientific
    Translations.

Barry, R. G., 1959. A synoptic climatology for Labrador-Ungava. Montreal:
    Arctic Meteorology Research Group, McGill Univ. Publ. in *Meteorology
    17.* 59 pp.

Belmont, A. D., 1961. Arctic meteorology (a ten-year review). in *Advances
    in Geophysics,* vol. 7. New York: Academic Press.

Committee an Polar Research, National Research Council, 1963. *Science in
    the Arctic Ocean Basin: Pt 2, Physical Sciences.* Washington, D. C.:
    Natl Research Council. Publ. 1086.

Estoque, M. A., 1960. Dynamical prediction of the arctic circulation.
    Tellus 12:41-52.

Fletcher, J. O., 1965. *The Heat Budget of the Arctic Basin and its
    Relation to Climate.* Santa Monica: The Rand Corp. Rept R-444-PR.
    179 pp.

_____, ed., 1966. *Proceedings of the Symposium on the Arctic Heat
    Budget and Atmospheric Circulation,* held Lake Arrowhead, Calif., 31
    Jan.-4Feb. 1966. Santa Monica: The Rand Corp. Memor. RM-5233-NSF.

Hare F. K., 1968. The Arctic. Royal Meteorol. Soc., *Quart. J.* 94:439-59.

Hare, F. K., and B. W. Boville, 1965. The Polar circulation. in *The Circu-
    lation in the Stratosphere, Mesosphere and Lower Thermosphere.* Geneva:
    World Meteorological Organization. Techn. Note 70. pp. 43-78.

Huschke, R. E., 1969. *Arctic Cloud Statistics from "Air-Calibrated"
    Surface Weather Observations.* Santa Monica: The Rand Corp. Memor.
    RM-6173-PR. 79 pp.

Keegan, T. J., 1958. Arctic synoptic activity in winter. *J. Meteorol.*
    15:513-21.

Kelley, J. J., Jr., D. T. Bailey, and B. J. Lieske, 1964. *Radiative
    Exchange over Arctic Land and Sea, Part I: Data 1962.* Seattle:
    Department of Atmospheric Sciences, Univ. of Washington.

Meteorological Branch, Department of Transport, 1967. *The Climate of the
    Canadian Arctic.* Ottawa: Queen's Printer. 32 pp.

Orvig, S., ed., 1970. *Climates of the Polar Regions.* New York: Elsevier
    Publishing Co. 370 pp.

Putnins, P. H. et al., 1962-65. *Studies on the Meteorology of Greenland.*
    Washington, D. C.: U.S. Weather Bureau and ESSA. Reports on Dept. of
    Army Project MIPR R-62-9-SC-00-9ꓶ

Reed, R. J. and R. K. Surface, 1959. *Arctic Weather Studies: Summer Season.* Seattle: Dept. of Meteorology and Climatology, Univ. of Washington. Scientific Rept. 5 under contraxt AF 19(604)-3063. 48 pp.

Rubin, M. J., 1963. Polar meteorology [triennial report to IUGG]. *Trans. Amer. Geophys. Union* 44:403-06.

Salmela, H. A. and N. Sissenwine, 1970. *Estimated Frequency of Cold Temperatures Over the Northern Hemisphere.* Bedford, Mass.: Air Force Cambridge Research Laboratories. Report AFCRL-70-0158. 23 pp.

Taylor-Ellis, E. C., 1968. *Windchill Nomogram, Envirometer (Frigorimeter) T-W-P-R Factor and Humidity in Boundary Layer Arctic Meteorology.* Fort Monmouth, N. J.: U. S. Army Electronics Command. Research and Development Technical Report ECOM-3303. AD-678 486. 12 pp.

U. S. Air Force, 1961. *Climatology of Alaska.* Washington D. C.: Government Printing Office. Weather Division Supplement to Report 444.

U. S. Navy, 1963. *Marine Climatic Atlas of the World: VI, Arctic Ocean.* Washington, D. C.: Government Printing Office. Chief of Naval Operations. NAVWEPS 50-IC-533.

Untersteiner, N., 1967. Polar meteorology [quadrennial report to IUGG]. *Trans. Amer. Geophys. Union* 48: 490-94.

Vowinckel, E., 1962. Cloud amount and type over the Arctic. Montreal: Arctic Meteorology Research Group, McGill Univ. Publ. in *Meteorology 51.* 32 pp.

Westbrook, J. H., 1961. *A Method of Predicting the Frequency Distribution of Windchill.* Natick, Mass.: U. S. Army Quartermaster Research and Engineering Center. 50 pp.

Wilson, C., 1967 and 1969. *Climatology: Northern Hemisphere, 1 and 2.* Part I, Sect. A3a and A3b, Cold Regions Science and Engineering series. Hanover, N. H.: U. S. Army Cold Regions Research and Engineering Laboratory. 141 pp and 167 pp. AD-656 447 and -674 185.

Zhakhov, S. I., 1969. *Influence of the Arctic on the Climate of the U.S.S.R.* Leningrad: Gidro... 84 pp. Translated by Joint Publications Research Service, 1971. JPRS 52756

Terrain

Landforms

The geology of the Arctic is not uniquely arctic since the earth's crust has migrated through geologic time. The major topographical elements of today's northern lands can only be understood by a reference to their geology. Their structure is roughly symmetrical about the Arctic Basin and has been instrumental in modeling the major elements of the surface form.

Three ancient shields formed predominently of Precambrian granites and gneisses are the main structural features of the land surfaces (Fig. 43). They are the Canadian-Greenland Shield in the western hemisphere, the Baltic or Scandinavian Shield in northern Europe, and the Angara Shield in north-central Siberia. In many sectors the shields extend beyond their exposed margins but are buried under younger flat-lying sedimentary rocks. A large part of the North European Plain in Russia and smaller areas in the Mackenzie lowland of northwest Canada developed in this way. The Angara Shield differs from the other shields in that only a small area is exposed; the remainder is buried under deep sediments which have experienced much faulting and in places have been linked with igneous activity. Between the stable shields and associated platforms are belts of strongly folded sedimentary rocks which are still today, in many areas, mountain ranges. Where the folding has been unusually intense and is of great age, as in Svalbard and northern Scandinavia, the physiography often differs little from the shield areas. In contrast, the younger fold belts, including those in the northwestern Queen Elizabeth Islands, the mountain ranges of Alaska, and the Poluostrov Kamchatka, have developed scenery that is typically alpine in many places. One orogenic belt that includes Kamchatka is strongly seismic and includes numerous active and recently extinct volcanoes. The underlying geologic structure is little known where unconsolidated sediments of Quaternary age bury the older rocks in the north Alaska-Beaufort Sea-east Siberian coastal plains and continental shelves and in the west Siberian lowlands.

The physical landscapes of the circumpolar regions contain major landforms, the origins of which may be traced to the distant geologic past, and minor landforms which have evolved in the last million years. The major elements, particularly in the shields, were already in existence before the onset of the Pleistocene glaciations. Practically universal in this category are the upland blocks which developed on ancient crystalline rocks. Today, with some later modifications, these uplands dominate the Arctic in eastern Canada, East and West Greenland, Svalbard, Scandinavia, and northern Novaya Zemlya. Other widely distributed physiographic provinces are geologically younger. Rimming the north Pacific Ocean is a volcanic mountain belt that is part of the zone that encircles the Pacific Ocean; a second, less conspicuous volcanic sector is developed within the Mid-Atlantic Ridge, principally in Iceland. Regions of the late Tertiary and Quaternary deposition form another group. These include the coastal plains in northern Alaska and adjacent to the Beaufort Sea; the deltas of the Mackenzie, Yukon, and Siberian rivers; and the west Siberian lowland.

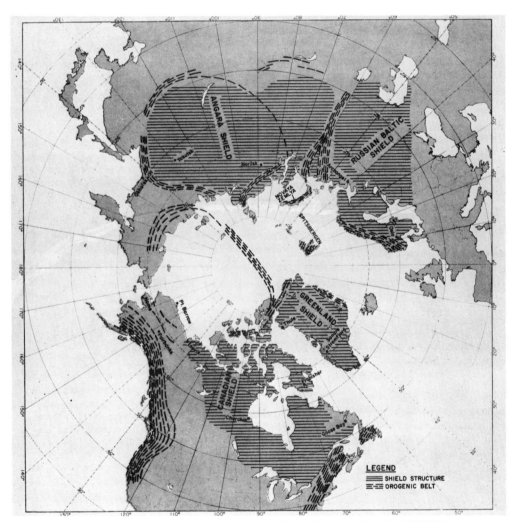

Figure 43. NORTH COLD REGIONS: MAJOR UNDERLYING STRUCTURES

Superimposed on the major elements are the modifications of the Quaternary. The most important of these resulted from the Pleistocene glaciations. Not all the circumpolar lands were glacierized as aridity was so intense in some areas that glacier ice failed to accumulate. Eventually all lands around the northern Atlantic and the Norwegian and Barents seas were at some period covered with ice sheets. The moisture of the north Pacific was less effective in penetrating into the western Arctic; and extensive unglacierized areas existed throughout the Pleistocene in northeastern Siberia, central and northern Alaska, and interior Yukon. The most conspicuous modification by the glacier ice was in uplands near the sea where outlet glaciers flowed down the river valleys to the ocean, resulting in the formation of the fiords that are such a striking feature of the upland coastal regions. Fiords developed at the same time else-where although their characteristics are usually rather different. This is particularly true of the south and southeastern coasts of Alaska, Peary Land, and Axel Heiberg and western Ellesmere islands. In all cases the fiords are curved rather than angular and are commonly longer and wider than the classic fiord. Channelled ice also excavated deep valleys on the continental shelves including the Amundsen Gulf Sea Valley and the troughs between many of the Queen Elizabeth Islands, all now submerged. During the Pleistocene glaciation the highest uplands near the sea began to develop alpine scenery - vertical-sided valleys and knife-edge mountain ridges. Typically found on the west coast of Spitsbergen, narrow zones of similar scenery are found at many places in northern Scandinavia, Greenland, and the eastern Canadian Arctic. By contrast, in the interior of the northern continents glacierization led to a reduction in relief, either by ice scouring as found in many shield areas (e.g. interior Finland) or by redeposition of debris in glacial landforms.

The Quaternary glaciations and changes of sea level brought significant changes to the landscapes of the Arctic. In the period since, geomorphic processes unique to northern areas have produced further changes. These result partly from low temperatures and the freezing and survival of ice in the ground, while other special processes occur in the arid high arctic because of the absence of a continuous vegetative cover.

A structural map of the circumpolar world suggests that there are close geologic links between the various continents. For physiographic purposes it is better to retain the basic continental divisions of North America, Eurasia, and the North Atlantic islands (Fig. 44). In the North American northlands the largest physiographic province is the Precambrian Canadian-Greenland Shield that occupies the Canadian arctic mainland, most of the islands south of Parry Channel, and a large part of Greenland. Across the vast area nearly 2,200 mi in diameter, crystalline granites and gneisses are the dominant rocks. Except where ice buries the land, the scenery is characteristically rocky and rolling with innumerable lakes and ungraded, fast-flowing streams. In North America, the shield superficially resembles a saucer. It is highest along the eastern margin from Ellesmere Island to northern Labrador where glaciated peaks reach 6,000 to 7,000 ft above sea level and fiords penetrate the coast. West of the highlands there is a broad upland zone, commonly between 1,000 and 2,000 ft above sea level. Within the shield are basins of considerable geologic age that are floored by younger rocks, mainly limestones. They have been partly submerged to form Foxe Basin, Hudson Bay, and the channels of the southern part of the Canadian Arctic Archipelago. The western margin is generally less elevated although it produces a conspicuous scarp where it overlooks the Mackenzie lowland. A belt of plains and low plateaus including the Mackenzie lowland and the plains south of Parry Channel surrounds the

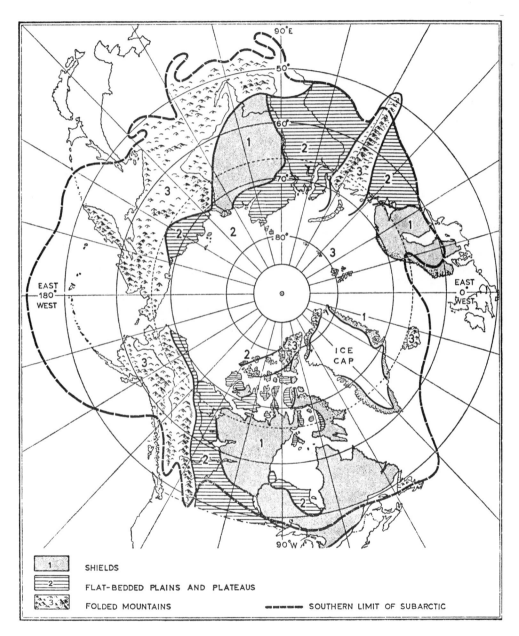

Figure 44.   PHYSIOGRAPHIC REGIONS

shield. The lowlands are developed on sedimentary rocks and are underlain by the shield in this area. The Greenland sector of the shield resembles an elongated saucer with a high mountainous rim. No young Paleozoic sediments are found within the Greenland Shield, but the island is apparently crossed by volcanic rocks that appear on the coasts in Scoresby Sund and Disko Bugt.

The Canadian-Greenland Shield, and associated platform areas, are partly surrounded by folded rock zones. The shield and this platform zone are regions of folded rocks of which three main groups may be recognized. The largest is the western Cordillera that includes the Cascades and Coast Ranges of western North America. The northern Cordillera in the Yukon Territory and Alaska may be divided into three provinces. The area adjacent to the Pacific Ocean is the Pacific mountain system which includes the Aleutian Ranges, the Alaska Range, and the Chugach and other mountains; on the north and eastern side of the Cordillera are the Brooks Range of northern Alaska and the Richardson Range of the Yukon and Mackenzie district; and between the two mountain belts is a complex area of plains and highlands drained by the Yukon and Kuskokwim rivers. The second folded rock province is in the Queen Elizabeth Islands and Greenland. It includes the parallel hill ridges on Melville, Bathurst, and Cornwallis islands and the alpine peaks of Ellesmere, Axel Heiberg, and Peary Land. The third province forms the mountains of northeast Greenland. Finally, along the edges of the Arctic Basin from Point Hope in northwest Alaska eastward to the Mackenzie and then along the outer northwestern islands of the Canadian Archipelago, is a coastal plain of sediments of late Tertiary and Quaternary age.

Several islands are found in the North Atlantic Ocean and the Norwegian Sea. All have structural links with the adjacent continents although physiographically they may be treated separately. The largest island, Iceland, is wholly of volcanic origin and lies at the intersection of the Greenland-northwest Scotland and the Mid-Atlantic ridges. Three hundred miles to the north-northeast is the small volcanic island of Jan Mayen. Farther north still is the archipelago of Svalbard. The terrain has evolved primarily on folded rocks although there is a great variety. The topography is typically mountainous in the west and generally plateau-like and often ice-covered in the center and east. Everywhere the uplands have been deeply dissected and the lower valleys drowned to produce fiords.

The Eurasian northlands contain several large upland regions separated by wide depressions. Two of the uplands, the Baltic Shield and the associated Russian platform in the west and the Siberian platform, are typical shield areas partly blanketed by younger sedimentary rocks. The Baltic Shield includes the Poluostrov Kol'skiy and the northern periphery of Scandinavia; it is an undulating upland with an average elevation of 1,500 ft that reproduces in many ways the landscape of the Canadian Shield. The surface of the shield declines in the vicinity of the White Sea, and east of Arkhangel'sk the Precambrian rocks disappear beneath sediments. Along the west side of the shield the Precambrian rocks are replaced by geologically younger, highly folded rocks; and there is a deeply dissected highland zone with numerous fiords and alpine peaks exceeding 6,000 ft. The central Siberian platform is conspicuously different. In the northwest is a high section developed primarily on flat-lying rocks through which the rivers flow in deep valleys and where mountains such as the Putorana exceed 6,000 ft. The extreme northeast part is generally lower.

Between the two shield and platform divisions, a belt of folded rocks

along the Ural-Novaya Zemlya axis produces a broad flat-topped upland with
a general height of about 3,000 ft. The Urals show little sign of glaciation, but Novaya Zemlya is dissected by glaciers, glaciated valleys, and
fiords. A second folded zone produces a vast highland massif of complex
mountains and plateaus in northeast Siberia. Many of the ranges are
arcuate and two of the largest, the Verkhoyanskiy and Cherskiy Khrebet,
both have peaks over 10,000 ft.

The west Siberian lowland province, over 500 mi wide, extends southward from the Kara Sea between the Urals and the central Siberian platform.
The lowlands are developed on horizontal sedimentary rocks covered with
deep glacial, alluvial, and marine deposits. They form a remarkably flat,
occasionally terraced, poorly-drained plain. The smaller, but in other
ways similar, north Siberian lowland province separates the hill ridges
of Poluostrov Taimyr from the central Siberian uplands to the south. The
eastern limit of these lowlands is the mouth of Khatanga River, but similar
plains occur discontinuosly far east along the coast and include the
Ostrova Novosibirskii.

Soils, Permafrost, and Vegetation

Most of the soils of the Arctic are quite young and poorly developed.
In large part this is due to the presence of continental glaciers which
covered the area and have retreated only in the recent geologic past.
Other reasons are frost action, the retarded biochemical activity resulting
from the low thermal regime, and a lack of adequate moisture due to the
slight precipitation. Drainage is frequently very poor as a result of the
presence of permafrost; hence many arctic soils are moist.

As a result of these conditions, the soils are usually shallow and have
not developed genetic horizons. Most commonly they are alkaline or
neutral but occasionally they may be acidic. In the islands north of the
mainland, polar desert soils are often found. They may show genetic
horizons, not only on more level surfaces but on some of the steeper slopes.
The surface is frequently as much as 50% coarse fragments, pebbles, and
rocks and can exhibit the characteristics of aridity: salt crusts, alkali
flats, and carbonate accumulations. In profile they pass from the desert
pavement of the surface to dark brown, sandy, gravelly loam to red-, gray-
and yellow-brown sands. Vegetation is always sparce and may cover less
than 1% of the surface.

Elsewhere, the soils range from bog to arctic brown to glei to subarctic
brown forest and wooded to podzol, depending upon parent material, slope,
exposure, vegetative cover, and the length of time since the area was last
covered by ice. The occurrence of the various types has been mapped on a
small scale for the entire region but detailed maps exist for only a few
areas which have been of concern for any of numerous reasons.

The vegetative cover of most of the arctic is best described by the
term tundra. Originally the Lapp word for the treeless areas of northern
Scandinavia, it has come to mean the entire plant community of the treeless
areas. It includes lichens, mosses, grasses, sedges, and woody shrubs.
Some tree species, such as willow, birch, and alder, may occur in sheltered
arctic valleys and may attain a height of 6 to 8 ft.

The arctic deserts are the least vegetated regions with their lichen-
covered rocks and scattered clumps of hardy perennials. The next most

developed community is the lichen-moss tundra which occurs on the coarse materials of tills, terraces, and strands. Further south this dry tundra contains increasing amounts of heath and berry-producing plants. When precipitation and the nutrient supply are adequate, these communities will completely cover the surface.

The wet tundras contrast markedly with the dry as they occur on finer-grained soils with poor drainage. The plant cover is a dense mat of grasses, sedges, and moss. As a result of the drainage, bogs are frequent in the low areas. Frost action leads to a hummocky surface in which the mounds are moss covered and the swales support the moisture-loving species. Finally, as the tree line is approached, the tundras begin to support increasing numbers of shrubs.

Despite the problems in defining it and its state of geographic flux, the tree line is the most obvious of the arctic boundaries. It is taken to be the poleward or altitudinal limit of standing trees; and in consequence there is a gradual transition from tundra, without trees, to small stands of spruce and larch to larger stands of greater numbers of species and finally the thick boreal forests of the subarctic (Fig. 45).

One of the unique phenomena of the Arctic is the presence of permafrost (Fig. 46). This perennially forzen state of the subsurface soil and rock leads to many of the surface conditions which distinguish the region, strongly influences the surface condition and vegetative cover, and creates many of the engineering problems which occur there. When permafrost occurs in bedrock or areas of coarse, well-drained materials it does not significantly alter conditions from those found elsewhere on the globe. However, in areas with poor drainage and fine-grained soil materials, it can be the controlling element. Throughout the area in which permafrost occurs the surface freezes and thaws annually with the passing of the seasons. The depth of the active layer varies with latitude and soil type from as little as a foot to six feet or more. Since the permafrost is impervious to surface runoff and roots, it may severely restrict plant growth and prevent water from draining as it would in other situations. The frost-induced swelling of the active layer causes a variety of irregular surface features, such as those illustrated in Figure 47, and further disrupts the root systems of the plant cover. Most prominent of the surface manifestations of permafrost is the patterned ground (Fig. 48) associated with the presence of subsurface ice wedges (Fig. 49c). On slopes, permafrost can cause massive slumping of the surface materials as they glide over the water-lubricated permafrost table or it can cause finer, less disruptive stripes and fingers of sloughed material to work their way downslope. Such conditions mix the soil layers, may expose buried layers of organic materials, and result in differing vegetative covers within very short distances.

Since it is a phenomena of temperature, any change in the thermal regime of an area can lead to thawing of the permafrost. Naturally this results in thermokarst topography and slumped banks and cliffs (Fig. 49); and when induced by human activity, it can significantly accelerate erosive processes (Fig. 50) or wreak havoc on structures which were not properly designed. The mechanical problem associated with the degradation of permafrost is that, upon thawing, the portion of it which was ice melts and the water runs off if a slope is present or the material loses its capacity to support an overburden. The amount of ice present in permafrost may vary from an insignificant number of minute crystals in porous materials to as much as 90% in some sedimentary deposits.

(a) Yukon-Tanana Plateau, near Fairbanks

(b) Yukon-Tanana Plateau, near Circle

(c) Yukon Flats, near Beaver Creek

(d) Yukon Flats, lower Chandalar River

Figure 45.   TOPOGRAPHIC TYPES IN THE CENTRAL PLATEAUS

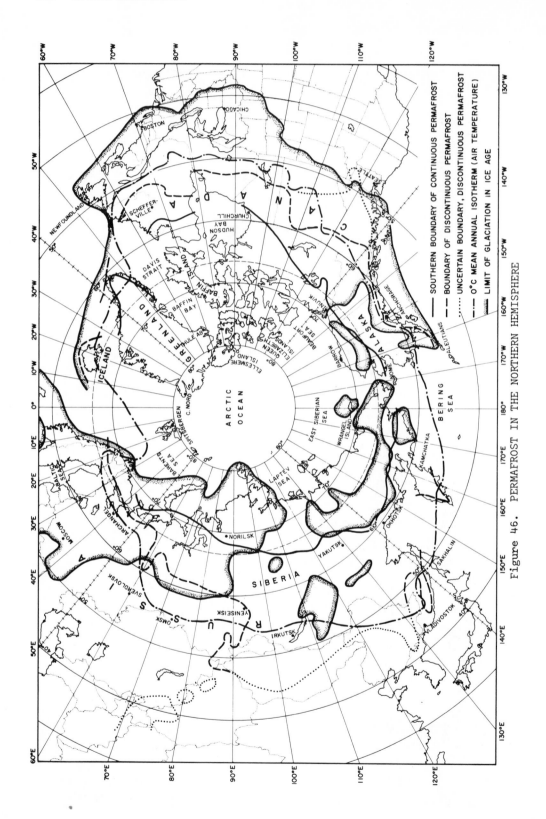

Figure 46. PERMAFROST IN THE NORTHERN HEMISPHERE

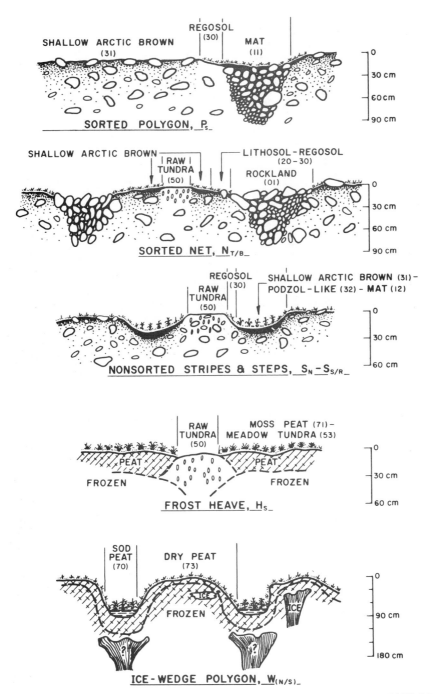

Figure 47.   VARIATIONS IN SURFACE FEATURES AND SOIL MORPHOLOGY AS
A RESULT OF FROST ACTION

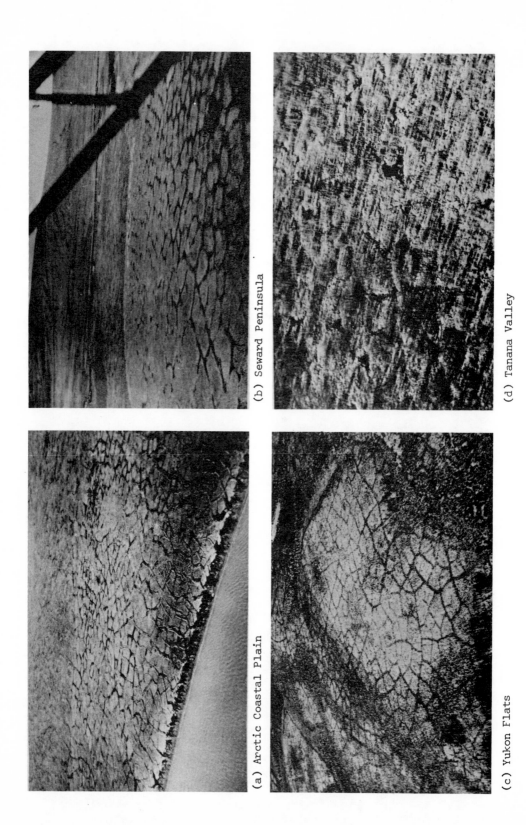

(a) Arctic Coastal Plain

(b) Seward Peninsula

(c) Yukon Flats

(d) Tanana Valley

Figure 48.   LOW-ALTITUDE OBLIQUE PHOTOS OF RAISED-CENTER TYPE POLYGONS IN ALASKA

(a) Massive ground ice, Sagavanirktok River

(b) Ledge of ground ice, Seward Peninsula

(c) Ice wedge, Nome

(d) Massive ground ice Kobuk River

Figure 49. TYPES OF ICE AND ICE-SOIL FORMS

(b) Seven-foot cavity in the "cat tracks" in 24 hours of thaw, Barter Island

(a) Unchecked highway culvert effluent

(c) Drainage ditch thaw near Umiat

Figure 50. ACCELERATED EROSION RESULTING FROM RUNNING WATER PASSING OVER FROZEN SOILS

The ability to travel on surfaces underlain by permafrost is clearly
related to temperature. During winter, when the active layer may be
frozen through and bearing on as much as a thousand or more feet of
permafrost, the surface will sustain extremely heavy loads and movement is
governed more by the surface roughness and slope than by bearing strength.
In summer, the load-bearing capacity of arctic terrains varies from the
pavements of polar deserts, which can sustain landings by large cargo
aircraft, to the boggy mucks of the muskeg which may fail at pressures as
low as 1 or 2 psi. Studies of the nature and extent of arctic lands and
soils are and have been conducted by many organizations, of which the Cold
Regions Research and Engineering Laboratory is prominent in this country,
while the mapping of it lies within the purview of the branches of the
Geological Survey.

Construction on and travel over permafrost can be accomplished but
requires that engineers and planners know and respect it and be prepared
to face larger costs than would otherwise be necessitated. One of two
courses must be followed - either the thermal regime must be left undisturbed or all permafrost-susceptible materials must be removed from the
area of concern. Where a single structure or reasonably permanent facility
such as an airfield is involved, it may be practical to consider evacuating
the frost-susceptible materials and replacing them with coarser material
which is not subject to frost action. The only other recourse is to leave
the permafrost intact and cover it with a sufficient amount of gravelly
fill to completely insulate the surface from frost action. It is usually
advisable to follow this course even if a building is to be set on piles
embedded into the permafrost. Such a plan may well necessitate vast
amounts of borrow and may require hauling it long distances. The alternatives are generally unwarranted or unacceptable.

Shorelines

Arctic littoral processes in the ice-free summer months do not differ
greatly from those in temperate latitudes. The differences are more of
degree than of kind, particularly as the annual period of wave action and
the amplitude of the waves is reduced in the presence of ice. However,
several distinctive processes are operative at breakup and freeze-up of
sea ice.

Sea ice has, in general, a secondary role to waves as an agent in
erosion, transportation, and deposition. During the fall, when air temperatures drop below freezing, an ice shelf commonly forms along arctic beaches
where there is a low tidal range as water from storm waves and spray freezes
gravel on the beach to leave layers of ice-cemented gravel and ice. Sand
and gravel are often washed onto the developing ice shelf and become incorporated. This ice shelf protects the beach against subsequent wave action
and ice shove. If pack ice moves onshore early in the winter, shorefast
ice with adhering debris may be shoved inland onto the beach, thus adding
material to it. During the winter, shorefast ice and offshore ice stop
all wave action. Pack ice at breakup, and also later in the summer, may
push onto the beach or impinge against the sea cliff, if present. Ice
moving onto a beach tends to act either as a plough or a raft. Where plough-
ing occurs, the ice planes and pushes debris into mounds and ridges, usually
below the upper limit of storm waves. Where rafting occurs, debris frozen
and incorporated in the ice may be transported onto the beach, locally
above the reach of storm waves. Usually storm waves soon rework most of
the transported material and by freeze-up little evidence of it is visible;

however, in high arctic seas that are permanently choked with ice, ice-push
ramparts are a normal feature at the rear of beaches.

On coasts where the tidal range is considerable, boulder barricades
are the most conspicuous sign of the action of sea ice. Typically there
is a narrow string of boulders parallel to the shore and several hundred
feet offshore. At low tide they are clearly visible above the water surface; at high tide, when they are submerged, they represent a navigational
danger on the approach to many open beaches. Generally the depth of water
increases rapidly beyond the boulder limit. The pushing and rafting of
boulders by the drifting sea ice that forms the boulder barricades is also
responsible for the development of boulder-covered flats which are exposed
at low tide near the heads of arctic bays. Beach morphology is affected
by grounded sea ice and permafrost ice. Oval ponds are produced by the
melting of lenses of ground ice that have developed in the backshore zone
of beaches. Hollows and soft areas on sand beaches are more likely to
result from melting of grounded ice floes.

There are strong regional differences between Pacific or western arctic
shores and those in the Atlantic, or eastern, Arctic. The former may be
defined as extending from Cape Chelyuskin in Siberia to the Beaufort Sea
and Amundsen Gulf. This sector is characterized by long stretches of
unconsolidated frozen sediments, shallow offshore depths, and small tidal
range. The Atlantic arctic coasts include those of the eastern Canadian
Arctic, Greenland, the Atlantic coasts proper, the Barents Sea, and to a
lesser degree the Kara Sea. Here the coasts are commonly bedrock.
Coarse-grained glacial sediments are widespread, and the tidal range is
moderate to high.

In the western Arctic, sea cliffs which may rise to 100 ft or more
front along hundreds of miles of coast. The cliffs are usually eroded into
unconsolidated frozen sediments with an ice content varying inversely with
the grain size. In sands and gravels, only a bonding cement occurs; but
in cohesive, fine-grained silty clays, clays, and peats, the ice content
(weight of ice to dry soil) may reach hundreds of percent. The frozen
sea cliffs retreat by undercutting, thermal erosion, and slumping. The
greatest erosion occurs during storm surges when the water level may rise
5 to 10 ft. When there is a combination of a high water level and strong
waves, the slumped debris at the foot of the sea cliff may be removed and
a notch 5 to 15 ft deep eroded into the cliff to produce an overhang in
the frozen sediments; this is followed by sediment failure and retreat of
the cliff face. Thermal erosion and slumping on steep cliffs poses a
hazard below, because of a constant downward rain of debris. Thermal
erosion may also produce glacier-like mud streams. Differential thermal
erosion is particularly marked along coasts where the large ice wedges of
tundra polygons are present. Gullies selectively etch out the ice wedges
to produce indentations or hanging valleys along the cliffs. In winter,
the sea cliff and beach zone is an accumulation site for large snow drifts
which persist and protect the cliff foot in early summer. Rapid slumping
from above may bury the snowbanks completely and some survive over the
summer, thus adding additional protection to the cliff foot for a second
summer season. The type of sediment in the sea cliff tends to be reflected
in the number and size of adjacent beaches and bars.

In the offshore zone, where pressure ridges may ground in depths reaching down to 100 ft, irregular depth fluctuations of 5 or more ft in
horizontal distances of 25 to 50 ft have been found superimposed upon the
gently sloping bottom. These irregularities have been attributed to the

grounding of pressure-ridge ice.

Offshore bars, baymouth bars, spits, tombolos, and other bar deposits are found along much of the Pacific arctic coast. This is to be expected where offshore depths are modest and the supply of debris from coastal recession and rivers is large. Offshore bars parallel hundreds of miles of coast, separated from it by a lagoon of up to several miles wide. In response to winds and currents spits form where there are directional changes in the coast. Driftwood and large logs become stranded on the bars and spits near a source of driftwood, such as east and west of the Mackenzie Delta. The higher parts of bars and spits rise well above sea level where they have been built by storm waves, ice shove, and wind action.

Large deltas are common in the Pacific portion and include the Lena, Indigirka, Kolyma, Colville, Mackenzie, and others. They terminate either in the open sea or, more often, in estuaries and bays fringed with bars. Deltas which build out into the sea have shoal water offshore from the distal islands. The rivers contribute sediment, principally fine-grained, in the early summer at breakup and after severe storms.

The main characteristics of the Atlantic shores are the spectacular cliffs which can be found in many sectors. In the Precambrian Shield areas the majority of cliffs are preglacial or, in the case of fiords, of glacial origin. These cliffs show little evidence of strong contemporary erosion subaerially or by waves. In contrast, many of the cliffs in younger sedimentary and igneous rocks, particularly in Svalbard and Iceland, have developed massive postglacial scree slopes that are active today. In some parts of the Atlantic Arctic, notably Scandinavia, a rock platform that **varies** in width up to several miles separates the cliffs from the sea. This feature, known as the strandflat, is locally drowned forming a skerry coast.

The main origin of beach material on the Atlantic coasts is glacial drift. The drift contained particles ranging in size from microscopic grains to boulders. Some were deposited as a heterogeneous mass (till); large quantities were laid down along valley walls by turbulent meltwater streams beside disintegrating ice masses as bottom or shore deposits of short-lived ice-blocked lakes or as outwash plains in front of glacial termini. Undoubtedly, many of these features still lie beneath the sea.

Blue clays of marine origin are an important source of beach materials. These sandy, fine-grained sediments are frequently exposed along the coast by stream or wave erosion. Their color is caused by the reduced state of iron in secondary minerals. They were deposited in sedimentary environments near the end of the glaciation when a rising sea level drowned the coastal area appearing from beneath the ice. Subsequently many of the submerged coasts were uplifted, so that these, and older deposits, have emerged from the sea. In the process, coarse sands and gravels have been spread on top of them by waves and currents.

The beaches can be a very complex mixture of fluvial, glacial, wind, and marine sediments. The backshore is often sand and gravel, sometimes with boulders breaking the surface and often with poorly developed dunes. The foreshore and offshore zones have their fine-grained materials washed away; and if the source of beach material contains coarse particles like gravel and boulders, these become concentrated in the zone of most intense wave action. This is strikingly apparent where boulder beaches

are developing in glacial till. Elsewhere shingle beaches and bars are
widely distributed. Except in shallow bays and troughs, the bottom tends
to drop away quickly. During storms, eroded beach sediment is easily
carried into deep water, from which it cannot be returned during calm
periods. This condition, as well as a frequent paucity of sediment,
contributes to the formation of relatively narrow beaches. If it were
not for the cover of ice which protects them from destruction by winter
storms, the attrition of beaches would be even greater.

Glacial and marine deposits which emerged from the sea during uplift
of the land have been reworked by waves, and a record of this has been
left along many coasts in the form of terraces and drift-free bedrock up
to levels of 100 to 750 ft.

More generalized descriptions of the shoreline characteristics are
given below. Detailed information concerning most of the arctic shoreline is lacking or of uncertain accuracy. The geological surveys of the
respective circumpolar nations map their arctic coasts with the greatest
accuracy possible and the hydrographic services chart the nearshore waters
and coasts and issue Pilots and sailing directions. Information of this
nature is, in general, available from the governments of the various
nations.

Regional Characteristics

North Atlantic

There is considerable uniformity in the topography around the northeast
Atlantic. Characteristically, the coasts are developed on crystalline or
intensely folded rocks. Flat-topped uplands dominate the landscape, with
altitudes varying in different areas from 2,500 to 5,000 ft. The uplands
are often intensely dissected into isolated pyramidal peaks, notably in
Spitsbergen. Straight-sided, linear valleys of great length are common;
the coastal sections are drowned forming fiord coasts. Surficial
sediments are typically coarse, clastic materials (sands, gravels,
boulders); and fine sediments are relatively rare. This is significant
because, although permafrost is found in the colder coastal area (Svalbard,
East Greenland), engineering problems due to its presence are minimal.
The main exception to these generalizations of the topography is along
the active volcanic zone that coincides with the Mid-Atlantic Ridge.

The environment of Greenland is everywhere dominated by the presence
of the inland ice sheet which, together with secondary glaciers, covers
five-sixths of the island. Ice-free areas are restricted to coasts; they
have a maximum width of about 120 mi, and even in these areas there are
numerous small ice caps and glaciers. On the east coast of Greenland the
margin of the inland ice stops short of the sea except south of Angmagssalik
and in the large outlet glaciers of the northeast at Nioghalvfjerdsfjorden,
Jøkelbugten, and Dove Bugt. At other points many smaller valley glaciers
calve icebergs into the Greenland Sea.

Greenland has the shape of an elongated basin with its major axis lying
north-south. In the interior of the island the earth's crust is depressed
by the ice sheet and in the north it lies 800 ft below sea level. The
rim of the basin is penetrated by deep valleys through which local and
inland ice glaciers move toward the sea. The rim is highest in the east
where it reaches 12,000 ft in the Gunnbjørns Mountains. Two major ice-free

areas are present in North and East Greenland - on the east coast between
Scoresby Sund and Germania Land and in Peary Land in the North. The
widest belt of ice-free land is around Scoresby Sund; but because of the
deep indentation of the coastline, the inland ice is never more than 44
mi from the sea.

Peary Land and the east coast north of 68°N has evolved on rocks that
are geologically younger than the shield; some are folded and others are
horizontal sandstones and basaltic lavas. The folded rocks have produced
a mountain topography not unlike the shield mountains except that the
lowlands are commonly broader, particularly in Peary Land. The horizontal
rocks, especially around Scoresby Sund, form plateau landscapes although
the table mountains are often so dissected that only peaks and ridges
survive.

A third topographic element characteristic of East Greenland, in
addition to the mountains and ice, are the fiords which are among the
largest and the deepest in the world. The fiords in Peary Land resemble
those of the northwestern Canadian arctic islands with wide-swinging
curves and great width that in many ways are more typical of drowned
river valleys than glaciated fiords. Elsewhere in the area they are
usually straight with sharp, angular breaks. All the east and north
coasts are underlain by permafrost. Unstable soil conditions and patterned
ground are found throughout the whole of the ice-free east coast although
they may be somewhat less common in the far north due to great soil
aridity.

The west coast of Greenland from Robeson Channel to Kap Farvel is a
deeply indented, fiord coast over 1,000 mi long. There are three distinct
topographic sectors. In the north, beyond Kap York is a small ice-free
area of sedimentary rocks that have developed a table-top plateau typical
of Peary Land and northeastern Greenland. For 390 mi between Kap York
and Upernavik, the inland ice approaches close to Melville Bay except for
a narrow, intermittent coastal strip of land and the offshore islands.

The third sector includes the remainder of the coast. It contains the
greatest amount of ice-free land and virtually the whole population of
Greenland. This central and southern strip of West Greenland has developed
primarily on granite and gneiss, Precambrian Shield rocks. An exception
is between Upernavik and the north side of Disko Bugt where there are
Tertiary basalts similar in age and characteristics to those south of
Scoreby Sund and in Iceland. They produce similar flat-topped tablelands.
The landscape of the Shield areas is characteristically deeply glaciated
with ice-smoothed rock knobs and hills. Along the coast are skerries
associated with an arctic strandflat. The fiords penetrate the full width
of the ice-free zone, effectively isolating the land into blocks. The
intervening uplands exceed 7,000 ft at several points and these are glacier-
covered. Southeast of Egedesminde the coast is especially divided by
inlets and is much lower than elsewhere.

Topographically, Iceland is a young country, directly or indirectly
entirely igneous in origin. It is characterized by straight lines and
rough-hewn slopes, a lack of the softly rounded outlines characteristic
of a mature landscape. Basalt-lava plateaus, which occupy nearly half
the island, consist of a mosaic of tilted blocks. They are separated by
fiords that have resulted from glacial deepening and widening of river
valleys originally guided by fractures. The highest mountain is 5,046
ft and many summits exceed 3,000 ft.

The landscape is very different in a median zone that crosses the island from southwest to northeast and is filled with Quaternary deposits. The landscape is generally that of a tableland with an inland elevation of 1,000 to 2,500 ft above which rise ice caps and volcanoes. Around the margins are lowland plains in which lava and ash are buried to a great extent beneath debris of glacier rivers.

Today only 1% of Iceland is covered with woods, although at the beginning of settlement about 1,100 years ago, about one-fifth of the country was wooded. Removal of the trees was followed by intense soil erosion. More than half of Iceland is now a desert or semidesert, and the nakedness and lack of woods is one of the most striking features of the country.

The coasts of Iceland are of two distinct types. Rocky coasts characterize the plateau basalt areas of the northwest, north, and east. These coasts are highly irregular in outline, incised with numerous fiords and inlets, and have spectacular seaward cliffs facing the open sea; in places the cliffs exceed 1,600 ft in height. The fiords are shallower than the classic Norwegian type. Shallow deltas have formed at the heads of the fiords and curved shingle spits project from fiord sides where the tributary streams reach the sea. On the inner sides of the spits are good natural anchorages which are quite deep, and many of the villages and towns in the fiords are built on them.

The west coast is lower than the fiord areas, and the coasts of Faxafloi and Breidafjorjur in particular are typical skerry. The southeast and south coast, from Hamarsfjordur in the southeast to Thorlakshofn, are sandy and smooth in ouline. Lagoons and long barrier spits and islands are common. These coasts have no natural anchorage. Most of the material building up the coast comes from debris-laden glacier rivers. The same type of coast on a smaller scale occurs where glacier rivers discharge at the heads of broad inlets in other parts of the country such as Heradsfloi in the northeast and Axarfjordur, Skagafjordur, and Hunafloi in the north. The bar along the south coast of the Snaefellsnes Peninsula consists mainly of shell sand.

Jan Mayen is wholly volcanic rocks, lavas, tuffs, and sands derived from them. The main landform is the volcanic cone of Beerenberg, the highest point on which is 7,500 ft above sea level. The southwest of the island is a lower hilly area that barely exceeds 2,600 ft. The connecting land between Beerenberg and the southwest hills is low and contains lagoons, separated from the sea by ridges of sand and gravel. The northernmost lagoon, Nordlagunen, is 130 ft deep. Sorlagunen, on the southeast coast, on the other hand, is so shallow that it dries out in the autumn. Large quantities of driftwood occur on the beaches. When not hidden in fog, Beerenberg may serve as an important landmark, visible from afar. There is no shelf around the island. The coast is steep and inaccessible over long distances, and skerries and pinacles occur in the sea close to those parts of the coast. Jan Mayen lacks sheltered anchorage and landing is exceptionally difficult.

From the sea Svalbard presents striking arctic scenery with rows of dark mountain peaks separated by bluish-white glaciers. The archipelago is composed of a major island, Spitsbergen, as well as Nordaustlandet on the northeast and many smaller islands. In the southern part of Spitsbergen many glaciers reach the sea, particularly on the east coast where they coalesce to form almost continuous glacier fronts with steep

ice faces. Icebergs formed from these glaciers are of limited dimensions
compared with Greenland or Baffin Bay icebergs. More than half of Spitsbergen and three quarters of Nordaustlandet are covered with glaciers. In
addition to the two large ice caps in Nordaustlandet there are others in
the northern part of Spitsbergen, north of Isfjorden, and in the southern
and southeastern part of the island. In contrast, in the area between
Isfjorden and Bellsund there are ice-free plateau mountains and ice-free
valleys.

Spitsbergen is deeply incised by fiords of which Hornsund, Bellsund,
Isfjorden, and Kongsfjord-Krossfjorden are the most conspicuous on the
west coast. Isfjorden is 55 mi long. On the north coast Woodfjorden
and Wijdefjorden are the larger ones. Wijdefjorden is 60 mi long.
The orientation of the fiords is principally derived from the geologic
structure.

A striking coastal feature is a low foreland in front of the steep
mountain sides. At its greatest development it rises from approximately
100 ft below sea level to about 160 ft above it. The surface is remarkably
even, sometimes with outcropping bedrock and sometimes covered with silt
and gravel. The foreland is often swampy with numerous ponds and lakes.
The width of the emerged foreland varies. In the southern part of Prins
Karls Forland the strandflat extends across the island and is almost 5 mi
wide. At Daudmannsyra to the north of the entrance to Isfjorden it is
6 mi wide. It is well developed between Bellsund and Isfjorden and from
Isfjorden to north of Kongsfjorden. It has great extension also on the
north coast of Spitsbergen. At some points, the foreland comes gently
down to sea level, whereas at other places it faces the sea in steep cliffs
10 to 30 ft high. At Björnöya, where the strandflat is well developed
on the northern part of the island, its sea cliffs are about 100 ft high.

Along the fiords of Spitsbergen, particularly in the Bellsund and the
Isfjord area, wave-built plains and terraces are common. These are depos-
itional features formed by longshore drifting created by wave currents.
Beach material is derived from streams which carry great quantities of
debris seaward during the summer and from neighboring cliffs. Large
cuspate forelands of sand and gravel are in this way formed and prograded
by the addition of successive beach ridges. The beach plains slope in
the direction in which the forelands prograde. Many extensive ridged
beach plains have surfaces sloping from 130 ft above sea level down to
the present-day beach, some of them even from 200 ft.

Björnöya is geologically related to Spitsbergen but in many respects is
dissimilar and there are no fiords, harbors, or glaciers. The island is
triangular in shape with the apex at the south and is about 11 mi across.
The north and northwestern sector is a lake-dotted plateau developed
mainly on horizontal sandstones. It is cliffed although the highest part
does not exceed 300 ft. In the southeast are hills, the highest of
which, not inappropriately, is Miseryfjellet (1,760 ft).

The greater part of northern Scandinavia geologically and topographically belongs to the Scandinavian Shield. The Precambrian rocks that underlie
it are of great age (Archaean) and are mainly crystalline granites and
gneisses; an exception is in the extreme northeast where somewhat younger
(Proterozoic) sedimentary rocks are found between the head of Porsangen
and Varangerenfjord. Southwest from Nordkapp along the Atlantic coast is
a belt of younger strongly metamorphosed sediments and intrusive rocks that
were incorporated in the Caledonian folding and contain a greater variety

of rocks than the shield.

The land mass is highest along the zone of Caledonian folding and heights between 3,200 to 5,000 ft are common and reach 6,500 ft at a few points close to the Norwegian-Swedish border. From there the land surface slopes gradually southeast, towards the Gulf of Bothnia. Numerous rivers flow across this slope in wide valleys often containing long, narrow lakes to the Gulf of Bothnia. The rivers flowing from the drainage divide to the Atlantic are in contrast short and turbulent. Near the coast the land mass is deeply entrenched by steep-sided fiords and in places separated by sounds from the mainland notably in the Lofoten. The combinations of highest mountains and deepest valleys (fiords) near the coast produces spectacular, rugged scenery in this area. There are numerous giant cirques on the mountain sides. When excavated from many sides of a mountain massif, the cirques leave only a skeleton of ridges and summits. A good example is the island of Moskenesoy, the westernmost large island in the Lofoten group. During the Ice Age the mountains were stripped of deposits and appear rounded and ice-smoothed or as roughly weathered peaks and escarpments. At many places along the fiords raised marine clay and sand deposits, of late glacial or postglacial age, form ledges and plains and also constitute the fill in the lower part of many valleys. Such terraces are found at 65 to 230 ft and even higher, above present-day sea level.

A second characteristic of the coastal topography is the strandflat, a belt of islands, skerries, and rocks and a rim of low foreland in front of steep mountain sides. The low foreland rises to a height of approximately 165 ft and may extend below sea level to a depth of about 100 ft. Generally the surface is neither flat nor continuous as the islands and peninsulas are separated by sounds and fiords. The summits rise to a uniform low height. Bedrock outcrops at many places on the strandflat, but often there is a thin cover of loose deposits ranging from clay to gravel.

The topography of the eastern part of northern Scandinavia, from Hammerfest to the Russian border, is of a different character. The interior is less mountainous and the relief lower. Most of the rolling surface lies between 1,000 and 1,500 ft above sea level. The hills drop precipitously to the sea and leave, in most places, no room for settlement.

Eurasian Arctic

All the Barents Sea coasts have an arctic environment, but permanent land ice is restricted to islands on the north and northeast sides. Several distinct physiographic provinces occupy the mainland coast and immediate hinterland on the south coast of the Barents Sea. In the west, granites, gneiss, and other crystalline rocks of the Baltic Shield underlie Kolskiy Poluostrov and Karelia. The shield is predominently a rocky, rolling upland with general elevations of 500 to 650 ft near the coast and rising to about 1,600 ft inland near the tree line. It is deeply dissected, especially near the Norwegian border where it is penetrated by deep, broad fiords that trend northeast-southwest. The land is covered with countless lakes and small, poorly organized streams; moraine ridges, eskers, and peat bogs are scattered over the surface. Along the coast there are often clearly marked terraces resulting from higher sea levels in the past. The surface of the shield descends toward the east and disappears beneath younger sedimentary rocks of the Russian Platform on the east side of the White Sea. These rocks dip gently to the southeast; on them are developed

broad plains crossed by escarpments that are highest near the White Sea
coast. Karst topography is well developed at several localities and the
lowlands particularly are marshy.

Lowlands extend from the edge of the shield to the Urals except where
they are interrupted by the uplands of Poluostrov Kanin and Timanskiy
Kryazh. The former is generally low-lying except in the north, where there
is a ridge of highly dissected hills. The summits are low, averaging 500
to 850 ft; at Mys Kanin Nos, where the hills reach the sea, they are under
500 ft but even so, the headland is in striking contrast to the alluvial
lowland in other parts of the peninsula. The only other rocky headlands
are where the Timanskiy Kryazh reach the sea at Cheshkaya Guba. This
range is formed of folded strata, and elevations in it reach 1,000 ft.

The lowlands of the Malozemel'skaya and Bol'sheze-mel'skaya tundras
separate the Timanskiy Kryazh and the Urals. The terrain is marshy, with
muskeg bogs and deep peat soils developed on thick postglacial marine
sediments and glacial deposits. Inland, sand dunes up to 300 ft high,
mark the outer margin of the glaciated area. The major features of the
coast are two large bays; Cheshkaya Guba and Pechorskay Guba. The latter
is the estuary of the Pechora River, which has formed a complex delta with
many small islands. Throughout, the coast is lined with spits and bars.

The Urals are a hilly upland composed of folded rocks. The highest
peak, Gora'Narodnaya, (6,200 ft) is 210 mi inland. Closer to the sea,
few points exceed 5,000 ft. The mountains trend northeast until 68°N
where they turn sharply to the northwest. The western slopes descend
steeply to a low plateau, and then to the lowlands; the eastern slope is
more gentle. The hills become much lower after the change in direction;
and 40 mi of lowland tundra separates them from the Khrebet Pay Kohoy,
the most northerly part of the range on the mainland. The Pay Khoy and
northern Urals have distinct glacial landforms including hanging valleys,
tarns, and ice-abraded rock zones.

The tree line extends from Varanger Peninsula in Norway, east through
the middle of the Kol'skiy Poluostrov, and then follows roughly the 67°N
parallel to the Urals - consequently all the Barents Sea coasts have
arctic vegetation, but the White Sea penetrates deeply into the forests.
South of the tundra proper, forest-tundra merges slowly into taiga forests.

A single large island, Otrov Kolguyev is present in the southern
Barents Sea. It is roughly circular, with a diameter of 50 mi. Altitudes
are everywhere low and only reach 500 ft in the center of the island.
Spits and sandbars line the coasts and separate lagoons from the open sea.
Surface drainage is poor and low tundra mounds are widely distributed in
marshes. In the north of the island the dominant vegetation is lichen
and moss tundra; in the south it is shrub tundra, with dwarf birch and
willow. Otrov Kolguyev and the adjacent mainland are underlain by deep,
continuous permafrost.

In the southeast corner of Barents Sea, Ostrov Vargach continues the
Ural structure. It is separated from Yugorskiy Poluostrov by Yugorskiy
Shar, a narrow strait 3 to 4 mi wide. The island is crossed by two
northwest-southeast trending hill ridges which attain an elevation of
600 ft. Where they reach the sea, the hills produce low cliffs but
elsewhere there are sandy beaches.

Novaya Zemlya is a massive land barrier that separates the Barents and

Kara seas. It consists of two islands divided by the narrow, winding,
steepsided Proliv Matochkin Shar. The islands are a structural continuation of the folded sediments of the Urals that curves in a southwest-
northeast arc for about 550 mi. Long, linear valleys, fiords, and
straight coastlines are characteristic of the topography and result from
intense faulting. The eastern side of the islands is somewhat lower and
less rugged than the west.

The southern part of Novaya Zemlya, for about 80 mi north of Proliv
Karskiye Vorota, is a plain that rarely exceeds 330 ft in the highest
parts and is covered with wet, hummocky tundra. At about 72°N the
interior is higher and rises gradually northwards for 120 mi at which
point the island has become a steep-sided, flat-topped block with an upland
surface reaching 3,300 ft. This sector is dissected by straight valleys,
many of which have been drowned to form fiords; and one, Matochkin Shar,
cuts completely across the upland.

Zemlya Frantsa Iosifa is an archipelago of several hundred islands on
the northeast margin of the Barents Sea between 80° and 82°N and 45°
and 65°E. The largest island, Georga, is about 70 mi long, but the majority are much smaller. The cessation of igneous activity was followed by
widespread faulting that disrupted the land mass and the surrounding
continental shelf into the archipelago and intervening deep channels. The
resulting plateau islands have steep, often cliffed shores and interior
uplands that reach 2,300 ft, although 1,000 ft is more typical. The
margins of the uplands have been eroded by ice to form cirques and glacier
troughs, but over 80% of the land is ice-covered. Outlet glaciers reach
the sea and produce icebergs, and in some localities form small ice shelves.

The west Siberian lowlands have developed on horizontal sedimentary
rocks that are buried beneath Quaternary glacial, marine, and fluvial
deposits. The monotony of the marsh-covered, ill-drained tundra landscape
is broken by occasional terraces and low moraines. The highest elevations
rarely exceed 500 ft and are found where bedrock approaches the surface
between the Ob' and Yenisey estuaries.

The shores of the Kara Sea are deeply indented by estuaries to form
peninsulas. In the west, the largest, Poluostrov Yamal, projects 240
mi northwards into the Kara Sea. It is a plain of sands and clays, the
highest elevation being in the south-central part of the peninsula
where a moraine reaches 330 ft. The west coast is occasionally terraced
and has occasional low cliffs, but in general the shores are low, flat,
and swampy. The surface of the land is covered with lakes and swamps
through which rivers appear to wander aimlessly. Ostrova Belyy, north of
the peninsula is similar topographically. Along the east shore, Obskaya
Guba is the drowned lower course of the Ob' River. It is over 320 mi
long and has an average width of 40 mi. At its head the mouth of the Ob'
has a limiting depth of only 8 ft, and seagoing ships cannot enter. A
branch of the main estuary, Tazovskaya Guba extends southeastward. South
of it is Trazovskiy Poluostrov, and north of it the very similar Gydanskiy
Poluostrov. The latter is a wide peninsula between the Ob' and Yenisey
rivers that is divided in the north by Gydanskaya Guba into two subsidiary
peninsulas. The interior is slightly hillier than the remainder of the
arctic lowlands, and ridges reach 600 ft. Along the coast the land is low
and swampy, with maximum elevations less than 100 ft.

The estuary of the Yenisey is 200 mi long. It marks the edge of the
lowlands as the land rises immediately east to the hills of Poluostrov

Taimyr. The mouth of the river itself has a minimum depth of 33 ft and
so is accessible to some seagoing vessels.

The treeless coast and hinterland of Poluostrov Taimyr are dominated
by Gory Byrranga, a mountain range parallel to the coast and about 45
mi inland with altitudes up to 4,000 ft. The uplands descend gently to
the north forming rolling terrain. The west and central coasts of the
peninsula are low-lying and highly irregular with innumerable offshore
islands. In the east, near Mys Chelyuskin, the coast is generally hillier.

The Kara Sea contains hundreds of islands, the majority of which are
close to the Taimyr coast. Ostrova Belyy, north of Poluostrov Yamal,
is the westernmost large island. Other islands include Ostrova Uyedineniya
in the central Kara Sea and Ostrov Vize and Ostrov Ushakova between
Zemlya Frantsa Iosifa and Severnaya Zemlya. These islands are composed of
recent deposits and have undulating terrain inland with low cliffs along
their coast. There is little vegetation.

Severnaya Zemlya lies north of Mys Chelyuskin between 78°N and 81°N.
There are four large islands in the archipelago and many small ones. Two-
fifths of the archipelago is ice-covered. The most southerly island,
Bol'shevik, is the second largest and is separated from the mainland by
the 32-mi-wide Proliv Vil'kitskogo. The western side is low while the
east coast is high and often cliffed. The interior has low, rounded hills
rising to about 3,000 ft. The remainder of the archipelago is separated
from Ostrov Bol'shevik by Proliv Shokal'skogo which has depths of 600 to
900 ft and is suitable for navigation as it is deep, wide, and often ice-
free in the summer. Oktyabr'skoy Revolyutsii is the largest island.
It resembles Ostrov Bol'shevik except that it has four small ice caps in
the corners of the island that are the remnants of a larger ice cap that
once covered the whole island; the highest elevation, 3,200 ft., is on
the northern ice cap.

The coast and hinterland bordering the Laptev and East Siberian seas
are composed of extensive lowlands backed by a highland region of mountain
ranges and high plateaus, several of which extend to the coast. There
are numerous north-flowing rivers; the largest, from west to east, are
the Khatanga, Anabar, Olenek, Lena, Indigirka, and Kolyma. The northern
Siberian lowlands extend eastward from the lower Yenisey River, where
they merge with the west Siberian lowlands, to the Kolyma River. They
form a lowland strip approximately 1,300 mi long that in places is 600
mi wide but narrows to 6 mi where uplands approach the sea. In the west
the lowlands occupy a basin that separates the hills of Poluostrov Taimyr
from the Siberian Plateau. This section is occupied by the Khatanga
River which is drowned in its lower part to produce an estuary more than
140 mi long. The mouth of the estuary is practically blocked by the
large island, Ostrova Begicheva.

Between the Khatanga and Lena rivers two ridges break the monotony of
the lowland. The Kryazh Pronchishcheva running parallel to the shore
between the Anabar and the Olenek rivers is a folded range with elevations
up to 1,000 ft. Kryazh Chekanovskogo, a ridge that rises to 1,650 ft,
runs northwest-southeast and separates the basin from the Lena River.
Another hilly sector occurs east of the Lena where the Verkhoyanskiy
Khrebet approaches the sea, but this is replaced east of Guba Buorkhaya
by an alluvial lowland. The lowlands have developed on unconsolidated
sands and silts that are underlain by continuous permafrost and contain
large quantities of ground ice. Pingos, thermokarst landforms, polygonal

ground, thaw lakes, and intricate periglacial drainage patterns are widespread. In some places the area of the lakes is equal to that of dry land;
and in the summer, much of the lowland is impassable to surface travel.
The majority of lakes are oval, shallow, (3 to 13 ft) and rarely longer
than 2 mi. The lakes and the rivers are interconnected; and when the rivers
are in flood they flow into the lakes, while at other times the lakes feed
the rivers. The relief is monotonously flat with gently rolling tundra
sloping imperceptibly to the north except where it is interrupted by low
morainic ridges. In striking contrast to western Siberia, east of the
Anabar deltas rather than estuaries are characteristic of river mouths.

Tundra, marked by conspicuous polygonal patterned ground and composed of
mosses and lichens with some herbaceous plants, dwarf birch, and willow,
occupies the coastal lowland. Taiga vegetation, with larch and white
birch, penetrates north along the valleys of large rivers and the tree
line nearly reaches the sea in the vicinity of the Lena.

The Lena River is more than 2,000 mi long. The delta, the third
largest in the world, is a complex of Quaternary sediments which begins
80 mi inland and has an area of 12,350 sq mi. It is made up of over a
thousand islands and sandbars. The depth and position of the intervening
channels are modified by tides and strong winds and the general fall of
water level in the summer. The shape and number of islands is altered
constantly by melting of ground ice, deposition, and erosion. Frost mounds
sometimes more than 100 ft high, frozen silt, and ice cliffs are widely
distributed and the whole delta is a mass of thaw lakes.

Northeastern Siberia, east of the Lena delta is a combination of coastal
lowlands, arch-shaped mountain ranges, isolated mountain groups,and plateaus.
The uplands have developed on folded sedimentary rocks, with granite intrusions usually underlying the highest peaks. The mountains are deeply
dissected but may have accordant tops. Summits above 6,000 ft are common;
all were modified by glaciers during the Pleistocene, which produced
hanging valleys, cirques, tarns, and moraines that descend to about 1,200
ft. The coastal lowlands (the Kolyma Plains) lack glacial features except
for a small area south of the Ostrova Novosibirskiye.

The peninsula of northeastern Siberia, when considered as a whole,
is dominated topographically by mountains, but only three ranges approach
close to the Arctic Ocean. In the west, the Verkoyanskiy Khrebet drop
sharply to the Lena River, but slopes are gentler on the east side.
Summits in the northern part of the range exceed 6,500 ft. East of the
Kolyma valley, a second group of ranges descend towards the coast in steep
escarpments crossed by deep canyons on the west side of Chaunskaya Guba.
A third mountain group, the Anadyrski Khrebet lies between the Anadyr
basin and the coast of the Chukchi Sea. The massif is divided at Zaliv
Kresta. The western section is highly dissected by deep glacial valleys
and has alpine mountains with elevations in the center up to 5,900 ft.
The eastern section is lower with rounded uplands and is crossed by broad
northwest-trending valleys. The northern part of the range backs the coast
a short distance inland from east of Chaunskaya Guba to west of Mys Shmidta.
Spurs from this range reach the coast and form cliffs and rocky points.
The Yukagirskoye Ploskogor'ya, south of the lower Kolyma, has a much dissected surface and broad, shallow valleys. There are some isolated
mountains with elevations up to 3,600 ft.

The only significant lowland area in northeast Siberia is a zone of
subsidence between the Koryaskiy and Chukotskiy highlands that has been

filled by deposits of the Anadyr River. Although the terrain is generally
flat, the volcanic and igneous rocks that underlie the alluvium project
through, producing low hill ranges at several points. Drainage in the
lowland coastal areas is inhibited, and marshes, thaw lakes, and lagoons
are widespread. Bars and spits are characteristic of the coast which
resembles closely the northern coast of Alaska and the Chukchi Peninsula.

The Yana, Indigirka, and Kolyma plains occupy most of the coastal
region of the East Siberian Sea. They extend from Guba Buorkhaya east
to the mouth of the Kolyma River and penetrate inland along the middle
and lower courses of the Indigirka and Kolyma. They are all close to sea
level and are broken only by lakes and the meandering distributaries of
the three rivers after which they are named. The coastal strip is a
low, swampy tundra with scattered areas of higher elevations, occasional
low cliffs, and some hills inland. The three large rivers have extensive
deltas. There are many lagoons and bays on the coast detached from the
sea by spits and bars and mostly with narrow entrances. North of the
Kolyma are six small rocky islands, the Ostrova Medvezh'i, which are the
only islands in the East Siberian Sea located an appreciable distance from
the shore.

Separating the Laptev and East Siberian seas are numerous low islands
known collectively as Ostrova Novosibirskiye. They are the much eroded
extension onto the continental shelf of the folded mountain ranges of
northeastern Siberia. The sediments on the Ostrova De-Longa were buried
by basalt lavas which today form the flat upper surface of the islands
and the precipitous black cliffs. Ostrov Benneta, the largest of the
group, is approximately 7 mi wide and the highest point, which is glaciated,
exceeds 1,300 ft.

The islands of the main and southern groups are generally low except
for the western third of Ostrov Kotel'nyy where hills reach 1,225 ft.
The uplands in this sector are developed on limestone, slate, and basalt,
each of which has a different scenery. The valleys are straight and deep,
a characteristic that has been attributed to faulting, and the coast has
several deep embayments. The central part of Ostrova Koteln'nyy, known
as Kemlya Bunge is a sandy, low, flat plain which is only slightly above
the level of the ocean and is occasionally flooded by seawater.

In the southern group, the interior of Ostrov Bol'shoy Lyakhovskiy
is also hilly, but elsewhere in the archipelago the terrain is flat and
gently undulating and does not rise above 300 ft. The plains are developed
on sands and silts which contain massive ground ice. The ice is concentrated in shallow valleys. Where it is found along the coast it forms cliffs
that in some places are 165 ft high. The ice has melted rapidly in the
20th century leading to important coastal changes and the disappearance
of two small islands. The coastal waters adjacent to the plain are exceptionally shallow. The islands have little vegetation and only the better
watered valleys have closed tundra.

Ostrov Vrangelya is 70 mi off the Poluostrov Chukokskiy. It is crossed
by two mountain ranges that separate the northern and southern lowland.
The summits are either flat or gently domed, the remains of an ancient
peneplain. The southern range is shorter than the northern but contains
the highest peak, Gora Sovetskaya (3,600 ft). In general the relief is
complex and highly dissected, with lattice drainage and some large, flat
intermontane valleys. West of the ranges are flat, low hills under 1,000
ft high; on the east is the Eastern Plateau, an undulating upland with

isolated flat-topped peaks with a maximum elevation of 650 ft. The
northern range is a gently rolling area, little dissected, with relic
mountains less than 2,000 ft high. It slopes gently to the northern
coastal plain, called Tundra Akademii.

Tundra Akademii is a flat plain of Quaternary marine sediments covered
with fluvial sands, gravels, and loams up to 100 ft thick. There are
also raised terraces left from marine transgressions in the interglacial
periods. The surface is cut by shallow river valleys; thermokarst depressions and lakes are common. There is a coastal bar on the northeast coast,
with a string of small lakes inside it. The southern coastal lowlands,
divided in the center by Zaliv Krasina, are relatively narrow and taper
to the east until they disappear. The western half is similar to Tundra
Akademii, except that the rivers are more entrenched and have steeper
gradients. On the east this tendency is more pronounced.

The easternmost Siberian mainland is dominated by the confused mountain
mass of the Chukostskiy Khrebet. The mountains are complex fold structures,
and in general the central and eastern parts of the range near the coast
have rounded outlines with elevations from 2,500 to 3,300 ft. In the
interior the highest summits exceed 6,500 ft. Although the mountains are
lowest near the Chukchi Sea, broad coastal lowlands are restricted to a
single plain that extends southeast from Amguyema River for 140 mi. The
eastern part of this plain is drowned to form Kolyuchinskaya Guba. Elsewhere along the coast hills frequently reach the sea, isolating small
plains.

The coast shows evidence of submergence and has an irregular outline
where the sea has entered valleys. The shallow inshore waters favor the
development of barrier bars and long sectors have straight sandy bars
and spits which separate lagoons from the open sea. The entire Siberian
coast lies beyond the tree line; and characteristically in the lowlands,
damp marsh tundra has developed on a terrain underlain by permafrost and
with inumerable small lakes.

East of Kolyuchinskaya Guba the mountains come closer to the coast and
at Mys Serdtse-Kamen elevations near the coast reach 2,000 to 3,000 ft.
Mys Dezhneva is a limestone mountain reaching 2,540 ft connected to the
mainland by a low isthmus.

North Pacific

At the western end of the Aleutian arc are the Komandorskiye Ostrova,
a group of four islands 90 mi from the Kamchatka coast. The terrain
of the two largest islands, Ostrova Beringa and Ostrova Mednyy, is rugged;
but although there is frequent seismic activity, there are not active
volcanoes and the maximum elevation is only 2,100 ft. The coasts are rocky
except at the north end of Ostrova Beringa.

The Asiatic land mass on the west side of the Bering Sea generally
experiences a harsher environment than Alaska. This is reflected in the
vegetation which is restricted to tundra and arctic desert in Siberia
as far south as 60°N and by the boundary of continuous permafrost which
is more than 80 mi farther south on the west side of the Bering Sea than
the east. Although the geologic history of northeast Siberia has many
points in common with Alaska the main topographic elements are not as clear-
cut or symmetrically distributed. The major physiographic regions are the

Poluostrov Kamchatka, the Koryakskiy Khrebet, Poluostrov Chukotskiy, the
Anadyr' Lowlands, and the north and west coasts of the Sea of Okhotsk.

Kamchatka is a peninsula, more than 600 mi long, that separates the
Sea of Okhotsk from the Bering Sea and the northwest Pacific Ocean. Two
main mountain ranges, divided by the broad valley of the Kamchatka River
dominate the peninsula. Forty volcanoes are known, almost all on the eastern
side of the peninsula; fourteen are active. The highest almost reaches
16,000 ft and many exceed 10,000 ft. In spite of the rigors of the land
the summers are sufficiently warm in the lowlands to support forests,
and permafrost occurs only sporadically near sea level. The west coast
lowland with maximum widths of 40 mi is considerably broader than the east;
the western marshy coastal plains are fringed in the central and southern
sectors by lagoons and offshore sand and gravel bars. Ostrov Kariginskiy
is a continuation of the more easterly interior mountain range. It
resembles the nearby east Kamchatka coast, being rugged and with maximum
elevation of about 3,000 ft.

The Koryakskiy Khrebet extends the rugged topography of Kamchatka
northeastward in a series of mountain chains that run roughly parallel
to the coast. Summit heights commonly exceed 5,200 ft in the interior,
and the coastline has occasional peaks with elevations reaching 4,000 ft.
The coast resembles the Pacific side of Kamchatka with large promontories
where the main ranges meet the sea.

The Poluostrov Chukotskiy highland block resembles the Alaskan Seward
Peninsula and consists of fold mountains. The ranges have no dominant
trend, although there is a tendency for the larger valleys to be aligned
in a northwest direction. The mountains have rounded contours with summit
elevations between 2,800 and 3,300 ft. There is strong evidence in the
landscape of former intense ice sheet erosion, particularly in the deep
U-shaped valleys and ice-smoothed hill tops. The southeast coast, where
the mountains are cut off at Bering Strait, has a deeply indented fiord
coastline. The nearby Diomede Islands in Bering Strait have steep rocky
shores and rounded relief.

Ostrova Kurilskiye run in a narrow concave arc along the southern
boundary of the Sea of Okhotsk. They are part of the Pacific volcanic arc
which extends from the Aleutians through Kamchatka, the Kuril Islands,
and Japan; there are over 100 cones in the island chain, of which 38 are
active today. The small islands in the chain are usually single volcanic
cones, while the largest are formed by a complex of connected cones.
All the islands are composed of ash and lava in alternate layers except
for the northernmost, Ostrov Shumshu, and the southernmost, Ostrov
Kunashir, which are geologically related to the adjacent mainland and are
of sedimentary origin.

The island of Sakhalin is over 500 mi long and is separated from the
mainland by the Strait of Tartary. Two mountain ranges, an eastern and a
western, dominate the relief of the island; both subside in the north
leaving an extensive lowland. The mountain ranges are separated by a
central lowland, 3 to 18 mi wide, which starts at Guba Terpentiya and
trends approximately northward before turning east with the Tym River to
form a coastal plain. The eastern range is higher than the western;
altitudes in the center reach 6,600 ft. The shores of Sakhalin are
relatively steep and rocky in the southeast, except where the central
lowland meets the sea at Guba Terpentiya. The western range is formed
of several parallel ridges, of which the westernmost is the highest and

has the sharpest relief. At the northern end the mountains become lower
and more gentle, and the coastal plain broadens to a substantial lowland
which finally merges into the northern plain. The eastern coast in the
center and north of the island is lined with almost continuous sandbars.

The mainland coast of the Sea of Okhotsk is over 1,000 mi long; and
although it is generally high and even mountainous, there are conspicuous
differences in several sectors. In the extreme west, the hill ranges
meet the coast at right angles, and deep bays and several large islands
are the result. From the Uda River northeastward to Okhotsk more than
300 mi away, the interior ranges lie parallel to the coast which is
exceptionally smooth and steep with no coastal plain. Between Okhotsk and
Magadan the coast is more irregular; and there are small plains, but they
diminish again east of the latter town. The northeastern coast is highly
irregular with rugged peninsulas and only occasional small plains with
lagoons and bars along the coast.

Alaska

With the exception of the Arctic Coastal Plain, Alaska is wholly within
the Western Cordillera physiographic province of North America. The
Cordillera in Alaska consists of parallel complex mountain ranges separated
by plateaus and lowlands. The west coast of Alaska cuts at right angles
across the northwestern margin of the province forming large peninsulas
that correspond roughly to mountain ranges. The two main peninsulas south
of the Chukchi Sea are the Seward and the Alaska. Between them, a third
blunt peninsula bounded by Norton Sound and Bristol Bay terminates in
Nunivak Island and has superimposed on it the Yukon and Kuskokwin deltas.

Seward Peninsula projects nearly 160 mi toward Siberia between Kotzebue
and Norton sounds. The geology is extremely complex and the interior is
dominated by a mass of uplands and mountain ranges. Across the center
of the Peninsula, the York Mountains and associated ranges reach nearly
3,000 ft. In the southern part the Kigluaik and Darby mountains include
the highest mountains in the Peninsula. From the sea, the overall appearance of the south side of the Peninsula is rugged and the relief in
the higher coastal areas is 1,600 to 2,300 ft. There is, however, considerable variation, and there are coastal lowlands between Cape Douglas and
Solomon (including the Nome area) and between Moses Point and Koyuk. The
upland coasts are sharply indented where valleys reach the sea. These are
filled with alluvial deposits, mainly gravels, in contrast to the northern
coast where silts are dominant. Along part of the coast, gravel spits
and bars are characteristic while elsewhere rock terraces are prominent
features.

The coastal highlands between Norton Sound and Bristol Bay are bisected
by the Yukon-Kuskokwim drainage complex. On the north side a highland
sector encircles the eastern and southern coasts of Norton Sound from
Norton Bay to the Yukon delta. In this area, hill ridges trend in a
northeasterly direction roughly parallel to the sound. The crests vary
in height between 1,600 and 2,000 ft and have been much rounded by frost
action and solifluction. Only small valleys reach the sea. The southern
highland sector extends southward from the Kuskokwim delta to the lowlands
surrounding the Nushagak River at the head of Bristol Bay. The hill
ridges have the same orientation as those south of Norton Sound, but here
are at right angles to the coast. Known as the Kuskokwim Highlands, the
rocks are more resistant and the scenery more rugged than in the Norton

Sound area. The hills rise 1,000 to 2,000 ft at the coast and increase
inland to heights of 3,000 to 5,000 ft. At Togaik Bay the hill ridges
project into the sea and form a number of small offshore islands with
maximum elevations of more than 800 ft. The ridges are separated by wide,
flat valleys filled with thick deposits of alluvium. Many of the landforms
were modified by intense mountain glaciation, particularly in the interior.

The twin delata of the Yukon and Kuskokwim rivers is the largest lowland
in the area. It is characteristically arctic, treeless, and underlain by
permafrost, with innumerable thaw lakes, deranged drainage, tundra
polygons, and pingos. The Nushagak-Kvichak lowlands at the head of Bristol
Bay have a deep mantle of Quaternary deposits. The coastal relief is
flat and monotonous; drainage is poor and continually shifting, resulting
in countless lakes, marshes, and sloughs.

The islands in the Bering Sea vary in size from the St. Lawrence
Island, which is over 80 mi long, to rocky islets. The majority are of
volcanic origin. The only appreciable sedimentary rock outcrops are on
St. Lawrence Island, where they form rugged relief in the southwest of
the island and contrast sharply with the remaining two-thirds of the island,
which is low with many lakes and marshes. There has been volcanic activity
in recent times, and a 2,070-ft volcanic cone dominates the center of the
island. The south coast is lined with barrier beaches, cuspate forelands,
spits, and lagoons.

St. Matthew and the Pribilov islands are rugged, hilly, volcanic
islands with elevations of 1,000 to 1,500 ft in the interior. Sea ice,
nearly continuous fog, and absence of harbors contribute to navigation
hazards around them. St. Matthew is a series of low peaks rising from
the sea and connected by low sand and gravel spits. Elevations are between
1,000 and 1,500 ft. Of the five islands in the Pribilov group only two,
St. George and St. Paul, exceed 20 sq mi in area and are inhabited.
Composed mainly of basaltic lava outflows, their highest elevation is
less than 1,000 ft.

Nelson Island lies in a re-entrant of the Yukon-Kuskokwim delta. It
is developed on sedimentary rocks and lavas which rise to about 100 ft
and contrast conspicuously with the nearby deltaic plains. The coasts
facing the sea are marked by precipitous headlands linked by beaches.
Nearby Nunivak Island is of volcanic origin and is surrounded by bluffs
between 50 and 400 ft high. Occasional dune formations occur along the
coast.

The Aleutian Range extends for 1,700 mi from near Anchorage to the
coast of Kamchatka. The range is continuous in the east where it forms
the Alaska Peninsula but is largely drowned in the central and western
sectors. It exhibits the characteristic pattern of the geologically young
island arcs found around the Pacific with high relief, steep topography,
strong earthquakes, and active vulcanism; almost 50 volcanoes have been
active in the last two centuries. Both the islands and the peninsula
are formed of lava outflows, volcanic cones, and calderas intermixed with
sedimentary strata formed by erosion of local igneous deposits. For the
most part the coasts of the Aleutian Range are lower on the north side,
the topography rising sharply to the south. Poor drainage, dunes, sandbars,
and lagoons characterize the Bering coast of the peninsula. The peaks
reach their maximum altitude on Unimak Island (9,978 ft) and in the Alaska
Peninsula (11,200 ft).

The northern Alaskan coasts are also dominated by mountain ranges but at many points they are far from the sea, and the lowlands are correspondingly larger than on the Siberian side. The principal mountains are the Brooks Range. They are relatively subdued in the western area where they are known as the de Long Mountains. The range is about 80 mi wide and has many peaks over 3,000 ft; a few rugged, glaciated summits exceed 5,000 ft. The mountains approach close to the sea between Point Hope and Kotzebue Sound. On their north flank is a broad foothill zone which is close to the coast northeast of Cape Lisburne. On the north side of the mountains and the foothills is the flat Arctic Coastal Plain that attains its widest development near Barrow.

Northwestern Alaska comprises a mountain sector, the Brooks Range; a foothills province; and a coastal plain. The same threefold pattern is found east of Point Barrow. The Brooks Range is 120 mi from the sea south of Point Barrow, but the distance lessens until along the U.S.-Canadian border it is only 25 mi away. The relief is often extremely rugged with east-west trending ridges. In the northern part accordant summits rise 7,000 to 9,000 ft. Extensive glaciation occurred in the Pleistocene, and there is evidence of ice tongues 35 mi beyond the mountain front. In the higher northeastern parts of the mountain group, small cirque and valley glaciers are common.

The southern portion of the foothills province consists of irregular isolated hills, east-trending ridges, and mesa-like mountains. In the north the structure of the foothills is much simpler and consists of folds of Cretaceous sediments. The hills rise from 600 ft in the north to 1,200 ft in the south.

The Arctic Coastal Plain slopes very gently from an average of 600 ft near its southern border to sea level along the coast. The plain has developed on ice-saturated sand, silts, and gravel of the Gubik formation. Ice volumes are often as high as 70% in the upper 20 ft of sediment. Consequently, if melting of the permafrost occurred, subsidence of the land surface might be as much as 12 ft in some areas, and could cause some low-lying coastal areas to be inundated. Organic material in the sections consists of plant and animal remains, some very old, preserved in the frozen ground. At a few localities, notably in the White Hills, lignite and coal are exposed. The plain is poorly drained and is covered with thousands of lakes and swamps. Thaw lakes are one of the most striking features of the coastal plain province. Covering over half the surface, the lake basins enlarge by thawing the frozen ground and often coalesce. They range from a few feet to several miles long and are up to 20 ft deep. Many of the lakes are elongated with their long axis having a pronounced N 15°W orientation.

Most of the rivers on the arctic slope originate in the Brooks Range. They cross the plain in shallow braided channels and have built large deltas in the Arctic Ocean. Most are navigable during the short summer by small boat in their lower reaches. Large seasonal fluctuations are common, with bank-full conditions during the spring compared to virtually no flow in the braided channels during the summer and fall. On the Colville River nearly half of the annual flow takes place in a three-week period following breakup. The rivers are generally frozen for eight months of the year.

The arctic coast is basically a barrier coast with sand spits, off-shore bars, and islands alternating with low bluffs for virtually the whole

distance. Between the bars and the mainland are shallow lagoons suitable
for the passage of small boats. On the mainland, behind the lagoons, is
commonly a bluff 15 to 40 ft high formed in frozen sediments. Point
Barrow is the most northerly point on the coast. It is a low spit of
sand and gravel about 4 mi long and 400 yards wide. The coast is
receding at most localities, the average loss reaching 10 ft per year.
Wherever the coast forms a point or is otherwise well exposed to the
sea, shore retreat can exceed 30 ft a year. Point Drew, Cape Simpson,
and Brownlow Point east of Flaxman Island have exceptionally rapid retreat.

Canada

The mainland coast of northwestern Canada, adjacent to the Beaufort
Sea, consists of three parts. In the west, the Yukon Coastal Plain,
which is only 2 mi broad at Demarcation Point where the Cordillera is
closest to the sea, widens to over 15 mi nearer the Mackenzie. It is
a monotonous land of open, often wet tundra crossed by the numerous
streams that drain the British Mountains. The plain has developed on
silts and sands which have been eroded by streams and waves and deformed
by glaciation into moderate relief. Low cliffs are common along the
coast; they are 20 to 40 ft high and are receding in many places at
about 1 ft per year. The sand from the cliffs is deposited on the beach,
which may be as much as 50 ft wide. The sand is slowly transported
offshore.

The Mackenzie delta occupies a former deep embayment in the coast that
has been filled with alluvial deposits brought down by the river. The
waters north of Shallow Bay are particularly shoal, with depths rarely
exceeding 20 ft as far as 17 mi offshore. Between the Blow River and
the inner parts of Shallow Bay recession reaches 10 ft per year. The
delta consists of thousands of islands surrounded by an intricate
network of channels and interconnecting lakes. At breakup, the water
level rises 10 to 15 ft in the middle parts of the delta and less in the
outer parts. During onshore storms, and at flood stage in early spring,
the delta is water-covered for tens of miles inland, and only branches
of submerged willows outline the channels. The coastline is barely
visible from the sea since the outermost alluvial islands are at sea
level. Some of the higher islands, such as Kendall and Garry islands
which are outside the recent delta, rise 200 ft above sea level. They
are the eroded, detached portions of an older delta.

East of the modern delta, the coast is formed by an old complex
Pleistocene delta which includes all the Tuktoyaktuk Peninsula. The
terrain is undulating, slopes seaward, and is disrupted only by low
swampy areas and higher sandy ridges. East of Atkinson Point half of
the surface is covered by shallow rounded lakes, many of which are
oriented with their long axis in a north-south direction. The coast is
low; sandy spits and parabolic sand dunes are common; and in places
recession reaches 10 ft a year. The most conspicuous features are the
pingos which are concentrated in groups in the area around Kugmallit Bay.
The coast from Anderson River north to Baillie Island is indented by
estuaries, indicating submergence; and the estuarine part of Harrowby Bay
is bordered by prominent terraces. Waters offshore are shallow along
the whole coast from Demarcation Point to Cape Bathurst, partly because
of fluvially transported silt and sand from the larger rivers. Sea
level fluctuates with changes in wind and pressure conditions; fluctuations
in Harrowby Bay reach 8 ft.

The Thesinger Bay coast of Banks Island resembles the Yukon coast; cliffs are up to 60 ft high in the east and 125 ft close to Cape Kellet. The fine sand and silt cliffs are cut rapidly back by marine erosion, and the sediments form a protective mudbank just below tide level. Occasional gaps are eroded by watercourses in the ridge-like coastline, and the lower reaches of some rivers include sandbars and lagoons. Except for two prominent ridges with bluffs immediately north of Cape Kellett, all of the west coast of Banks Island is low. The rivers, of which several rise near the east coast, enter the Beaufort Sea in flat open valleys and often have braided channels and shallow lakes. Between the valleys, the terrain is rolling and rises to a height of several hundred feet a few miles inland. Along this coast the unconsolidated sediments containing ice lenses are being rapidly cut back, helped by a slow sinking of the land. Along the Barnett Bay coast offshore islands provide protection from wave and ice erosion, and crustal sinking has led to a drowned coastline.

The whole of the area is north of the tree line although in Coronation Gulf northern extensions of the boreal forest project north along the rivers and, in the case of Coppermine River, reach to within a few miles of the sea. Along the mainland coast west from Kent Peninsula, there is a southern variety of arctic tundra with thickets of willow and birch bushes in sheltered localities and a rich proliferation of species. East of Kent Peninsula and on the southern islands the vegetation is visibly poorer, but nonetheless forms closed tundra communities. In the northern sector of the islands where the summer temperatures are significantly lower and drought conditions develop on the deep shattered bedrocks, there is a striking impoverishment of the species and there are broad areas of rock deserts.

The Canadian Shield on the mainland west from Dease Strait is composed predominantly of sedimentary and volcanic rocks, and the topography and terrain are consequently unlike most shield areas. Everywhere the shores and coastal lowlands are overlain by quantities of silt and fine sand deposited in a high-level sea that existed at the close of the glaciation. Several distinct coastal sections can be recognized resulting primarily from the type of bedrock.

Along the south side of Dolphin and Union Strait there is rolling hill country developed on sedimentary rocks. Although altitudes inland exceed 2,000 ft, the drift is generally so thick that rock outcrops are rare, except where they form cliffed headlands. Slopes are long and gentle, and the impression from the coast is rather of rolling lowlands than an upland region. The mainland coasts of Coronation Gulf, Bathurst Inlet, and Dease Strait form a second region that contrasts strongly with the coasts farther west. The igneous rocks commonly form spectacular cliffs, in many cases rising several hundred feet out of the sea. In Coronation Gulf and Bathurst Inlet the lavas form strings of elongated islands which have a cliffed side and a gently sloping backface. Typical of this part of the coast is the great variety of rock types and consequent landforms. The shores include cliffs, volcanic shingle strandlines rising in steps from the water to more than 650 ft, and flat silt beaches.

South of Queen Maud Gulf the dominant rocks are granites of the Canadian Shield. The land slopes gently to the north and passes imperceptibly beneath the sea producing shoals and many islands. In summer the inshore water is extremely muddy, and the coast is one of the most difficult in the Canadian Arctic for ship operations. Similar crystalline rocks are exposed around Chantrey Inlet, but the relief is somewhat greater, and low cliffs and bluffs rise out of the water to form hills several hundred feet high. Adelaide Peninsula, south of Simpson Strait, is similar to the large islands north of the mainland. The shores are shallow and contain numerous islands, the majority of which are submerged drumlins.

The southwestern islands have uplands in two areas - the first in central and eastern Banks Island and western and west central Victoria Island, and a second on the eastern margin on western Prince of Wales Island, Somerset Island, and Boothia Peninsula. Between the two regions is a broad lowland which shows many minor differences but has an overall uniformity of terrain.

The southern highland zone reaches Amundsen Gulf in Nelson Head and Cape Lampton; heights exceed 2,000 ft and cliffed coasts or cliffs fronted by a narrow coastal strip are typical. This area contrasts strongly with the northeast upland which is basically a tableland that is between 1,000 and 1,500 ft in the east; it drops to the west where it has been dissected by deep valleys, some of which are drowned forming Castel and Mercy bays. The central lowlands of Banks Island are rolling plains with few rock outcrops and a surface covered with glacial drift, sand, and gravel.

The western Victoria Island uplands are separated from Banks Island by Prince of Wales Strait which is about 8 mi across at its narrowest and more generally about 12 mi wide. In the northwest corner of Victoria Island, corresponding roughly to Prince Albert Peninsula, there is rolling hill country in the interior, but the shores are usually low-lying and drift covered, although at a few localities near the coast altitudes may exceed 1,000 ft. Southeast of Prince Albert Peninsula, roughly as far as a line from the north side of Prince Albert Sound to Hadley Bay, is an area that resembles the Coronation Gulf sector with cliffed escarpment coasts, particularly in the north, and gently dipping back slopes. In the southwest, overlooking Prince Albert Sound, the relief is not as great. Characteristic features of the western upland of Victoria Island are the long inlets, some of which penetrate nearly 80 mi into the island.

The eastern upland includes a strip of hills, not more than 4 mi wide on the east side of Prince of Wales Island, that exceed 1,000 ft in height and reach the coast in steep slopes and cliffs. Across Peel Sound on Somerset Island a similar shield coastline extends between Aston Bay and Wrottesley Inlet. Somerset Island is essentially a tableland. In Boothia Peninsula Precambrian rocks form the hilly backbone of the peninsula with limestone hills and plains on either side.

Between the two uplands the lowlands of the Victoria Basin are nearly 250 mi across. The central, lowest part is drowned and forms M'Clintock Channel and Victoria Strait, which separate Prince of Wales and King William islands from Victoria Island. The coasts are remarkably uniform over considerable distances. Typically, the beaches are formed of shingle; behind them the coast rises in strandlines produced during the emergence of the land in postglacial times. The elevated beaches are separated by low marshy hollows and shallow lagoons. At a few localities, glacial deposits modify the general effect because of the presence of drumlinoid islands and occasional low morainic hills. Glacial landforms are more prominent inland because even where the till is thick on the coast, the surface was washed over by the postglacial sea and strandlines were impressed on them. The most impressive of these hills is in the Rawlinson Peninsula of

western Prince of Wales Island. In detail the land rises at varying rates
away from the sea. In some places, as in the southern part of Victoria
Island, the plains fail to rise above 200 ft for many tens of miles whereas
in the northeast corner of Victoria Island they slope steeply up from the
water.

The Queen Elizabeth Islands have the shape of a right-angled triangle
with a 650-mi base along Parry Channel. East of the 90° meridian including
Ellesmere and Devon islands, access is from Baffin Bay. Within the remainder of the area are five islands each with an area greater than 2,000
sq mi and many scores of smaller islands.

The three largest southern islands, Melville, Bathurst, and Cornwallis,
have a variety of topography as they cut across the three main geologic
regions of the archipelago. Melville Island, the largest of the three, is
also the highest with points in excess of 3,000 ft. In the southwest is
a plateau rising to over 2,000 ft and deeply cut by fiords and steep-sided
valleys. Cliffed coasts with surfaces as high as 1,000 ft are comparable
to the upland coasts of the central Arctic. A belt of folded rocks that
has developed parallel hill ridges and valleys runs from northwest to
southeast across the center of the island. The northwest coast of Melville
Island consists of fiords, but elsewhere the coasts are much lower with
deltaic river mouths and long smooth coastlines. The Bathurst group of
islands, with Melville Island, are similar, each with a southern plateau
and hill ridges traversing the remainder of the island. Cornwallis Island,
the smallest of the three, is topographically more uniform. The southeast
corner is a plateau that dips rather gently towards the north into low
rolling country in which perhaps the most conspicuous element, as on all
the other islands, is the absence of close vegetation associations.
Grinnell Peninsula is somewhat higher but in other ways is topographically
comparable to the group.

The central islands, including Prince Patrick, Mackenzie King, Borden,
and the two Ringnes islands, are low-lying with only occasional points
above 1,000 ft. Close to the coast and particularly in Prince Patrick
Island, gravel surface deposits are widespread; elsewhere the soil is
generally derived from the underlying rocks and often contains much fine-
grained material which is particularly susceptible to solifluction.
Indeed, the solifluction in this area is probably more striking than in
any other part of the Canadian North. Only occasionally, and notably
on Ellef Ringnes, is there higher ground which reaches the sea in cliffs.
Appearing at several points on the islands are the low hill domes developed
around gypsum intrusions.

Axel Heiberg Island differs strikingly from the other islands. It is
essentially a mountain mass broken into two parts through the center. Both
the northern and southern uplands are covered with ice caps. The western
side of the island contains deep valleys and fiords toward which valley
glaciers flow from the main ice caps. Between the fiords are peninsulas
with local ice caps and often extremely rugged scenery. In contrast the
eastern and northeastern sides of the island are generally lower, consisting
of low hills through which outlet rivers from the main ice cap flow toward
Nansen and Eureka sounds. This coast is generally lower.

Ellesmere, Devon, and Axel Heiberg islands form the most northerly
and the highest part of the mountain rim of the eastern Canadian Arctic.
Ice caps are widely distributed, and movement by land and sea is restricted
by ice and the terrain. The highland block is deeply penetrated by fiords

and wide channels that split it into separate islands and topographical units. The main height of land is near the east coasts and consequently the major fiords open westwards into the Sverdrup Basin.

Complex mountain ranges developed principally on the folded sedimentary rocks occupy a large part of central and northern Ellesmere and Axel Heiberg islands. The higher peaks have an average elevation of 6,600 ft and, in the United States Range, exceed 9,500 ft. Although many of the fiords have high cliffed sides, narrow coastal lowlands occur at many points. The mountains are generally ice-covered and outlet glaciers reach the sea at the head of several fiords. A lower, essentially glacier-free region of plateaus and hills, roughly 30 mi wide, crosses the mountainous region from Robeson Channel to Fosheim Peninsula.

Between Buchanan Bay in eastern Ellesmere Island and Cape Sherard at the entrance to Lancaster Sound, the most northerly sector of the Canadian Shield forms the Canadian coast. Rugged alpine mountains with peaks reaching 6,600 ft are nearly covered by ice caps, and the only ice-free areas are close to the sea and occasional nunataks.

Central Devon Island and the south coast of Ellesmere Island west of Starnes Fiord are backed by plateaus of horizontal sedimentary rocks having upper surfaces at 1,500 to 2,000 ft. There are many small fiords often with cliffed sides. Elsewhere narrow coastal plains are typically covered with elevated shingle strandlines.

Prince Regent Inlet and its extension as the Gulf of Boothia is the most easterly of the large sounds that penetrate south from Parry Channel and, in so doing, separate the islands of the southern half of the Canadian Archipelago. On the western side, a structural arch forms Boothia Peninsula and Somerset Island. South of Bellot Strait the coast is mainly developed on shield rocks that produce low hills with a maximum elevation of about 1,000 ft. Between Thom and Pelly bays the shield is strongly fractured resulting in long, steep-sided inlets and rectangular islands. At two points, Simpson Peninsula and northwest Boothia Peninsula, Palaeozoic limestone forms coastal plains characterized by elevated shingle strandlines inland. In the southeast of the island, the coast rises slowly inland to low hills; but north of Cresswell Bay the cliffs over 1,000 ft high are practically continuous.

The east side of the Gulf of Boothia is in several respects a mirror image of the west coast. In the southern half, the west side of Melville Peninsula is a shield coast where hills reach the sea, except for a narrow limestone plain in Committee Bay which includes Wales Island. North of Fury and Hecla Strait, hilly terrain is replaced by limestone plains from Agu Bay to north of Bernier Bay. Farther north both sides of Bordeur Peninsula have naked rock hills and plateaus with cliffs and steep shingle slopes forming the coasts.

Borden Peninsula has greater topographic variety than the peninsula and islands to the west, but it is basically the same. It consists of complex barren plateau and hill ranges. Over long distances the coasts are cliffed or have narrow coastal plains; only at the heads of Eclipse Sound and Admiralty Inlet do the coasts become lower and provide access to the interior.

The eastern coasts of Bylot and Baffin islands are an area of scenic magnificence with high ice-covered mountains rising abruptly from long

fiords that penetrate far into the interior. The fiords attain their
greatest development in the north between Pond Inlet and Cape Henry Kater
where many are more than 60 mi long. The coast is flanked by a continental
shelf 16 to 24 mi wide. A limited number of soundings are available from
the fiords. In Inugsuin Fiord there is a sill at the entrance at a depth
of 325 to 340 ft whereas the maximum inner depth is 2,050 ft and at the head
of the fiord the water is still 330 ft deep. Eglinton and Sam Ford fiords
also appear to possess sills at 330 ft and 475 ft respectively.

Fiords and mountains face the open sea north of Cape Hunter and the
coastal scenery is composed of sheer cliffs, mountain peaks, fiords, and
deep glaciated transection valleys. Coastal cliffs in the Buchan Gulf
tower 5,000 ft above the sea. The highest mountains occur in the middle
sectors of the fiords, and elevations of over 5,000 ft are common. Farther
west the mountains become more massive, the amount of glacial erosion
decreases, and the fiord heads lead steeply onto the rolling interior
plateau at 1,500 to 2,500 ft. Between Royal Society Fiord and Coutts
Inlet the alpine peaks of the middle fiord area are replaced by steep-
sided flat-topped mountains that are usually sites for ice caps when the
mountains exceed 3,000 ft. Numerous glaciers descend to sea level from
these sources, especially in the middle fiord areas.

South of Cape Henry Kater the coast recedes to form Home Bay. Although
the mountains are massive and summit elevations range from 2,500 to 3,600
ft, the topography is more subdued than farther north and there are few
glaciers. From the southeast side of Home Bay to Cape Mercy at the
entrance to Cumberland Sound, the coastal scenery is again spectacular
with fiord walls rising sheer to 4,000 ft in places and mountains with
summits exceeding 5,000 ft. Many peaks are alpine in character although
flat-topped mountains characterize the land around Okoa Bay north of the
Penny Ice Cap. Fiords are numerous and penetrate up to 35 mi inland.
Most of the high tops are covered by ice caps from which glaciers descend
to and near sea level. North of Cape Dyer the coast trends southeast-
northwest, but this changes to S 30°W at the Cape.

The southeast side of Baffin Island extends for 290 mi between Cape
Dyer and Resolution Island. The coast is penetrated by two major inlets,
Cumberland Sound and Frobisher Bay, while farther south an even larger
break in the continental margin forms Hudson Strait. The north shore of
Cumberland Sound is deeply indented with fiords, with mountains close to
the sea that exceed 5,000 ft. The head of the sound is lower than the
sides, and valleys through hilly terrain provide routes to Nettiliing
Lake and the Foxe Basin lowlands. The summits rise again on the south
side toward Hall Peninsula, which has numerous fiords, large rocky islands,
and uplands close to the sea that are ice-covered. A similar coastal
pattern occurs around Frobisher Bay. The north shore is broken by many
fiords; at the head a lowland leads northwest towards Amadjuak Lake
while the south side is an almost unbroken line of cliffs.

The east coast of Canada from Bylot Island to the Atlantic provinces
is essentially a highland region that blocks penetration into the interior
of the continent. At two points the continental margin is breached by
submerged depressions. In the north between Baffin Island and Labrador,
Hudson Strait leads westward to drowned basins in the center of the
Canadian Shield which form Hudson Bay and Foxe Basin. The second gap
between the southern edge of the Canadian Shield and the Appalachians
constitutes the Gulf of St. Lawrence. Between Hudson Strait and the Strait
of Belle Isle the continent faces the northwestern sector of the Atlantic

Ocean known as the Labrador Sea. All the interior seas and the coastal
belt of the Labrador Sea have arctic or subarctic environments and heavy
sea ice late in winter and spring.

Foxe Basin is a circular depression of great geologic age in the
Canadian Shield. Almost all the islands in the basin are developed on
limestone and in few places do they rise more than 100 ft above sea level.
Occasionally bedrock is exposed on the islands but generally a mantle of
frost-shattered limestone boulders forms the surface. The low relief and
the effects of the postglacial marine transgression restrict drainage,
and marshes and ponds are widespread. Old sea-beach ridges are found almost
everywhere on the islands recording the continuing slow emergence of the
land. Extremely shallow water occurs around many of the islands and those
parts of the mainland which are formed of similar rocks. Offshore bars,
spits, mud flats, and lagoons are a dominant element on the shores. The
largest island, Prince Charles Island discovered in 1948, is in the northeastern part of the basin. Rowley, Bray, Kock, Jens Munk, and Spicer
islands, together with Baird Peninsula, have similar topography. Air
Force Island resembles the others with the exception of a Precambrian
rock outcrop at the northern end.

The east coast of Melville Peninsula from the vicinity of Hecla and
Fury Strait to beyond Parry Bay is also a low-lying area of limestone,
with very little variation in relief and a typically flat, monotonous
topography. The limestones are replaced by Precambrian crystalline rocks
25 to 30 mi west of Hall Beach. On the granites and gneisses of this
group, rugged hills and uplands with a high proportion of exposed bedrock
contrast sharply with the lowlands.

The largest plain around Foxe Basin is the vast flat or gently sloping
area in western Baffin Island known as the Great Plain of the Koukdjuak.
A striking characteristic of the plain is the profusion of small, nearly
circular coalescing lakes, ponds, and marshy depressions that have resulted
from the melting of ground ice combined with the effect of wind-directed
wave action on the pond margins. On the southwest side the plain passes
imperceptibly from limestone onto granites. After many miles the bedrock
ridges break the terrain and the remainder of Foxe Peninsula is mainly
an area of crystalline granites and gneisses forming diverse hilly
topography with elevations over 1,000 ft above sea level.

Southampton Island combines the two basic relief types of Foxe Basin
(and Hudson Bay). While the north and northeast coast consists of
highlands of Precambrian rocks with steep cliffs rising abruptly from
Foxe Channel, the south and southwestern part of the island is made up of
gently sloping limestone plains and plateaus.

Hudson Bay is a larger version of Foxe Basin. A central depression
in the Shield now forms the bay. The result is a wide variety of landforms which include: areas of rugged topography with outcrops forming
hilly sectors of widely varying relative relief; subdued areas of flat
aspect often at low level and sometimes covered by shattered rock debris
or glacial material; lowlands that have developed on Palaeozoic limestones;
and more restricted areas formed on metamorphic rocks that occur in folded
belts or belts of steeply dipping strata and are mainly restricted to the
east side of Hudson Bay where they produce prominent escarpments and ranges
of hills.

The west coast of Hudson Bay between Roes Welcome Sound and Churchill

is shield country. In the north a narrow rocky coastal plain gives way
to an interior plateau and a hilly area with elevations over 1,000 ft near
Wager Bay. South of Chesterfield Inlet there is a striking change in
physiography. The Hudson Bay lowlands are an enormous area of low relief
and poorly developed drainage. A great part of the area is composed of
wet muskeg and swamp with islands of unconsolidated glacial material.
This region which is over 180 mi wide has a very shallow gradient toward
Hudson Bay. Extensive raised marine beaches and deposits are found great
distances inland. The Hudson Bay lowlands continue to the head of James
Bay; but on the east side of the bay, Precambrian granite-gneiss rocks
again appear. Inland from the complex island-studded east shore of James
Bay the land rises over 500 ft within about 40 mi; the area is a complex
of lakes, rivers, and poorly drained muskeg.

On the east side of Hudson Bay, north of Cape Jones, the Precambrian
Shield rocks are fringed along the coast by a series of island escarpments
which extend as far as Cap Dufferin near Port Harrison. These escarpments
also occur on the mainland where they exceed 1,500 ft above sea level in
places. They have steep east-facing slopes or cliffs and gentle western
slopes toward Hudson Bay. The interior of the central part of the east
coast is a rocky upland with numerous lakes and a complex drainage pattern.
Elevations 40 mi inland from Richmond Gulf exceed 1,500 ft. Northward,
heights decrease as far as the latitude of Cape Smith, where a bold range
of hills trends southwest-northeast with heights over 1,000 ft. The
northwestern part of the Ungava Peninsula is marked by the impressive
cliffs of Cape Wolstenholme while inland a relatively even plateau reaches
an average height of 1,400 ft.

Seventy miles offshore on the 60th parallel are the Ottawa Islands.
They are the northernmost of a complex chain of islands extending southward almost as far as James Bay. The largest group is the Belcher Islands.

Hudson Strait is essentially a parallel-sided basin about 65 mi wide
and nearly 400 mi long. The south side is broken by the deep embayment
of Ungava Bay. With the exception of the limestone plateau that forms
Akpatok Island in Ungava Bay, all the coasts are developed on shield rocks.
The north shore is everywhere rocky, cliffed, and often very rugged. The
coast rises slowly from the southeast corner of Baffin Island to about 1,000
ft in the center of the strait around Big Island. Farther west there is an
overall decrease in altitude and the coast becomes shallow and is deeply
indented with many islands. The land is higher on the south side of Foxe
Peninsula. The Quebec shore of Hudson Strait is high and cliffed between
Cape Wolstenholme and Wakenham Bay; but farther east it decreases in height,
and low hills and rock plains form the west side of Ungava Bay. The east
coast of the bay is low, but rises close to Cape Chidley to become hilly.

Northern Labrador between Nain and Cape Chidley is mountainous; in
the Kiglipait, Kaumajet, and Torngat ranges peaks in excess of 3,300 ft
not uncommonly rise directly from the sea, and the highest points are
over 5,000 ft. The coast is deeply indented by fiords and a few small
glaciers manage to survive.

South of Nain the coast gradually becomes lower; and hills, bare rock
ridges, and intervening rocky lowlands characterize the coast as far as
the Strait of Belle Isle. The coastline is low, irregular, and fretted
with numerous islands and bays. Everywhere it is barren even though trees
are found a few miles inland. Sandwich Bay is a major indentation, and
Hamilton Inlet is even larger. In the south the land rises to 1,500 ft

within 8 mi of the coast although along the faulted coastline of the
strait the coast is quite bold. Several apparently drowned river valleys
are notable features in the south. Lake Melville is contained in a steep-
sided inlet with elevations approaching 2,000 ft on the south side in the
Mealy Mountains.

Physiographically, Newfoundland is several plateaus that decrease
in elevation in a northeasterly direction. The highest surfaces are in
the west and southwest, where boulder-covered uplands reach 1,500 to 2,000
ft; while on the northeast side rocky plains and low hills disappear under
the Atlantic.

Two topographic sectors may be recognized on the Atlantic coast
between Strait of Belle Isle and St. John's. In the north is the straight
fault-guided coast of the east side of the northern peninsula. Inland
the ground rises rapidly to the barren summits of the Long Range Mountains.
Rivers have eroded deeply into the mountains, and the drowned lower sections
of the valleys break the straight coast with many small inlets. At the
north end of the peninsula elevations are less and embayments are larger
than farther south.

The remainder of the northeastern coast comprises rocky headlands and
peninsulas formed where hill ranges reach the sea; they are separated
by submerged lowlands that include Notre Dame, Bonavista, Trinity, and
Conception bays.

The coasts of the Gulf of St. Lawrence exhibit strong contrasts as a
result of the presence of three very different structural regions in the
area. The Quebec shore is formed by the southern edge of the Canadian
Shield; this is usually a scarp face 1,000 to 1,500 ft high that drops
gradually toward the Strait of Belle Isle. The precipitous scarp is
separated from the sea at many points by a narrow rocky coastal plain
a few miles wide. Rivers pouring out from the interior deposited large
sand deltas when the sea was higher than today, and these deposits often
mantle the coastal lowland.

The south and east coasts of the gulf have developed on rocks of the
Appalachian-Acadian Province. Some rocks, notably granites, have proved
highly resistant to erosion and form upland coasts, while others, particularly sandstones and shales, are weak and form the lowland coasts that
ring much of the southern part of the gulf. In the first category are
the high, often cliffed, coasts of Gaspe Peninsula, Cape Breton Island,
and much of the west coast of Newfoundland. Lowland coasts are present
on the eastern shores of New Brunswick, Prince Edward Island, and northwestern Nova Scotia; they are generally sandy with highly developed
spits and beach bars which virtually close the long estuaries that
characterize the coasts. In a few areas the lowlands end abruptly in
sandstone cliffs that are 10 to 100 ft high.

The Magdalen Islands, which are part of the lowland group, consist of
isolated sandstone and glacial till islands joined by sand bars. Anticosti
Island in the north of the gulf differs from other parts. The island
is developed on Palaeozonic limestone and has low cliffs and rocky
ledges along the coasts.

Bibliography

Berg, L. S., 1950. *Natural Regions of the U.S.S.R.* New York. 436 pp.

Bird, J. B., 1967. *The Physiography of Arctic Canada.* Baltimore: Johns Hopkins Press. 336 pp.

Burk, C. A., 1965. *Geology of the Alaska Peninsula - Island Arc and Continental Margin.* Geological Society of America, Memoir 99. 250 pp.

Douglas, R. J. W., ed., 1970. *Geology and Economic Minerals of Canada.* Ottawa: The Queen's Printer. 838 pp.

Dunbar, M. and K. R. Greenaway, 1956. *Arctic Canada from the Air.* Ottawa: The Queen's Printer. 541 pp.

Frost, R. E., 1950. *Evaluation of Soils and Permafrost Conditions in the Territory of Alaska by Means of Aerial Photographs.* Vol. 1. Lafayette: Purdue University, Engineering Experiment Station. 50 pp. plus figs.

Gvozdetskii, N. A. and N. J. Mikhailov, 1970. *Physical Geography of the U.S.S.R. (Asiatic Part).* Moscow. 450 pp. Translated by U. S. Army.

Military Geology Branch, 1966-7. *Atlas of Asia and Eastern Europe to Supplement Detection of Underground Nuclear Testing.* 5 Vols., multiple authors. Washington, D. C.: Geological Survey.

Mil'kov, F. N., 1964. *Natural Regions of the U.S.S.R.* Moscow: Izk'vo. Sotsialno-economicheskay Literatury. 188 pp. Translated by U. S. Army.

Needleman, S. M., ed., 1969. *Earth Science Applied to Military Use of Natural Terrain.* Bedford, Mass.: Air Force Cambridge Research Laboratories Report AFCRL-69-0364. 206 pp.

Needleman, S. M., D. W. Klick, and E. E. Molineaux, 1961. *Evaluation of an Arctic Ice-free Land Site and Results of C-130 Aircraft Test Landings: Polaris Promontary, North Greenland 1958-1959.* Bedford, Mass.: Air Force Cambridge Research Laboratories. Report AFCRL 252. 70 pp.

Pressman, A. E., R. L. Stitt, J. H. Montanari, and R. R. Blesch, 1961. *Terrain Analysis of Ice-free Land Sites in Arctic Canada.* Philadelphia: Aero Service Corp. Final Report 0047-30 under contract AF19(604)-6182. 456 pp.

Raasch, G. O., 1962. *Geology of the Arctic.* 2 vols. Toronto: University of Toronto Press. 1411 pp.

Rachlin, J. and D. Alvesron, 1971. *Suitability for Cross-country Movement of Air Cushion Vehicles in Arctic U.S.S.R.* Washington, D. C.: Military Geology Branch, Geological Survey. 21 pp.

Sater, J. E., 1969. *The Arctic Basin.* Washington, D. C.: Arctic Institute of No. Amer. 319 pp.

Scott, R. F., 1969. *The Freezing Process and Mechanics of Frozen Ground.* Hanover, N. H.: U. S. Army Cold Regions Research and Engineering Laboratory. Cold Regions Science and Engineering Monograph II-D1. 65 pp. AD-697 136.

Sømme, A., ed., 1960. *A Geography of Norden*.   Oslo.   362 pp.

Stearns, S. R., 1965. *Selected Aspects of Geology and Physiography of the Cold Regions*. Hanover: Cold Regions Research and Engineering Laboratory. CRSE Report I-A1. 39 pp.

_____, 1966. *Permafrost (Perennially Frozen Ground)*. Hanover, N. H.: U.S. Army Cold Regions Research and Engineering Laboratory. Cold Regions Science and Engineering Monograph I-A2. 77 pp. AD-642 730.

Suslov, S. P., 1961. *Physical Geography of Asiatic Russia*. San Francisco: W. H. Freeman and Co. 594 pp.

Thiel, E., 1957. *The Soviet Far East*. New York.

Tushinskii, G. K., ed., 1966. *A Physical Geography of the U.S.S.R.* Moscow: Education Publishing House. 679 pp. Translated by U.S. Army.

Williams, H., ed., 1958. *Landscapes of Alaska*. Berkeley. 148 pp.

Introduction

The arctic population is but a small fraction of the total population of the circumpolar countries. The tendency is, therefore, to consider the significance of arctic resources mainly in terms of their meaning for peoples who live outside the arctic, most of them far removed from that area. For this reason, a crucial question in the evaluation of the importance of arctic resources to the countries concerned, including the United States, is the feasibility of economic transportation of the resource to non-arctic markets. This, in turn, tends to focus attention on the arctic areas in which resources can be successfully exploited only by overcoming the special transportation problems associated with arctic conditions, such as ice, cold, permafrost, and other well-known conditions. A resource that cannot economically be moved to population centers to the south is of little practical importance to the circumpolar countries. In view of the above factors this survey of arctic resources is mainly confined to the resources of the arctic regions that can be tapped only from ports, rail or road heads, landing fields, or collection points which are in the Arctic and must operate under arctic conditions. The subarctic, therefore, receives minor attention.

In a practical sense, arctic resources are important to the United States and other countries to the extent that they may help to satisfy an existing or potential demand. Aside from the potential demand for rare minerals or other critical substances that might be found in the Arctic, it appears that major interest is focused upon energy fuels. This situation results mainly from the anticipated heavy future demands of industrial society. The interest in the Arctic is whetted in turn by indications that the arctic region is, in fact, rich in precisely those resources. The resource survey, therefore, emphasizes energy fuels of the region, which means mainly its oil and gas resources.

U.S. Arctic Resources

The U.S. arctic resources of interest to this survey are contained in the state of Alaska and its continental shelf and are confined mainly to the areas in and north of the Brooks Range (see Fig. 51). The Kobuk River basin and parts of the Yukon River basin north of the Kuskokwim Mountains are of lesser concern. Within the regions mentioned, movements of resources must be through ice-covered waters or through permafrost areas to a meaningful extent, and naval protection of the sources, storage, and transportation of the resources would also involve operations in ice-covered waters.

Energy Resources

Hydroelectric Power

The hydroelectric power generation capacity for all of Alaska was only 84 thousand kilowatts in 1967.[1] However, for the whole of Alaska, the estimated water power potential is 32,511 thousand kilowatts, the greatest of any state.[1] Most of the potential is in the Kuskokwim and Yukon river basins. The water power potential of the northern region of the state, by comparison, is quite small. The readily available coal, gas, and oil energy sources make fossil fuel power plants competitive with hydroelectric plants. The small population and limited industries in Alaska will also limit the development of hydroelectric power in the future, particularly in the northwest region.

Coal

Coal is widely distributed throughout many parts of Alaska (See Fig. 52). The deposits range from extensive coal fields to isolated small occurrences. The principal coal fields are in five major regions: the northern Alaska region along the North Slope of the Brooks Range; the central Alaska region, including Nenana coal field on the north flank of the Alaska Range; scattered occurrences on the Seward Peninsula and in the Yukon and Kobuk River basins; the Cook Inlet-Susitna region; the Alaska Peninsula region; and the southeastern Alaska region. The last three are not, properly, in the arctic regions of the state. Total production in Alaska to the end of 1963 was about 14.6 million tons, composed mainly sub-bituminous coal from the Nenana field in central Alaska for the Fairbanks area and 5.6 million tons of bituminous production in the Matanuska field in the Anchorage area. Very little coal has been produced elsewhere in Alaska. The total Alaska production, however, which was between 800 and 900 thousand tons annually after 1953, increased to a total of 4.36 million tons in 1969.[2]

Coal-bearing rocks are known or inferred to underlie most of the part of Alaska which extends northward from the northern foothills of the Brooks Range to the arctic coast and eastward from Cape Lisburne at least as far as the Itkillik and lower Colville rivers. The area of known and potential coal-bearing land is about 58,000 sq mi. Estimated coal resources

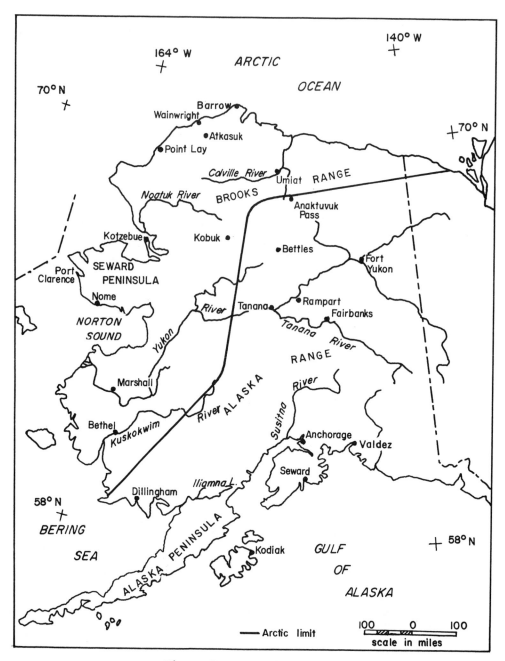

Figure 51. ARCTIC ALASKA

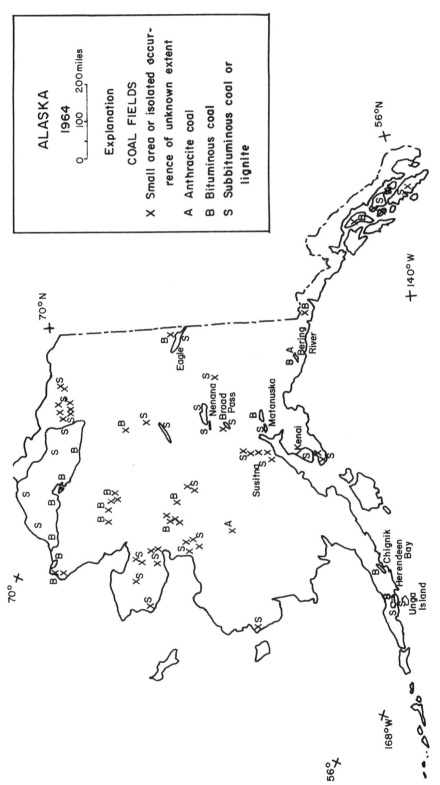

Figure 52.   COAL FIELDS OF ALASKA

for the region are estimated as high as 120,197 million tons, of which 19,292 million tons are bituminous and 100,905 million tons sub-bituminous.[3] The U.S. Bureau of Mines has reported that northwestern Alaska has "immense coal resources, as yet only sketchily outlined" in the area between Point Hope and Point Barrow north of Bering Strait on the Chukchi Sea.[4] The coals are believed to be capable of producing metallurgical quality coke by blending with as little as fifteen percent of strongly coking coals.[4] The estimated coal reserves of the remainder of Alaska, mainly sub-bituminous coal and lignite, were estimated by the U.S. Geological Survey in 1964 at 10,000 million tons[5] but in 1969 the Bureau of Mines mentioned 15-20 million tons in the Bering River (Gulf of Alaska) area alone.[4]

The total U.S. coal resources as shown in Figure 53 are estimated at 3,210 billion tons, of which half may be recoverable.[1] Total U.S. coal production in 1968 was 556 million tons, about the same as in 1950.[1] A recent estimate of the Department of the Interior of 220 billion tons of U.S. mineable coal at or below present cost levels works out to cover 400 years' supply at present rates of production, and is more than 100 times present annual production of energy from all sources.[1] The coal resources of Alaska rank fourth - behind North Dakota, Montana, and Illinois.[6]

About half of the U.S. coal production is used to generate about half the U.S. electricity supply. It has been estimated that by the year 2000 coal will furnish only about 30 percent of the power for generation of electricity.[1] However, that estimate is based partly on a substantial increase in nuclear-powered generators, a somewhat shaky assumption. The future of the coal mining industry in Alaska is dependent on a number of factors, including the growth of industry and population in Alaska and the U.S. and world demand.[7] Involved in this picture, obviously, will be the competitive position of Alaska coal in terms of relative cost. Coal shipments from Alaska to the lower 48 may well be unlikely. Foreign markets in countries such as Japan may have greater promise. The fact that some U.S. companies, such as Morgan Coal Company of West Virginia and Kaiser Steel Corporation, have been planning exploration as recently as 1970 would seem to indicate that potential values are thought to exist.[7] In a recent interview, a group of Japanese stated that they are in need of one million tons per year of low volatile or medium volatile coking coal.[8] There may, therefore, be a market for Alaskan coal.

Oil and Gas

It has become dramatically apparent during the last three years that potentially the most economically important arctic resource of the U.S. is the stored energy which exists in the onshore and offshore north Alaskan oil fields. The major petroleum areas of Alaska are shown in Figure 54.[9] Of the several areas shown, only the areas north of the Yukon should perhaps be considered arctic. However, it is mainly in those arctic areas that the greatest reserves are believed to exist, and the most spectacular finds to date have been in the North Slope area where dramatic discoveries were made at Prudhoe Bay on the Atlantic-Richfield-Humble Oil Co. lease in 1967.

Oil production in the state of Alaska has been significant only since 1957, but has increased notably in recent years. Production has been concentrated in the Cook Inlet area in southern Alaska. Crude petroleum output has increased in value during a three-year period as follows:[10]

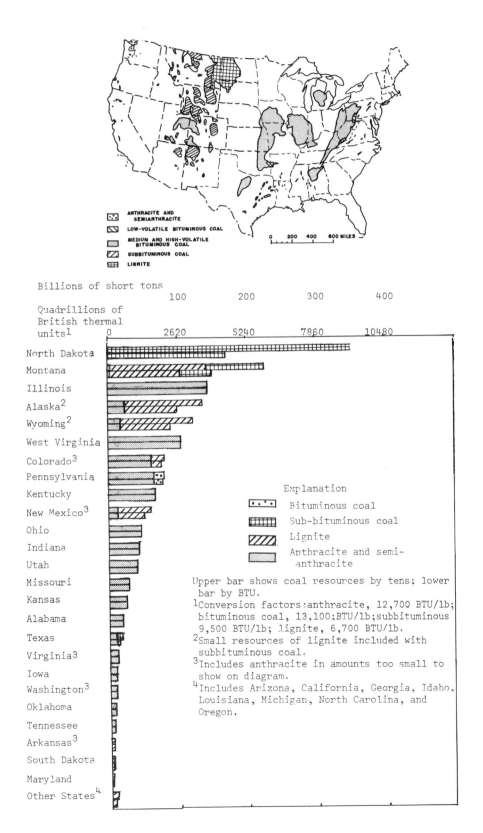

Figure 53. COAL RESOURCES OF THE UNITED STATES

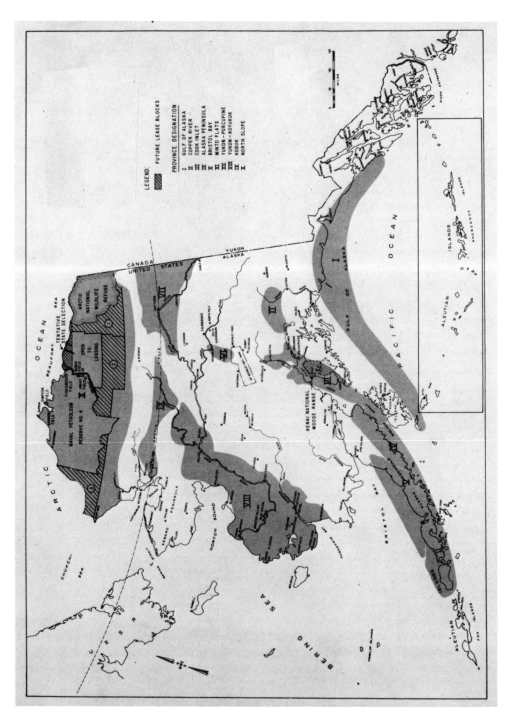

Figure 54.   PETROLEUM PROVINCES OF ALASKA

1967	$ 88,187,000
1968	179,500,000
1969	214,464,000

Natural gas production has also increased, but not at a similar rate. Corresponding values were:[10]

1967	$ 7,269,000
1968	8,400,000
1969	12,665,000

It should be noted that the value of the 1969 oil and gas production was approximately 88 percent of the total value of all Alaskan mineral production for the year. Nevertheless, the total Alaska crude production in 1968 of about 66 million barrels was relatively minor in comparison with the one billion barrels produced in Texas alone.[1] However, the importance of arctic Alaska's oil and gas is not to be expressed in terms of present production but in terms of proved and potential reserves. Aside from some gas production used locally from the Barrow and Gubic fields, the North Slope production now awaits resolution of the transportation problem. Meanwhile, exploration and some drilling has continued since the 1967 discovery at Prudhoe Bay.

As late as 1967 the total Alaskan reserves were estimated at only 381 million barrels.[1] (Total U.S. reserves were then placed at 31.377 million barrels.) Of this about 80 million barrels were attributed to the North Slope, at Umiat and Simpson in the Naval Petroleum Reserve No. 4.[5] The discovery in the Prudhoe Bay area has drastically altered the reserve status. Since the end of 1967 numerous estimates have been made, and high and low estimates have been produced. For example, The American Petroleum Institute and the American Gas Association, in outlining the U.S. oil and gas reserve position as of January 1, 1971, gave the following figures:[11]

U.S. total proved oil reserves -
                        38,001,335,000 barrels
Proved Alaska reserves -
                        10,148,824,000 barrels
Proved U.S. gas reserves -
                        290,746,408 mil cu ft
Proved Alaska reserves -
                        31,130,751 mil cu ft

Thus the proved Alaska reserves, of which 9.7 billion barrels are attributed to arctic Alaska, were, for oil, 26 percent and for gas, 11 percent of the U.S. total. The estimates, which included North Slope reserves for the first time, moved Alaska from eighth to second among the states in oil reserves; and it was considered only a matter of time until Alaska moves ahead of Texas, which was credited with 13.2 billion barrels of proved reserves. The estimated gas, including 26 trillion cu ft of Prudhoe Bay reserves, places Alaska third behind Texas and Louisiana.

A monumental study by the National Petroleum Council on future petroleum reserves in the United States which appeared in 1970[12] appraised the Prudhoe Bay North Slope reserves at 31.3 billion barrels in place, plus 43.5 billion barrels speculative in place, and estimated as recoverable about 30 billion barrels. It should be noted that the above estimates did not include NPR No. 4, the Wildlife Range, nor the Chukchi Sea and Beaufort Sea offshore areas. Estimates for the NPR No. 4 reserves have been made;

and range upward from 4.5 billion barrels, a figure that probably is much too low.[13]   Offshore potential reserves have not been assessed for specific areas. However, the National Petroleum Council has been cited as estimating total U.S. potential offshore reserves out to a depth of 200 meters as possibly 600-780 billion barrels of oil and 1,640 to 2,220 trillion cu ft of natural gas. A roughly equivalent amount is estimated for the 200-meter to 2,500-meter depths.[14] The NPC reported also that the U.S. has already drilled out to depths of 400 meters and predicted that eventually the industry will be capable of drilling and producing in water depths of 4,000 to 6,000 ft (1200 to 1800 meters). The U.S. Geological Survey has recently conducted a reconnaissance marine geologic survey of the Chukchi Sea area of 55,00 sq mi and has reported structural features that suggest the need for further investigation of "what may be the western extension of the Barrow arch."[15] The Beaufort Sea is itself a promising area.

In summary, if one takes the 30 billion barrel estimate of North Slope recoverable reserves, and adds 10-15 billion barrels from NPR 4, plus an equal amount from the Wildlife Range and the offshore areas, the total for northern Alaska reaches totals of 50 to 60 billion barrels. Much higher figures are mentioned, especially for the offshore areas, but those are highly speculative for the present. It should be noted that estimates of proven reserves are lower than the above figures; the API total for Alaskan "proved reserves" being, as noted, just over 10 billion barrels.

The estimates of gas reserves in arctic Alaska are more speculative. The National Petroleum Council in 1970 estimated reserves of 238 trillion cu ft.[12] The American Gas Association "proved reserves" figure for January 1, 1971 was "only" 31 trillion cu ft. Potential reserves are obviously much greater, and estimates up to 438 trillion cu ft have been noted (See Fig. 54). The estimates of 238 to 438 trillion cu ft may be compared with the National Petroleum Council's estimated potential U.S. gas reserves of 1543 trillion cu ft.[17]

Thus if the National Petroleum Council estimates for total U.S. potential oil and gas reserves - 432 billion barrels of oil and 1543 trillion cu ft of gas [17] - are taken as a base, the arctic Alaska contribution to those totals might run as high as 14 percent and more for oil, and the gas percentage might run as high as 20 to 28 percent. It should, of course, be emphasized that these figures are unproven and provide only speculative bases for projection into the petroleum future for the next two or three decades. The president of one U.S. oil company has forecast, for example, that between now and 1990 the U.S. will consume 150 billion barrels of oil. At the present consumption rate of 5.4. billion barrels a year the arctic Alaska reserve would perhaps equal U.S. consumption for 10 years. The anticipated increased consumption rate for oil - doubled or tripled by the year 2000 - would correspondingly reduce the number of years below 10.[18]

As has been noted, the production of oil and gas in northern Alaska awaits the provision of transportation facilities. The projected rate of production and delivery over the next decades, therefore, can only be calculated from plans, not hard facts. The pipeline (48-inch) method has been estimated as capable of transmitting at increasing rates up to 2 million barrels a day by 1980 (730 million barrels a year) and perhaps double that amount by 1990 if another pipeline were added.[19] Carrying the projected production onward to the year 2000, one finds that total delivery estimated in the years 1972 to 1990 would be roughly 14 billion barrels, and with two pipelines thereafter delivering 1.4 billion barrels a year, the total delivery capacity from 1973 to 2000 would be roughly 28 billion barrels. That is approximately the total conservative estimated North Slope reserve and about half the estimated potential reserves mentioned above for all of arctic Alaska.

Other Minerals

Metallic Minerals

Metallic mineral resources, particularly gold and copper, were main-stays of the Alaskan economy from about 1880 until shortly after World War II.[7] The peak year for metal mining was 1916, when $48 million worth of metals was extracted in all of Alaska.[9] In 1963 the value of metals extracted was less than $8 million,[9] and in 1967 the figure had dropped to less than $7 million.[7] Some authorities expect a continuing decline, despite the fact that the metallic mineral resources of Alaska are large and varied. The extent to which Alaska's mineral wealth will be developed will in the long term be dependent on the basic economic factors of prices and costs of production of additional units.[20] North-western Alaska is at a particular economic disadvantage in mining because of a short operating season, remote location causing high shipping costs of materials both in and out, high capital outlays required for facilities used under severe weather conditions, and high labor costs. Thus, mining in northwest Alaska is likely to continue to be restricted to certain scarce and valuable metals that can be marketed economically.

The known metal resources in the Alaska region are large and varied. (Figs. 55 through 59 show the major metal deposits in Alaska.) To date, no significant amounts of metal mineral deposits have been reported north of the Brooks Range. However, there are unknown potentials in the enormous continental shelf areas off northwest Alaska. The crest and the North Slope of the Brooks Range and the Arctic Coastal Plain are believed to be unpromising in this regard.[7] The area to the east and north of Kotzebue Sound has not shipped metallic ore. There has been some placer gold production along the Kobuk River, and occurrences of iron ore, nickel, and lead are known at Ruby Creek.

The largest known arctic Alaskan copper reserve of 100 million tons of 1.2 to 1.6 percent copper ore occurs in the Ruby Creek area. Esti-mated potential production is 60,000 tons of copper concentrate annually.[9] The concentrate might be barged down the Kobuk River to Kotzebue, during the summer months. Kennecott Copper Corporation owns the deposits. The U.S.G.S. has recently reported a copper deposit estimated at more than 200 million tons in the Orange Hill area in the Nabesna Glacier district in eastern Alaska. The copper ore in Alaska, as elsewhere, is mixed with varying amounts of gold, silver, lead, and zinc.

Other metallic minerals in Alaska are iron ore, antimony, tin, tungsten, bismuth, mercury, and platinum. Most of these are not found in arctic Alaska, unless the Yukon River area is included. A small high-grade residual iron ore deposit has been found near Nome, with 0.5 to 1.0 million tons of 10 to 45 percent iron.[5]

The potentially significant metals of the arctic or near-arctic region of Alaska are copper at Ruby Creek; gold, tin, and tungsten in the Seward Peninsula; and mercury in the Kuskokwim River Basin. The copper concentrate

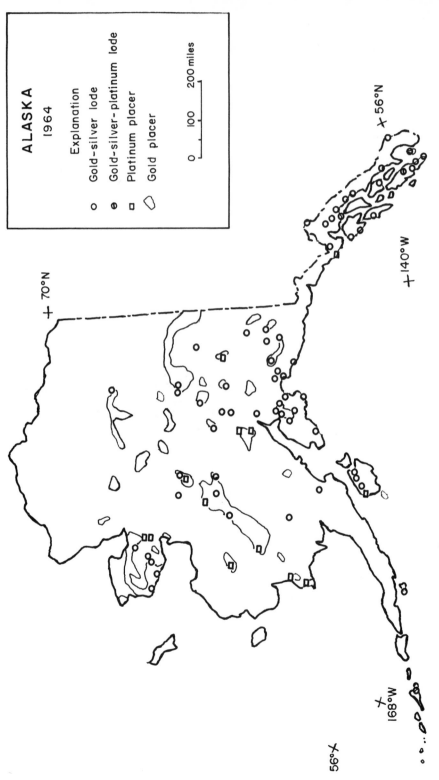

Figure 55. GOLD, SILVER, AND PLATINUM IN ALASKA

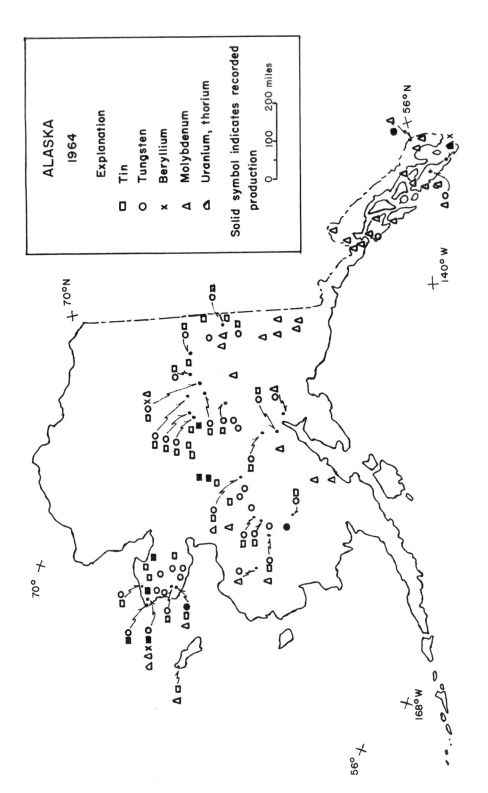

Figure 56. TIN, TUNGSTEN, BERYLLIUM, MOLYBDENUM, URANIUM, AND THORIUM IN ALASKA

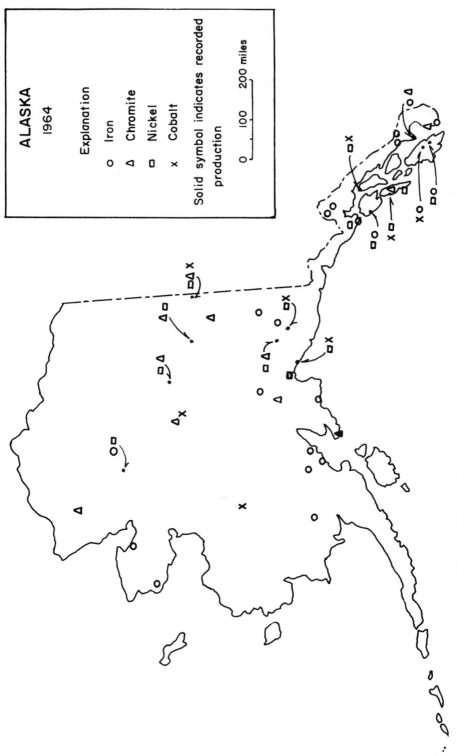

Figure 57. IRON, CHROMITE, NICKEL, AND COBALT IN ALASKA

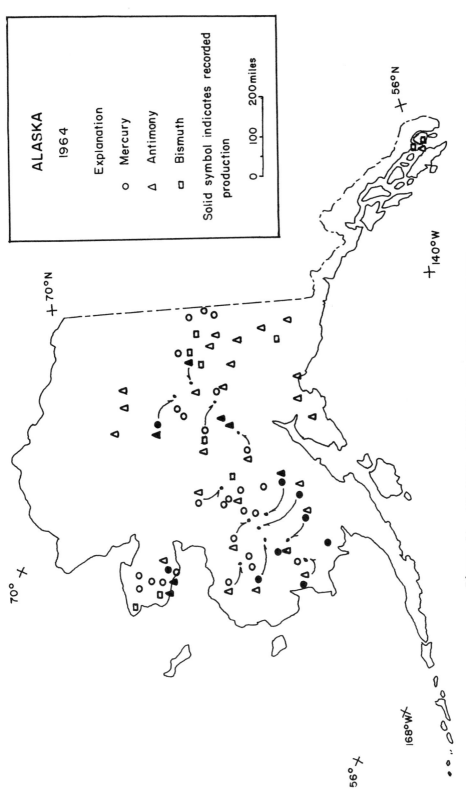

Figure 58. MERCURY, ANTIMONY, AND BISMUTH IN ALASKA

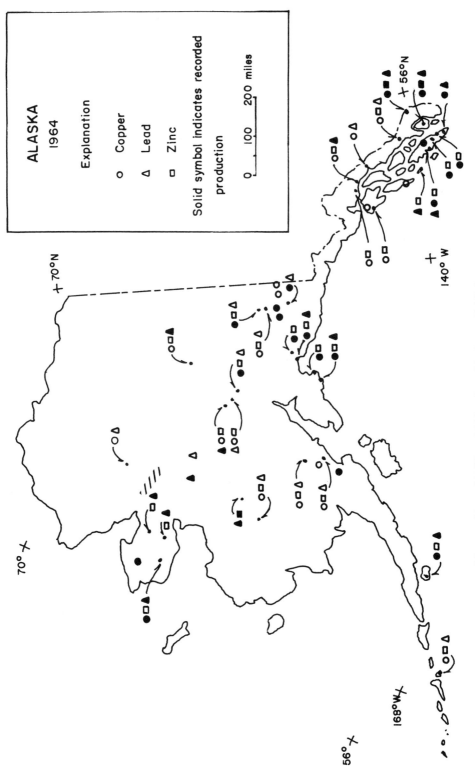

Figure 59. COPPER, LEAD, AND ZINC IN ALASKA

production potential of 60,000 tons annually at Ruby Creek would not be immediately critical to the nation's economy, since over one million tons have been produced annually in recent years by the U.S. with about 500,000 tons from Arizona alone.[21] However, long-range forecasts of the copper demand through the year 2000 are 50 percent above proven resources.[22] Assistant Secretary Hollis M. Dole of the Department of the Interior has forecast a tripling of the U.S. demand for copper by 2000.[23] Thus the copper at Ruby Creek could become economically and strategically important in the next decades.

Production and reserves of tin, tungsten, and mercury in Alaska are not great, although a potential production figure of 5,000 flasks annually of mercury in the Kuskokwim area makes it a significant potential source of that metal.

In the near future the arctic Alaska metal of significance could be mercury, and in the longer range copper may be increasingly important.

Nonmetallic Minerals

The production and known resources of nonmetallic minerals in arctic Alaska are limited, as shown in Figure 60.[5] One of these is asbestos. Deposits at Kobuk have shown limited potential, and in 1960 the U.S.G.S. announced a discovery in the Yukon-Tanana upland near Eagle on the Alaska-Yukon Territory border. No estimate of reserves were given for the find, which was 60 mi west of the newly opened Clinton Creek deposit by Cassiar Asbestos on the Canadian side.[4] Estimated fluorite reserves at Lost River have recently been upped from 2 million to 10 million tons by the U.S.G.S.[21] Annual production in the U.S. amounted to 250,000 tons in 1966. Hence the Alaska reserves might well be significant in this resource which has importance to the aluminum and steel industries. A worldwide shortage is said to exist, and the trend is toward greatly increased consumption of fluorite.[23]

Extensive resources of predominantly low to medium-grade (8% to 25%) phosphate rock occur in the central portion of the arctic slope of Alaska in the Tiglukpuk Creek-Kiruktahiok River area, and substantial amounts of phosphate rock of unknown thickness and grade are indicated in the eastern Brooks Range.

There has been a limited graphite production in the Kigluack Mountains of the Seward Peninsula. Reserves are estimated at 65,000 tons of rock containing 52% of graphite.[5]

Other known nonmetallic minerals in the area include barite, with 41 claims filed upstream from Circle City in 1969; and garnet, as well as mica, found on the Seward Peninsula. In recent years the second-ranking mineral produced in Alaska has been sand and gravel. Production figures for 1969 show that the value of petroleum production alone was higher, with sand and gravel production valued at $18,615,000, down slightly from 1968.[12] If and when the trans-Alaska oil pipeline and the service roads are built in northern Alaska, the sand and gravel supplies will be much needed and in considerable quantities.

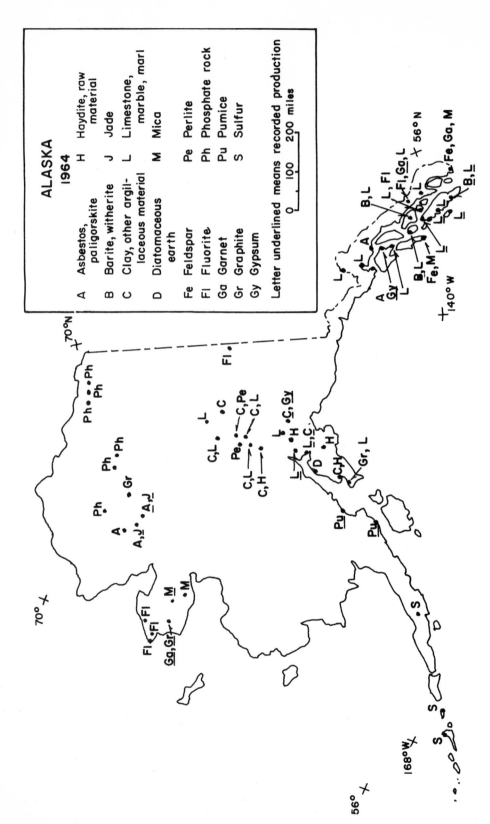

Figure 60.   NONMETALLIC MINERALS IN ALASKA

Other Natural Resources

The areas of Alaska bordering those parts of the ocean that are ice-covered a significant portion of the year include the area north of the Brooks Range, the Seward Peninsula, the lowlands of the Yukon and Kuskokwim rivers, and the Bering Sea islands. Much of the region is treeless tundra with permafrost.

Subsistence hunting and fishing are basic to the economy of this region. Hunting and trapping of fur-bearing animals provide the main winter income for many people. The median family income is very low. There has been no significant commercial production of timber or fish in this northwest region and none is anticipated. The principal resources of arctic Alaska are, as stated, its minerals.

Population

The areas of Alaska bordering the Arctic Ocean, Chukchi Sea, and Bering Sea are very sparsely populated. The land areas of interest in Alaska include that north of the Brooks Range, Kobuk River basin, Seward Peninsula, and the Yukon River basin bordered on the south by the Kuskokwim Mountains, as shown in Figure 51.

It is estimated that in the middle 1960's about 30,000 people, consisting mostly of Eskimos, lived in this far north and far west area. This compares with a 1970 total state population slightly over 300,000. The Northwestern senatorial district had a 1964 population of 14,912.[25] To this must be added the western portion of the Central district, which had a population of 60,990. Most of the population of this district is centered around Fairbanks, so it is estimated that the western part has only about 15,000 people. Less than 10,000 people live above the Seward Peninsula and north of the Brooks Range. About 1,000 men have been on the North Slope for oil drilling.

Table 12 shows the major towns in the Far North.[25] The largest town is Nome on the Seward Peninsula with a population of 2,316. Other major towns include Barrow in the north and Kotzebue on the Chukchi Sea.

TABLE 12

Towns in Far North Alaska

(above 100 in population)

Barrow	2,201	Wainwright	274
Kotzebue	1,656	Kiana	216
Noorvik	384	Kivalina	142
Selawik	348	Shungnak	135
Point Hope	324	Kaktovik	124
Noatak	275	Anaktuvuk Pass	107

It is projected that the total population of Alaska will be nearly 400,000 by 1980.[26] This is expected to result from petroleum development and production on the North Slope, continued growth of forest products

industries, and stabilization and diversification of the fish products
industries. Of a total anticipated civilian workforce of 159,800 in 1980,
the oil and gas industry is expected to employ 4,300 and mining 2,400.[27]
Most of the manufacturing related to North Slope petroleum production should
take place around Anchorage where a growing petrochemical complex and other
factors make the prospect an economic operation. Even so, the area from
Fairbanks north should have a population increase from 68,000 in 1969 to
96,000 in 1980.

Transportation

The Alaskan transportation net is made up of motor roads, railroads,
rivers, sea routes, air modes, and pipelines for oil and gas. Figures 61
and 62 show the Alaskan surface routes and air routes.[28] Figure 63 shows
the coastal traffic.[16] Motor roads and railroads are used in the south-
central region, while shipping and aircraft are used throughout Alaska.
Ships and barges accounted for most of the tonnage to, from, and within
Alaska.[16] About 15 percent is moved by the Alaska Railroad. Truck and
air accounted for only a few percent.

Shipping

Due to severe ice conditions ocean access to the northwest is limited
to summer months. Traffic flow to and from this region amounted to 71,000
tons or 7 percent of total Alaskan traffic in 1964.[16] Movements northbound consisted of general commodities, while southbound movements were
primarily fish. About one-third of the total tonnage was southbound. Commercial cargo moves almost entirely through Dillingham, Bethel, Kotzebue,
and Nome. Only Bethel has the dock facilities or water depth to accommodate
large vessels. The other towns must use lighterage vessels for cargo
transfer.

Seasonal activity from May to October is possible along many of
Alaska's navigable rivers. Recent movements in the northwest region have
occurred on the Innoko, Kobuk, Koyukuk, Kuskokwim, Kvichak, Noatak, Nushagak,
and Yukon rivers. Traffic has been from 30,000 to 50,000 tons in recent
years.[16] Shallow-draft vessels carry general cargo, equipment, supplies,
minerals, and furs.

The activity of oil companies on the North Slope in recent years has
changed the structure of the shipping in the northwest. The ocean route
up around Point Barrow is open for about 6 weeks. Arctic Marine Freighters
delivered 100,000 tons of cargo to the North Slope in the summer of 1969.[29]
In the summer of 1970 the waterborne shipment from Seattle to the North
Slope (3,200 mi) was 185,000 tons of drummed oil and construction materials.[30] Twenty-one tugs and 41 barges were involved in the northbound
tow of 25 days. Included were 117,000 tons of 48-inch trans-Alaska
pipeline, 6,000,000 gallons of bulk fuel, and 45,000 tons of general cargo
for Prudhoe Bay.

Point Barrow is a bottleneck in the North Slope shipping because the
polar ice pack is never far offshore. It has been suggested that a ship
canal be built through the low, level, lake-studded terrain south of Barrow
exiting in Admiralty Bay or, if necessary, going to the Smith Bay, bypassing
Cape Simpson.[31]

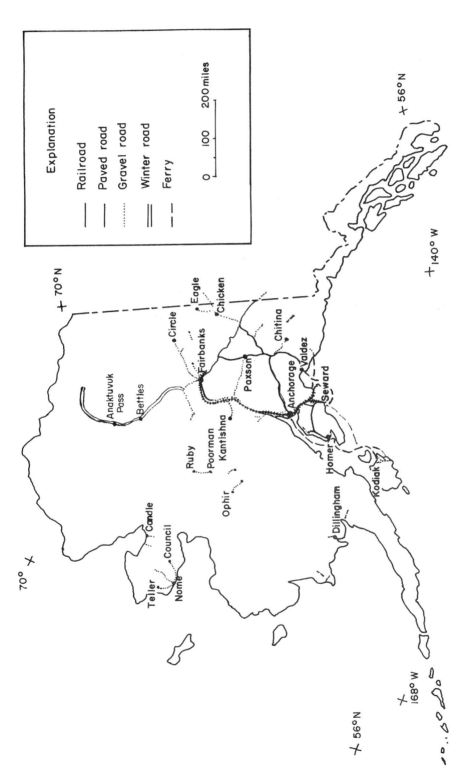

Figure 61. ALASKAN SURFACE ROUTES

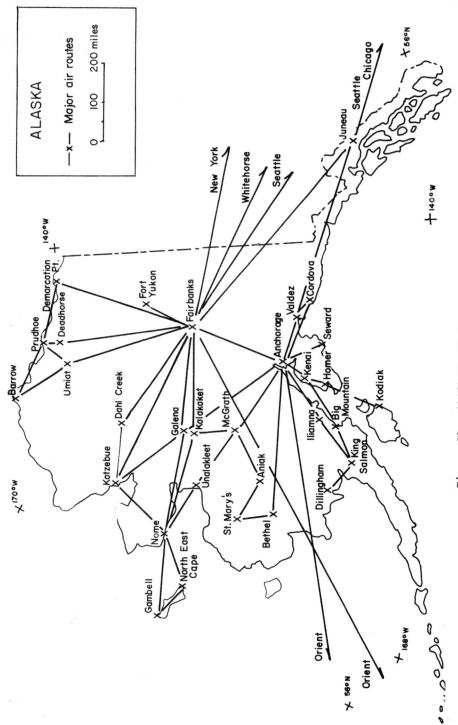

Figure 62. ALASKAN AIR ROUTES

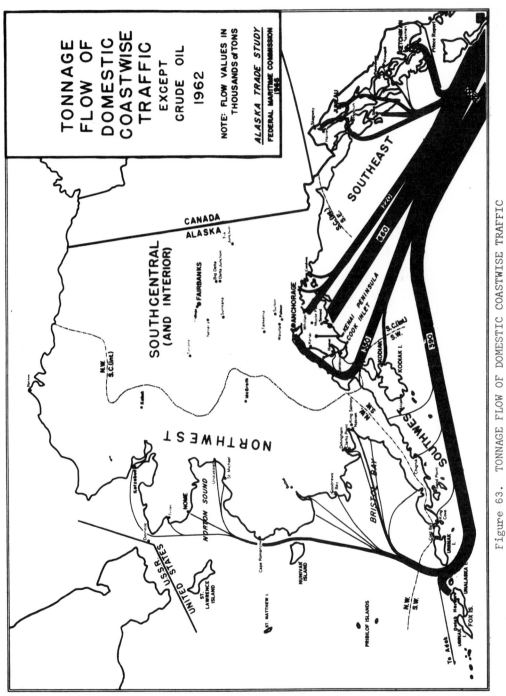

Figure 63. TONNAGE FLOW OF DOMESTIC COASTWISE TRAFFIC

II–6

Barge shipping also flows on Canada's Mackenzie River and along the Beaufort Sea to Prudhoe Bay. In 1969, 206,000 tons were shipped on the Mackenzie River and annual tonnages were increasing.[32] Some of this cargo went to the Canadian drilling sites. At the rate of $80-$125 per ton from Seattle, barge transportation to the North Slope is still the cheapest. Air transport can range up to $170 per ton from points in Alaska. Truck rates over the winter road, when it was in use, were running as high as $240 per ton. In the future, the barge traffic to the North Slope is expected to continue to increase as the petroleum fields are developed.

There is the future possibility of supertankers bringing oil from the North Slope through the Northwest Passage or around Greenland to the east coast market. The Newport News Shipbuilding and Dry Dock Company was awarded a contract in the spring of 1970 by Humble Oil and Refining Company to develop a design for these icebreaker supertankers.[33] The contract contains options for tanker construction and licensing provisions that would permit Newport News Shipbuilding to use the Humble design for other customers.

Each of these giant icebreaker tankers would displace 250,000 dead-weight tons and could haul between 1.5 and 1.75 million barrels of oil. A fleet of 30 to 40 supertankers - each costing $60-$90 million - could carry 2 million barrels of oil per day by 1980.[34] The cost of moving oil by tanker to the east coast has been estimated to be $ .60 per barrel lower than by a transcontinental pipeline.[26] The decision to build the super-tanker fleet has not yet been made, however, by Humble Oil Company.

Since the waters off the North Slope are shallow, the supertankers would have to anchor 6 to 25 mi from the coast. Bringing the oil out from the coast and providing permanent terminals is a key problem. Ice islands and Herschel Island have been suggested.

An alternate method of shipping the oil by 170,000 ton nuclear-powered submarine tankers has been proposed by General Dynamics Corporation.[35] Costs for such a submarine tanker may be as much as $175 million. The company says they could be ready in 3 to 6 years.[36]

Railroads

There are no railroads serving northwest Alaska or the North Slope. The existing Alaska Railroad is 483 mi long from Seward to Fairbanks. An additional 54 mi of branch lines serve the coal mines and military installation. In fiscal year 1963-64, the railroad carried a total of approximately 1,507,000 tons, for an average haul of 138.6 mi.[16]

The NORTH Commission has recommended that the railroad be extended to the Umiat area on the North Slope and Kobuk on the South Slope of the Brooks Range.[37] Whether this extension will be achieved depends partly on the results of the current $3-million transportation corridor survey underway.[37]

Motor Roads

There are few roads in Alaska; most of them are concentrated in the south-central region. Over 75 percent of Alaska's area is more than 100 mi from any road. By the end of 1962, Alaska's primary highway system, built through federal aid, consisted of 1,209 mi of paved and 472 mi of unpaved roads. At that time there were also 1,721 mi of secondary roads, of which 98 percent were unpaved.

In the northwest, gravel roads exist from Nome to the towns of Teller, Taylor, and Council. A gravel road connects Ophir with McGrath and Poorman with Ruby. A winter ice road was opened in the spring of 1969, connecting Livengood above Fairbanks to the North Slope area around Umiat. Three hundred forty-three trucks carried 7,464 tons of equipment and supplies for this 420-mi road to the North Slope in the spring of 1969 before the April 15 thaw forced closing of the road.[29] Another 139 vehicles, mostly scapers and dump trucks, were sent up the road to be used by the oil companies on the North Slope. Truck frieght costs were roughly the same as those incurred by air shipment; and trucks have the advantage of being able to deliver goods to the work site without the extra handling costs from airport to work site.

The future northwest traffic may be substantially increased by the petroleum activity on the North Slope. Sixty miles of an all-season road to the North Slope following the proposed path of the Alyeska pipeline had been completed by the summer of 1970 before work ceased because of the permit delay. The road was completed in 1970. Road networks will expand on the North Slope as the oil fields are developed.

Air Routes

Alaska has more general aviation aircraft per capita than any other state - one aircraft for each 100 residents.[30] Because of the lack of roads over much of the state, passenger and freight transportation by scheduled airlines and chartered and private aircraft are all-important. There are many small gravel airports throughout the state that serve light aircraft and the larger Hercules air freight aircraft. In addition, commercial airlines maintain scheduled passenger flights with many villages using a variety of propeller and propjet aircraft. Scheduled flights with small jet aircraft connect the arctic towns of Nome, Kotzebue, Barrow, Umiat, Prudhoe Bay, and Deadhorse with Anchorage and Fairbanks. Anchorage is also linked to Europe, the Orient, Juneau, Sitka, Seattle, Chicago, and New York. Fairbanks is linked to New York, Seattle, Whitehorse, Juneau, the Orient, and Europe.

Aircraft are playing a significant role in the North Slope activities. They can operate during all seasons - in the winter when the rivers and seas are frozen and in the summer when the tundra becomes swampy. Complete drilling rigs have been moved to the North Slope via aircraft. Aircraft will continue to play a key role in the North for movement of personnel and critical freight. The Boeing Company is even advancing an idea of moving North Slope oil by containerized aircraft.[36]

Pipelines

Pipelines will play an important role in the transportation of oil and gas within and from Alaska. Small pipelines are currently used in the south-central region for transporting petroleum from producing fields. Future emphasis will be on large pipelines to transport oil and gas from the North Slope to U.S. markets on the east coast, midwest, and Pacific coast.

A Trans-Alaska Pipeline System (TAPS) Company was formed by several
oil companies to transport the oil from Prudhoe Bay to the port of Valdez
(800 mi) (see Fig. 64). This 48-inch line is expected to cost approximately $1.3 billion and to have an initial capacity of 500,000 barrels per
day and eventually a maximum capacity of 2 million barrels per day with
12 stations.[32] The proposed pipeline route is over extremely rugged
and difficult terrain and in an area of extreme environmental conditions.
TAPS encountered difficulties in obtaining the necessary releases and
rights-of-way to proceed. As a result of the pipeline's being delayed,
TAPS was dissolved and the Alyeska formed in 1970. The planned pipeline
would serve primarily the U.S. Pacific coast markets using conventional
tankers from Valdez.

The pipeline would be laid through the earthquake belt across 200
mi of marshy tundra and 300 mi of permafrost, forest, and swollen glacial
rivers. Temperatures range from -80°F in winter to +90°F in summer. Before
reaching Valdez, the proposed line will climb the Alaska Range where even
the lowest passes are raked by 100-mile-an-hour winds. The next barrier
is the Chugach Mountains where winter snows often measure 10 ft. The pipe
must be laid in such a manner as not to melt the permafrost which could

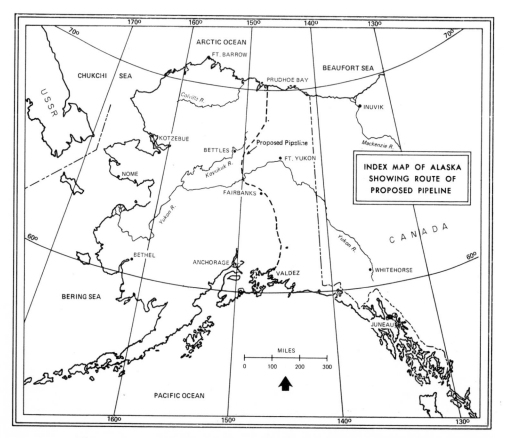

Figure 64. PROPOSED ROUTE OF THE TRANS-ALASKA PIPELINE

cause breaks in the pipeline. The oil must be heated to flow under the cold
environmental conditions. There also has been concern about the probable
interference with caribou migration pattern. There are native claims on the
land which Congress is presently trying to settle. The extended delay in
the granting of a permit suggests that it cannot be in service before 1973
or 1974.

The Mackenzie Valley Pipeline Research Company, Ltd., composed of four
oil and two pipeline companies, was formed to explore the merits of laying
a 48-inch crude line from the North Slope to Edmonton, Alberta. The proposed line would generally follow the Mackenzie River from the arctic coast
south. At Edmonton, the line would connect with existing facilities of
Trans-Mountain and Interprovincial Pipeline Companies serving the mid-west
area. The proposed route would cross several hundred miles of permafrost
(see Fig. 65).[38] A proposed gas line would be laid simultaneously with
the Mackenzie Valley Pipe Line or parallel to it.[39]

Figure 65. PROPOSED MACKENZIE VALLEY CRUDE LINE

A fourth proposed pipeline is for the transportation of gas from
Prudhoe Bay to markets in the midwestern U.S. and in Canada. That line
would be built in three segments and would be a 48-ince pipeline extending
for 1,550 mi from Prudhoe Bay to a point in Alberta where it would connect
with Alberta gas trunk's existing 2,800-mi transmission system. From
Alberta the gas would be connected to major pipeline systems for export to
U.S. and Canadian markets. The pipeline would have an initial capacity of
1.5 billion cu ft of gas daily, rising to 3 billion cu ft daily by 1980.
Completion of the first phase is projected for 1974.[40]

Canadian Arctic Resources

    The Canadian Arctic stretches from Alaska to Greenland and includes the Canadian Arctic Archipelago (or arctic islands). The area of interest has an approximate southern boundary that follows the tree line from the Brooks Range in Alaska, dips southeastward to encompass the southern part of Hudson Bay, and thence continues eastward to the Labrador coast (see Figs. 66 and 67). The Mackenzie River basin is included because of the importance of that northward flowing river to activities in the Arctic. Thus the Far North plus portions of the Middle North will be examined.

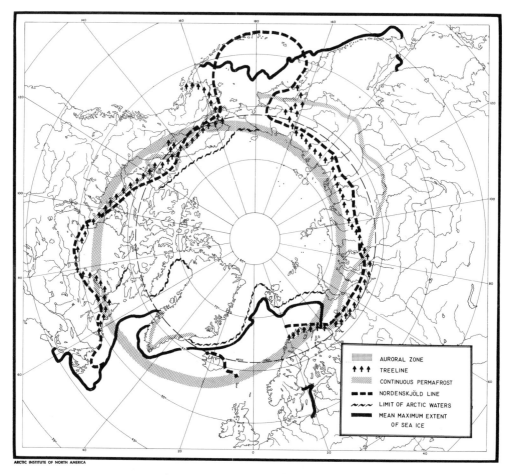

Figure 66. THE ARCTIC REGION

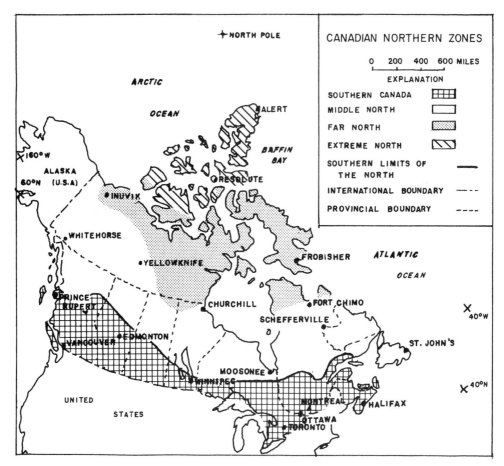

Figure 67. CANADIAN NORTHERN ZONES

Energy Resources

Coal

Among the economically significant energy resources of arctic Canada coal is not included. Production north of 60° has been confined to the Yukon Territory where coal production reached a high annual value of $123,675 in 1963. By 1968 production of coal was no longer indicated in the mineral production statistics for the Territory.[41] 1969 statistics similarly failed to record any coal production.[42]

Water Power

In the Yukon Territory and the Northwest Territories water power is of special importance in the development of mining areas such as Mayo and Yellowknife. In the Yukon, most water power resources are on the Yukon River and its tributaries. Although thorough surveys have not been made, recent partial surveys show that the rivers flowing into the Great Slave Lake and the South Nahanni River, which drains into the Mackenzie River, have considerable potential.[43] Currently there are four hydroelectric generating plants operating in the Yukon and a like number in the Northwest Territories.[41] The potential water power development of arctic Canada may be gleaned from a 1970 statement by the Northern Economic Branch of the Canadian Department of Indian Affairs and Northern Development: "In total, the water flow in these four principal basins is approximately equal to two Fraser Rivers, one Columbia River and one St. Lawrence River. The future requirements for water in municipal and industrial development is therefore well assured if proper care is exercised in resource development."[41] It should be emphasized that hydroelectric power is of much greater significance in the Middle North than in the Far North. That is not to say that power lines may not penetrate the Arctic from sources farther south. Table 13[43] shows preliminary statistics for installed hydro- and thermal-electric generating capacity by province (1968).

TABLE 13

Installed Hydro- and Thermal-Electric Generating Capacity,
By Province, By December 31, 1968*

Province	Hydro	Thermal	Total
		Thousands of Kilowatts	
Newfoundland	819	112	931
Prince Edward Island	---	77	77
Nova Scotia	163	543	706
New Brunswick	562	551	1,113
Quebec	11,035	762	11,797
Ontario	6,413	4,876	11,289
Manitoba	1,184	369	1,153
Saskatchewan	586	691	1,277
Alberta	616	1,435	2,051
British Columbia	3,531	1,515	5,046
Yukon Territory	18	15	33
Northwest Territories	35	26	61
CANADA	24,962	10,972	35,934

*Preliminary

Nuclear Thermal Power

Development of commercial power generation in thermal plants using heat generated by nuclear reactors is a major contribution of Canada to energy resource technology. That development has centered around the CANDU reactor which uses a natural uranium fuel with a heavy water moderator. However, all three major nuclear power plants are in southern Canada.

Oil and Gas

Oil has been produced at Norman Wells in the Mackenzie Valley from the middle of the 1930's to the present. Current annual production is only about 750,000 barrels. In the area south of Norman Wells, oil and gas exploration activity has been building up over the past four or five years. That activity is actually an extension of activity in northern Alberta and northeastern British Columbia.[44] A pipeline is being built to the Beaver River and is expected to be extended to Pointed Mountain later.

Major oil production in Canada today takes place south of the arctic region, including the rich Athabasca tar sands. It does not impact directly on the importance of the Canadian Arctic. However, this production has led to the construction of high-capacity pipelines, e.g. from Edmonton, Alberta toward the Chicago area in the U.S. These pipelines may well have significance for the future transportation of oil and gas from the Arctic.

The Prudhoe Bay 1967 discoveries in Alaska had immediate repercusions in Canada. Potential oil and gas finds in arctic Canada had long been the subject of mild interest, and extensive leases had been registered by several oil companies. After 1967, however, Canadian arctic exploration and drilling was given explosive encouragement. Panarctic Oils, a consortium with government capital input was organized as an instrument for the early prosecution of intensified activity. The basis for the interest and activity was mainly the simple fact that the geologic features of the Canadian arctic region, including particularly the Mackenzie Delta region, the arctic islands area, and the Sverdrup Basin (see Figs. 68 and 69), were known to have promising geologic formations as did those of the Alaska North Slope and were therefore attractive to oilmen.[45]

In the year 1970, 72 wells were drilled in the Northwest Territories, the Yukon Territory, and the arctic islands for a total drilling of 369,885 ft.[8] High-pressure gas and some indications of oil were found by Panarctic Oils in 1969 at Drake Point on Melville Island. Panarctic also, on March 25, 1971, spudded the world's northernmost test on Ellesmere Island. Panarctic's Fosheim N-27 is only 700 mi from the North Pole on Fosheim Peninsula.[47] The spring of 1971 has brought on other tests by Sun Oil on Longheed, Bathurst, and Somerset islands. Panarctic's well on King Christian Island, D-18, blew on October 25, 1970, becoming the second devastating blowout for Panarctic.[48] Also, in 1971, a new consortium, Magnorth Petroleum Ltd., of Calgary, was formed to push exploration in the arctic islands. The consortium, formed by 10 Canadian and 2 U.S. firms approved a $1-million exploration budget.[49] Meanwhile, Gulf Oil Canada and Mobil Oil Canada have joined forces to explore their vast offshore areas in the Canadian Arctic. Imperial has drilled 10 more wells in the Mackenzie Delta between November 1970 and March 1971 as part of the 1971 drilling spurt.[47] The chances have been estimated as high that a major strike is imminent. In fact, an Edmonton report of a new Imperial Oil strike may confirm this. More than 600 exploratory wells are predicted for drilling north of 60° during the next five years.[50]

In spite of all the activity in the way of exploration and drilling, it is still possible to give only speculative estimates of total reserves that exist in arctic Canada. However, estimates have been made by many

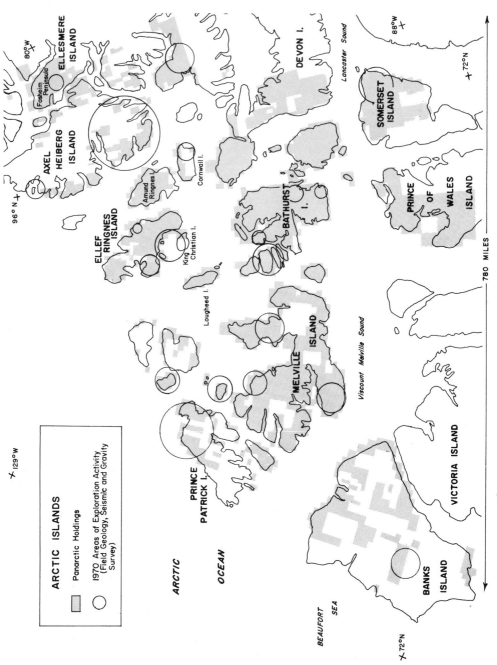

Figure 68. OIL AND GAS ACTIVITIES - ARCTIC ISLANDS

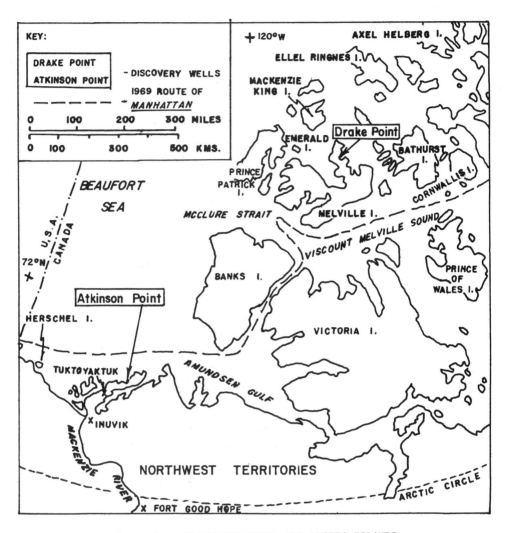

Figure 69. MACKENZIE DELTA AND ARCTIC ISLANDS

competent private and official sources and may provide figures that will later be more sharply refined.

First as to oil potentials above 60°, the lowest estimate in the past two years was that of the Northern Development Branch of the Department of Indian Affairs and Northern Development, which estimates 50 billion barrels.[41] That figure has been used by others who have suggested estimates in the 50-54 billion barrel range as a conservative estimate.[51] Edgington, Campbell, and Cleland, on February 1, 1971, placed the potential oil reserves at 80-120 billion barrels in the arctic islands alone, plus 20-30 billion in the Mackenzie Delta.[52] In 1969 the Canadian Petroleum Association was cited as calculating the arctic reserves at 120.8 billion barrels of crude.[53] The Association added an estimate of 19.6 billion barrels of natural gas liquids, for a total of 140.4 billion barrels.[54]

The highest estimates were made by the *Oil and Gas Journal* (U.S.) in August 1970.[55] It estimated current reserves at 53.95 billion barrels and "undiscovered potential" at 202 billion barrels, for a total of 256 billion barrels.

In summary, the recent estimates ranging from "conservative" to "undiscovered potential" range from 50 to 256 billion barrels of oil and liquid gas reserves in arctic Canada. The estimates, therefore, range from slightly more than present "proved reserves" for all of North America to a total more than five times that amount. (The estimates cited do not all give figures for recoverable oil.)

The estimates of natural gas potential from arctic Canada are equally spectacular. Roughly, estimates range from the figure of 300 trillion cu ft given by the Department of Indian Affairs and Northern Development[41] to the 724.8 trillion-cu-ft estimates of the Canadian Petroleum Association;[54] and the *Oil and Gas Journal* figure in August 1970 was 710 trillion cu ft.[55] The higher estimates are approximately two and a half times present proved reserves for all of North America.[53] The above figures suggest why the Department of Indian Affairs and Northern Development, which administers Canadian oil and gas regulations, reported in late 1970 that the "permit" acreage had increased from 100 million to 350 million acres since the Prudhoe Bay discovery.

Other Minerals

Table 14 shows the mineral production in arctic Canada from 1960 to 1969, and Figure 70 shows known locations of mineral resources in northern Canada as of 1969. As is indicated by the table, the small-scale minerals industry of northern Canada prior to 1964 was based largely on gold production. Together with silver it accounted for 75 percent of the value of production in the Yukon and Northwest territories.[42] In 1963 the two territories produced about equal amounts. Between the years 1964 and 1967 the value of mineral production in the NWT increased more than sixfold. In 1968 and 1969 new mines in the Yukon Territory more than doubled from 1967. The consequence was that annual production, which had been in the $30- to $35-million range before 1964, rose to $153.2 million in 1969.[42] In 1970 nine private companies were mining metals, one company was mining asbestos, and four companies were preparing mines for production.[42]

The Oil and Minerals Division of the Department of Indian Affairs and Northern Development concluded (1970) that, "In addition to recent large investments in new mines, confidence in the future is abundantly indicated by the tremendous expansion in exploration."[42] It pointed out that before 1964 less than 6,000 claims (0.2 km^2) were recorded annually in the two territories. In the five years 1964-1969, five major staking rushes occurred - in the Pine Point area with 27,000 calims, in Coppermine River area with 39,000 claims, in Vangorda Creek-Ross River area with 10,000 claims, in Artillery Lake area with 8,000 claims, and in Casino Creek area with 10,000 claims. The high point was reached in 1968 with 53,000 claims recorded.

Metallic Minerals

Extensive iron-bearing formations are located in many northern areas of Canada. More than 139 million tons of direct-shipping ore, grading 68

RECENT AND FUTURE MINERAL DEVELOPMENTS IN NORTHERN CANADA

TABLE 14

Mineral Production Chart, 1960 to 1969

Northwest Territories

Mineral		1960	1961	1962	1963	1964	1965	1966	1967	1968	1969(a)	Cumulative Totals (kg)
Gold	$	14 194 631	14 449 028	14 974 924	14 609 250	15 586 182	17 071 580	15 990 133	14 356 476	13 285 459	12 935 473	
	kg	13 003	12 672	12 449	12 036	12 841	14 082	13 187	11 827	10 957	10 671	123 725
Silver	$	70 659	73 419	84 814	107 216	91 312	1 490 754	2 325 407	3 429 755	8 677 365	3 911 170	
	kg	2 472	2 422	2 264	2 409		33 116	51 694	61 585	116 673	63 024	335 659
Copper	$	315 016	270 440	194 928	10 281		354 342	672 065	538 077	833 169	550 920	
	kg	471 737	420 245	285 220	14 804		427 466	678 940	513 071	785 695	485 889	4 083 067
Nickel	$	2 669 645	2 604 789	1 503 837								
	kg	1 729 903	1 546 484	816 922								4 093 309
Lead	$					823 279	25 677 695	31 472 562	35 665 535	33 636 984	31 037 000	
	kg					2 778 523	75 144 531	95 555 249	115 556 332	113 524 822	92 988 000	495 547 547
Zinc	$					1 111 016	28 596 474	57 128 344	60 852 900	57 504 129	67 012 000	
	kg					3 556 505	85 903 051	171 612 030	190 496 033	184 992 005	199 584 000	436 143 624
Pitch-blende(d)	$	9 231 698										
	kg	430 884										430 884
Cadmium	$						516 635	2 769 372	2 551 920	774 060		
	kg						84 297	486 894	413 411	123 198		1 107 800
TOTAL	$	26 481 649	17 397 676	16 758 503	14 726 747	17 611 789	73 707 480	110 357 883	117 394 663	114 711 166	115 446 563	

Yukon Territory

Mineral		1960	1961	1962	1963	1964	1965	1966	1967	1968	1969(a)	Cumulative Totals (kg)
Gold	$	2 652 004	2 371 494	2 050 255	2 084 215	2 183 611	1 698 975	1 639 103	675 725	911 338	991 700	
	kg	2 429	2 079	1 704	1 717	1 799	1 400	1 352	556	751	818	14 605
Silver	$	6 416 956	6 538 897	7 551 814	8 450 755	7 894 196	6 462 393	5 868 217	6 701 756	4 806 384	5 770 808	
	kg	224 460	215 743	201 598	189 898	175 363	143 557	130 451	120 337	64 625	92 991	1 559 023
Lead	$	2 166 638	1 712 198	1 615 980	1 867 647	2 744 235	2 766 953	2 386 684	2 141 959	970 629	4 663 120	
	kg	9 202 125	7 606 788	7 389 201	7 701 496	9 261 793	8 097 754	7 246 316	6 939 948	3 275 872	13 970 880	80 692 173
Copper	$		257 098	132 990					3 409 779	5 097 157	8 084 127	
	kg		399 519	194 594					3 251 368	4 806 800	7 130 002	15 982 283
Coal	$	97 156	114 221	115 198	123 675	98 150	85 626	46 390	15 791			
	kg	6 573 843	7 826 633	7 771 766	8 363 107	7 345 025	8 942 256	5 761 003	1 942 688			53 526 321
Zinc	$	1 789 287	1 528 100	1 438 554	1 514 520	1 855 512	2 000 396	1 729 027	1 373 151	748 206	5 201 045	
	kg	6 097 555	5 505 533	5 392 974	5 375 480	5 939 735	6 009 135	5 193 951	4 298 561	2 406 996	15 490 440	62 610 360
Cadmium	$	206 604	228 296	231 328	326 124	428 399	386 192	306 336	265 997	147 716	243 600	
	kg	65 997	64 722	61 006	61 637	59 976	63 013	53 858	43 091	23 510	31 752	528 562
Asbestos	$								406 371	8 684 125	12 701 400	
	kg								2 296 273	64 612 652	89 412 400	156 321 325
TOTAL	$	13 328 645	12 750 304	13 136 119	14 366 936	15 204 103	13 400 535	11 975 757	14 990 529	21 365 555	37 655 800	

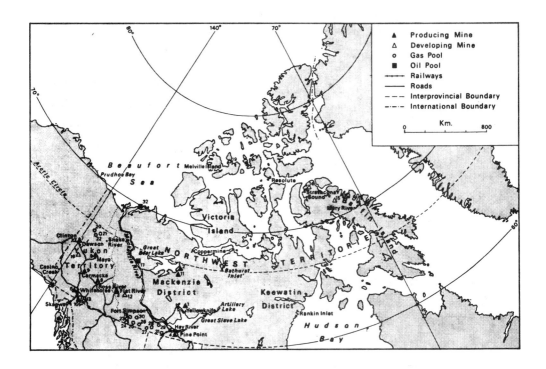

1	Giant Yellowknife Mines Au	17	Norman Wells	Oil
	Con-Rycon Mines Au	18	Pointed Mountain	Gas
2	Echo Bay Mines Ag Cu	19	Drake Point	Gas
3	Canada Tungsten Mining W Cu	20	Chance	Oil and gas
4	Pine Point Mines Pb Zn	21	Birch	Gas
5	United Keno Hill Mines	22	Blackie	Gas
	Pb Zn Ag Cd	23	North Beaver River	Gas
6	New Imperial Mines Cu	24	Beaver River	Gas
7	Cassiar Asbestos Corporation Asb	25	Bovie Lake	Gas
8	Anvil Mining Corporation Pb Zn Ag	26	Celibeta	Gas
9	Yukon Coal Co C	27	Island River	Gas
10	Arctic Mining and Exploration Au	28	Trainor Lake	Gas
11	Terra Mining and Exploration Ag	29	Rabbit Lake	Gas
12	Cadillac Mines Ag Pb	30	Netla	Gas
13	Venus Mines Ag Au	31	Cameron Hills	Gas
14	Strathcona Zn Pb	32	Atkinson	Oil
15	Baffin Iron Fe			
16	Casino Cu Mo			

Figure 70.   MINERAL, OIL, AND GAS DEVELOPMENTS
IN NORTHERN CANADA, 1969

percent iron or better, have been outlined in the Mary River area of
north-central Baffin Island. One of the major obstacles to developing that
project is the short shipping season. Immense low-grade deposits have been
found also in the central Yukon. Additional sources are known on either
side of the Foxe Basin. With problems of transportation and benefication
(concentration) and a need for long contracts at stable prices, development
of the low-grade ores may not occur for many years. They do constitute a
reserve in case of future need. Considering the predicted cumulative
demands for iron and steel in the U.S. alone, the anticipated demand to the
year 2000 exceeds reserves by 40 percent. Canadian low-grade ore might
later therefore be of strategic importance.[22]

A 3-million-ton copper deposit has been outlined in the Coppermine area
of the Canadian Arctic. Further mineralization occurs between Coppermine
and the Bathurst Inlet and on Victoria Island. In the Casino Creek area,
west of Carmacks, recent exploration has indicated a very large low-grade
copper-molybdenum deposit. Indications of porphyry copper-type mineralization have been encountered in widely spaced localities in western Yukon
Territory.[42] In April 1967, New Imperial Mines began production from an
open pit copper mine 10 miles from Whitehorse. New Imperial began exploration in 1956 and by 1965 had outlined reserves of 5.5 million tons of ore
grading 1.2 percent in several mineable deposits. The concentrated
product - 2,000 tons per day - is being shipped to Skagway for onward transfer to Japan.[42]

Lead-zinc proved reserves in the Pine Point area exceed 40 million tons
(a Cominco, Ltd. subsidiary is the producer) with a combined zinc-lead grade
of 9.4 percent. Total capacity is 8,000 tons per day. There are reports of
another deposit in the area which is expected to grade 13 percent and contain
1.4 million tons. More may be found. Several additional deposits may be
brought into production in the Anvil district (120 mi northeast). Significant high-grade deposits have also been outlined north of Resolute and
Strathcona Sound on northern Baffin Island. Underground development has
already begun in the 12-million-ton Strathcona Sound deposit.[42] The Anvil
Mining Company development near Ross River is estimated to have reserves of
63 million tons grading 9 percent and also 31.1 grams of silver per ton.
Fuel for the concentration process is provided by the total coal output of
the Tantalus Butte Mine near Carmacks, which produces 12,000 tons per year.

Canada Tungsten Mining Corporation is the only tungsten producer in
Canada. It operates a 300-ton-per-day mine in the Flat River area close
to the Yukon-NWT boundary. The deposit in 1959 contained 1.5 million tons,
of which less than half has been mined. The Selwyn Mountain region, southeastern Yukon Territory, contains at least one deposit in excess of one
million tons, and it is considered likely that further deposits will be
found.[42]

Gold and silver are found in many parts of the Canadian north and a
number of high-grade gold and silver prospects are thought to exist in the
Yukon. Silver is also a by-product of the Anvil lead-zinc mines and of the
New Imperial copper mines. The Mayo district near Great Bear Lake and the
area west of Lake Simpson are also potential silver producers. Gold and
silver do not, as of now, constitute resources of great strategic importance
among the Canadian arctic minerals. Some nickel is mined east of Artillery
Lake but production is minimal.

Nonmetallic Minerals

The most significant of nonmetallic minerals found thus far in arctic Canada is asbestos. The principal find is the Clinton Mine in Yukon Territory operated by Cassiar Asbestos Corporation. The main ore body is said to contain 14 million tons of asbestos ore containing 6 to 7 percent fibre. An additional body of 9 million tons of lower-grade ore lies to the west of the Clinton mine. Prospecting in the Yukon Territory is expected to discover additional ores.[42]

Some sulphur is to be found in the arctic islands.[56]

Other Natural Resources

Other natural resources, such as forests, fish, and game, are not significant in the Canadian Arctic. Trees do not grow there and agriculture in the frozen grounds is not practical. Fish and game, though, are important to the native economy. Forests, of course, are of great importance in the Middle North.

Industries

Other than the mining and the exploitation of oil and gas, there appears to be no logical base for industrial development in the Canadian Arctic in the near future. There is no significant industry now located there. There has, however, been considerable penetration of industry into the Middle North.

Manufacturing

The high cost of shipping materials both into and out of the Arctic, the shortage of local skilled labor, the great expense of providing amenities for imported labor, the lack of communications, and other costs and climatic factors all tend to make the construction and operation of manufacturing facilities uneconomical. A small refinery at Norman Wells has been in operation for many years, but its products are used in the area and are not exported south.

In the case of metals, it is presently cheaper to ship ore concentrates to more temperate regions for refining. The only industrial activity pertaining to metal production, then, will be the mining of the ores and the operation of plants to produce the desired concentrate.

In the case of oil and gas, wells will be drilled and fields developed. Small refineries for processing products required locally probably will be built (such as the ARCO plant in the Prudhoe Bay area of Alaska). For gas, it may be more economical in the Arctic to operate facilities to convert the gas to the liquid state for shipment by sea rather than by pipeline.

Farther south, in the Middle North, is another story. For example, Thompson, Manitoba is a town that was built to serve the nickel mines of the International Nickel Company. The company now produces about 75 million pounds of nickel a year at Thompson and the capacity is being increased to 100 million pounds a year. The town of about 10,000 people

is essentially a self-run open community. The whole development was paid
for by the company without government assistance. The company built and
paid for a railway spur about 40 mi long from the Pas-Churchill railway
line. International Nickel Company also built, owns, and operates a power
plant on the Nelson River at Kettle Rapids. The town has a single purpose -
the production of nickel. It is often spoken of as "sweet suburbia in the
North."[57]

At Fort McMurray, in the Middle North, 230 mi northeast of Edmonton,
Sun Oil Company has built a $300-million plant for the extraction of up to
45,000 barrels of high-grade crude per day from the Athabasca tar sands.[58]
The Alberta government has now authorized production of 150,000 barrels per
day, and several companies are competing for this development.[57]

Other developments in the Middle North could be cited. However, since
they do not impact directly on operations in the Arctic Ocean, the two cited
examples will suffice as illustrative of the kind of industrial developments
that have and will take place in the Middle North. Further, as the obstacles
of the subarctic are overcome, it can be expected that significant industrial
activity will penetrate the Arctic. Nevertheless, this is unlikely to occur
in the foreseeable future, certainly not through the next decade.

Other Industry

Agriculture is nonexistent in the Arctic. Commercial fishing in the
Arctic is largely limited to the Arctic char, a delicacy fish which is
air-shipped to luxury markets in Canada and the U.S. There are a few fish
canneries.

Small service-type industries, such as repair and maintenance shops,
will develop as communities are established or enlarged to accommodate
personnel required in the mining and oil production. Also, there will be
industrial activities associated with transportation facilities as arctic
transportation systems are established.

Population

Population figures in this section are from a 1966 census. Table 15,
for all of Canada, gives the population of broad lateral zones (Fig. 67)
by province or territory.[59]

In order to place the population of northern Canada in perspective,
southern Canada is mentioned first. The most densely populated area of
Canada lies near the Canada-U.S. border. Its major cities - Montreal,
Toronto, Vancouver, Winnipeg, and Ottawa - are within 100 mi of this border.
Southern Canada, i.e. the area south of the Middle North, has 19,278,380 of
Canada's total population of 20,014,880.[59]

The Middle North (essentially subarctic in character) provides the main
routes of northward pioneer penetration. Its total population is 210,546 -
approximately 1 percent of Canada's total population.[59] Populations of
principal towns follow:

Flin Flon	11,104
Whitehorse	5,031
Yellowknife	3,241

Schefferville	3,178
Goose Bay	3,040
Churchill	1,878
Moosonee	925

The Far and Extreme North, the zones which together form the Canadian Arctic, have a population of 17,954.[59] This is less than one-tenth of 1 percent of Canada's total population. Population figures for principal communities of the Canadian Arctic follow:

Inuvik	1,248
Cambridge Bay	531
Frobisher	512
Tuktoyaktuk	409
Coppermine	230
Resolute	153

TABLE 15

Population of Zones, By Province or Territory
Canada, 1966

Province or Territory	Southern Canada	Middle North (essentially sub-arctic in character)	Far and Extreme North (basically the Canadian Arctic
Newfoundland & Labrador	448,487	44,909	0
Nova Scotia	756,039	0	0
Prince Edward Is.	108,535	0	0
New Brunswick	616,788	0	0
Quebec	5,754,115	23,699	3,031
Ontario	6,945,635	15,235	0
Manitoba	902,929	60,112	25
Saskatchewan	937,251	18,093	0
Alberta	1,448,683	14,520	0
British Columbia	1,867,918	5,756	0
Northwest Territories	0	13,850	14,888
Yukon	0	14,372	10
CANADA	19,786,380	210,546	17,954

It is evident from the above statistics and the large areas to which they apply that the Canadian Arctic is sparsely settled. It is likely to remain so for a very long time. Exploration and development of extractive resources alone do not stimulate large increases in population. Minerals may be reduced to concentrates in the Arctic for more economical shipment. However, refining plants in the Arctic for minerals or oil are not yet economically sound. The prospect of other manufacturing activity is even more remote. Population pressures are unlikely to force occupation of the empty arctic spaces. For the foreseeable future it is concluded that there will be only moderate population growth in the Canadian Arctic, due principally to mineral and oil exploration and production, including ancillary services required. Population will remain scattered in small communities, rather than concentrated in a few large population centers.

Transportation

Of all the items that affect development in northern Canada, after climate, transportation is easily the most important. Transportation systems are minimal in the Canadian Arctic. They are somewhat better developed in the Middle North. Canada's railroads and air routes are shown in Figure 71.[59] It also shows the 1969 route of the *S. S. Manhattan* through the Northwest Passage. Figure 72 shows the northern roads of Canada.[61] The Mackenzie River system and connecting arctic coastal routes are shown in Figure 73.[62]

Considering the Canadian North as a whole, a partially integrated pattern of water, land, and air transportation operates through relatively few centers such as Whitehorse, Yukon Territory; Yellowknife, Resolute, and Frobisher Bay, Northwest Territories; Churchill, Manitoba; and Fort Chimo, Quebec. There is little east-west movement within the Arctic or Middle North. The broad pattern is the movement into the North of general and package freight and the movement out of ore concentrates. To the south, these northern routes connect with the fully integrated Canadian system of east-west highway, rail, and air routes.[57]

Special situations, such as support of the Distant Early Warning System (DEW line), the distribution of petroleum products from Norman Wells, and, more recently, the activities of the oil companies in the Arctic, have resulted in departures from the generalities stated above.[57]

The possible development of year-round arctic tanker routes to satisfy the requirements of developing Alaskan North Slope oil, as well as pipelines that may be constructed for this purpose, may have a major impact on future trends of transportation development in the Canadian Arctic.

Railroads

While no railroads extend into the Canadian Arctic, the railroads of the Middle North are worth considering. Some provide links with arctic river and sea transportation.

The White Pass and Yukon Railway is a diesel-powered narrow-gauge railroad that operates between Whitehorse, Yukon Territory and Skagway, Alaska. This is the main outlet for concentrates from the Yukon to the Pacific. There is concern about the ability of the railroad to handle predicted tonnages as the Yukon develops.[57]

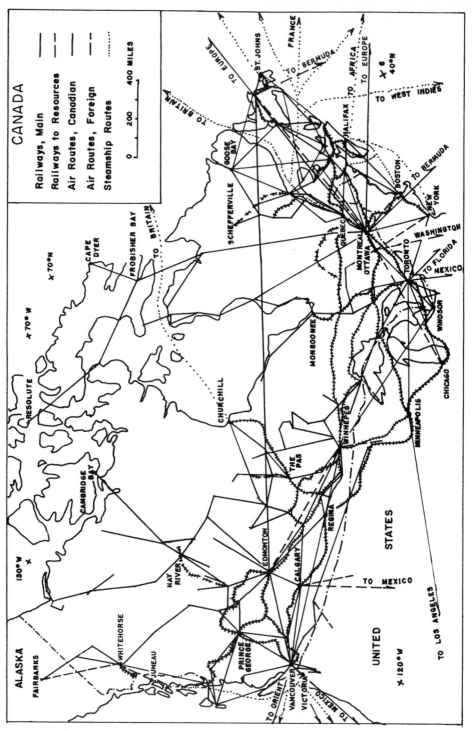

Figure 71.   RAILROADS AND AIR ROUTES OF CANADA

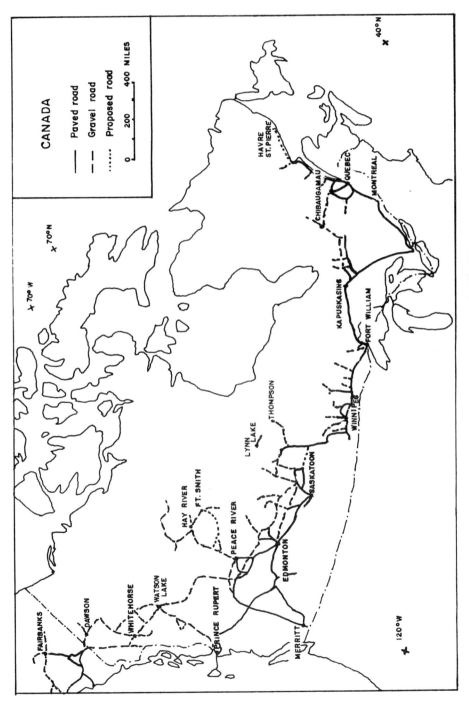

Figure 72.   NORTHERN ROADS OF CANADA

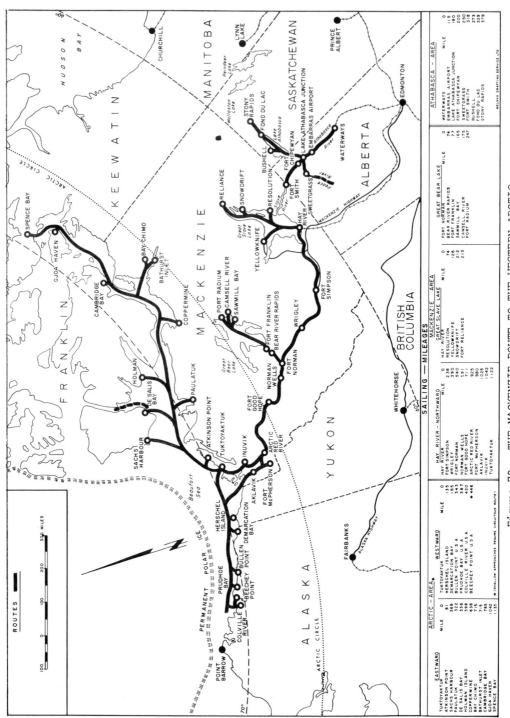

Figure 73. THE MACKENZIE ROUTE TO THE WESTERN ARCTIC

The Great Slave Lake Railroad is operated by the Canadian National system. It connects with the main system at Roma, Alberta and extends northward to the south shore of Great Slave Lake at Hay River and thence eastward to Pine Point. Hay River is the connecting point to the water transportation system in the Mackenzie River basin.[57] Although built principally to export lead-zinc concentrates from the Pine Point mines to the smelter in British Columbia, this railroad has generated traffic by developments other than the mine about equal to the ore tonnage that the railroad carries. This additional traffic is made up largely of agriculture and forest products. Up to a point of northerness, there is potential growth of traffic on a rail line such as the Great Slave, but farther north there are no forests and no farms.[63]

The Northern Alberta Railway connects Edmonton and the main rail system with Waterways, from which a tug and barge service operates on the Athabasca and Slave rivers. This railroad serves the Athabasca oil sands and also the Beaverlodge uranium mining area.[57]

A line of the Canadian National system runs from The Pas to Churchill at the edge of the Canadian Arctic on the west shore of Hudson Bay. This railroad was built principally as an outlet for wheat from the central provinces to the sea. Another railroad connects The Pas with Lynn Lake and provides a spur to Flin Flon. This is a significant mining railway.[59]

The Northern Ontario Railway connects Cochran on the main railroad network with Moosenee at the south end of James Bay, the southern extension of Hudson Bay.[57]

As the means of shipping out large tonnages of iron ore from Schefferville, Quebec, which is practically on the Labrador border, to the sea at Sept Iles, where the St. Lawrence River emerges into the Gulf of St. Lawrence, is a railroad operated by the Iron Ore Company of Canada.[57]

A railway, to be successful, has to depend on a high degree of permanence and a variety of two-way traffic. Conditions in the Canadian Arctic are not yet conducive to railways from this point of view.[63] No plans are now known for extension of railways into the Canadian Arctic.

Canadian railways as a whole loaded 186 million tons of unduplicated freight in 1967, and carried each ton an average distance of 447 mi. Freight traffic in terms of ton-miles was over 94,000 million.[59]

Motor Roads

There are no highways in the Canadian North, except gravel roads in the subarctic areas of western Canada. The Alaska Highway connects with the integrated highway system farther south at Dawson Creek, British Columbia and runs west and north through Whitehorse, Yukon Territory to the Alaska Border at the 141st meridian near the head of the Tanana River and on down the Tanana Valley to Fairbanks, Alaska. In Canada, it is a well-maintained full-width gravel road.[57]

From Haines Junction, west of Whitehorse, the Haines cutoff runs southward across a narrow extent of British Columbia to Haines, Alaska, not far from Skagway. Also from the Alaska Highway, branch roads spread widely to points in the Yukon and British Columbia. Most of these give access to mining areas.[57]

The Klondike Highway runs northward from Carcross through Whitehorse and Carmacks to Dawson. From there a road runs westward to connect with the Alaska Highway system. The Dempster Highway is being pushed northward toward Fort McPherson. Roads also run from Johnsons Crossing and from Watson Lake to Ross River. Another road has been extended west to near Carmacks to serve the Anvil Creek mining area.[57]

The Mackenzie Highway, maintained to a standard comparable to that of the Alaska Highway, generally parallels the Great Slave Lake Railway but extends much farther. It runs eastward and southward from Hay River to Pine Point and Fort Smith and northward to Yellowknife, Northwest Territories. A branch is being pushed down the Mackenzie River to Fort Simpson. These roads aid mineral developments.[57]

Within the next decade, roads can be expected to penetrate to the arctic coast. For instance, there has been some talk of an all-season road from Yellowknife to Coppermine.[61] The increased tempo of exploration activity along the arctic coast may lead, at least, to winter roads, as in Alaska.

Shipping

The Mackenzie watershed (see Fig. 73) is the one major water system used for navigation in the development of the vast area of northwestern Canada. It is the only inland water route extending through to the North American Arctic and is the main navigation route for movement of freight into the western Canadian Arctic. It has been used for moving oil rigs and supplies to the North Slope area of Alaska since 1963.[64]

The Mackenzie with its tributary rivers and lakes totals 3,274 mi of navigable channels. For purposes of comparison, the Mississippi River system with its principal tributaries, i.e. the Missouri, Ohio, and Illinois waterways, totals 3,866 mi - not a great deal more than the Mackenzie.

Essentially, the only transportation system operator using the Mackenzie watershed is the Northern Transportation Company, Ltd., a crown Corporation. The company operates barges and tugs from the road and rail head at Hay River and other points throughout the Mackenzie River system. It operates a service along the arctic coast from Tuktoyaktuk at the mouth of the Mackenzie. It serves the arctic coast (Canada and Alaska) from 95° to 150°W and the arctic islands to 72°N. Tuktoyaktuk has a governing depth of 13 ft and is usually open from mid-July to early October.[60] Operations are seasonal. The open season for the Mackenzie system and adjacent coastal waters normally extends from two to five months, generally decreasing as the more northerly areas are reached.[60][64] The Canadian government provides one icebreaker to support the coastal operations. 260,000 tons of cargo were shipped down the Mackenzie in 1969, with 10 percent of that to the North Slope.

For comparative purposes, the freight tonnages handled at the 12 major ports in Canada are shown in Table 16.[59] It is apparent that tonnages now handled in the western Canadian Arctic are minor compared to those in Canada as a whole. It is noted that the port of Sept Iles, whose tonnage includes the iron ore from northern Quebec, ranks second in tonnage handled in Canadian ports.

In the eastern Arctic of Canada many ships each year operate over a number of routes to many localities. An important segment of marine

TABLE 16

The Twelve Major Ports of Canada, 1967

Port	Total Freight Handled (million tons)	Foreign as % of Foreign & Coastwise	Loaded as % of Loaded and Unloaded
Vancouver, B.C.	24.1	56	72
Sept-Iles/Pointe Noire, Quebec	22.6	85	96
Montreal, Quebec	18.5	54	45
Port Arthur & Fort William, Ontario	15.3	28	91
Hamilton, Ontario	10.0	65	6
Port Cartier, Quebec	9.5	98	97
Halifax, Nova Scotia	9.0	72	46
Quebec, Quebec	7.0	51	33
Toronto, Ontario	5.8	64	9
Saint John, New Brunswick	5.6	75	39
New Westminster, B. C.	5.3	30	68
Sault Ste. Marie, Ontario	4.5	69	9
All Ports	238.2	55	57

transport is the shipment of grain from the central provinces to Europe from the railroad at Churchill, Manitoba through Hudson Bay and Hudson Strait.[57] Ordinary freighters for many years have been able to reach the port of Churchill in summer (from mid-July to late October). Churchill has a 30- to 32-foot water depth alongside the docks and a 28-foot depth in the approach channel.[60]

Canada's Department of Transport, in effect, runs a commercial shipping company.[45] It uses naval supply ships, chartered motor vessels and larger ships, and several icebreakers. 1966 records show approximately 100,000 tons of shipping to the eastern Arctic handled by the Department of Transport.[57]

Some of the ports served in the Canadian Arctic by seasonal shipping are Resolute, Eureka (on Ellesmere Island), Frobisher, and small settlements on the periphery of Hudson Bay and Ungava Bay, e.g. Fort Chimo.

The government of Manitoba has initiated rail-water transportation to

Europe from Churchill and is considering other possible harbor sites on the
west shore of Hudson Bay. The purpose is export of both minerals and
forest products from northern Manitoba and possibly the Keewatin district
of the Northwest Territories (in eastern Canada).

Off-Road Vehicle Transportation

Off-road vehicle transportation is important in arctic areas. A
variety of low-ground-pressure vehicles are used. For hauling heavy freight
over virgin land, the most common solution has been the tractor-hauled sled
train. Given the need for repeated hauls, a winter road of compacted snow
may be built, such as the one in Alaska to the North Slope oil fields. Summer thaw, however, makes the tundra terrain virtually impassable.

Surface-effect vehicles (SEV) may play a significant role in development of surface transportation in the Canadian Arctic.[60] As yet that type
of vehicle does not have a sufficiently favorable payload-fuel-distance
relationship to make it commercially competitive with other forms of transportation. For special purposes, however, it may be useful.

The exploration phase of mineral development (including oil and gas) in
the Canadian Arctic is increasing demands for off-road transportation. Tonnage figures are not available.

Air Transportation

The Canadian air transportation net for scheduled air lines is shown
in Figure 71. The principal arctic centers provided with regular service
are Inuvik, Tuktoyaktuk, Coppermine, Cambridge Bay, Resolute, Churchill, and
Frobisher. There is a well-developed network in the Middle North and southern Canada. In addition to scheduled air service, there are a number of
small companies and charter operators who fly to any place that has business
activity and the facilities to handle aircraft.[57] The operations of
Canadian air carriers for 1966 and 1967 are shown in Table 17.[60] Foreign
air carriers serving points in Canada are not included.

Except during the short ice-free open-navigation season, air transport
is the key to getting around in the barrens and throughout the Arctic
Archipelago.[57]

New high-capacity cargo aircraft may have an increasing role. A
generalized study by the Arctic Institute of North America showed that
seasonal sea transport of 30,000 tons per year of copper concentrates from
Coppermine to Tokyo might cost $56 per ton, including stockpiling, whereas
a C-5 type aircraft might do the job for $71 per ton. The gap is not as
large as might be expected.[57]

As in Alaska, complete oil rigs can be flown into the Arctic by C-130,
and premium transportation of that type is used to avoid delays due to
seasonal shipping.

The possibility of year-round, or nearly year-round, sea transportation
has been discussed in connection with development of Alaskan North Slope
petroleum industry, and the advantages of year-round tanker service are
obvious, particularly in the face of pipeline difficulties and costs.

TABLE 17

Operations of Canadian Air Carriers, 1966 and 1967

	Scheduled Carriers 1967	Non-Scheduled Carriers 1967	Total 1967	Total 1966
Operating Revenues ($millions)	475.1	68.5	543.6	460.6
Passengers (unit toll)	393.8	0.6	398.4	331.2
Goods (unit toll)	81.3	63.9	145.2	129.4
Charter and Contract	11.9	45.7	57.6	54.7
Specialty and Non-Flying Services	8.1	15.2	23.4	17.4
Net Income after Taxes ($ millions)	6.2	4.9	11.1	15.7
Revenue Traffic Carried				
Passengers (millions)	8.1	0.8	8.9	7.5
Goods (lb., millions)	252.2	114.7	366.8	357.1

An advantage to Canada in opening a year-round Northwest Passage is the favorable impact it would have on mineral development. Surely, for example, the Mary River iron ore on Baffin Island would be exploited. Even nearly year-round sea transportation would permit exploitation of many minerals that cannot now be economically produced and shipped.

If the Northwest Passage is chosen as the route and routes north of the arctic islands are not developed, Canadian government policy can affect the competitive position of Alaskan crude. This can be done through levy of user charges for the indirect costs of aids to navigation and through enforcement of the recently enacted Canadian laws and regulations concerned with oil pollution in this area.

The Canada Act to Avert Oil Pollution Disasters in Arctic Waters establishes authority to inspect shipping and to control and resulting pollution within a line running from the Yukon-Alaska boundary around the Arctic Archipelago at a distance of approximately 100 mi and thence down Baffin Bay to 60°N latitude, halfway between Canada and Greenland. Among other things, the Act gives powers of inspection and allows for the application of government standards to all construction work in the area and to incoming shipping.

Cost comparisons that have been made between tanker and pipeline delivery to the east coast of the United States vary considerably. Generally, they show tanker delivery to be significantly cheaper. It is believed that the ultimate decision as to whether or not to use tankers for exporting oil

from the North Slope and Canadian Arctic to the east coast of the United
States and Canada and/or directly to Europe will depend on economic factors.
It appears to be technologically impossible.

Pipelines

The discussion of pipeline projects and proposals to move oil/gas from
northern Alaska has indicated that there is much interest in Canada in the
possible construction of such pipelines up the Mackenzie Valley, either
originating in Alaska or perhaps tapping only Canadian oil and gas. Planning, research, and corporate activity has reached the point where it was
reported in January 1971 that an expenditure of $350 million by five company
groups is contemplated for 1971.(67)

The four principal planning groups were Interprovincial Pipeline,
Trans-Alaska, Alberta Gas Trunk Line Company, and Mountain Pacific Pipeline,
Ltd. Interprovincial was one of the original partners in the Mackenzie
Valley Pipeline Research Company, Limited. It was the first group to study
the feasibility of a crude oil line from Prudhoe Bay to Edmonton. The plan
would envisage that from Edmonton some oil would be transmitted via Interprovincial to midwestern U.S. and some by Trans-Mountain to west coast
refineries.(67)

Trans-Canada heads a six-company study group which is spending $12
million to study the feasibility of a northern Alaska-central Canada-midwest
U.S. gas pipeline. The projected line would be 2,500 mi of 48-inch pipe.
The estimated cost would be $2.5 billion. Trans-Canada already has 453 mi
of 36-inch pipeline and 230 mi of 42-inch gas pipeline. Several U.S. companies are among the partners, including ARCO, Humble, and Sohio.(12)

Alberta Gas Trunk Line Company, Limited reportedly plans to spend $200
million on a study of a gas pipeline from Prudhoe Bay to the Alberta-
Northwest Territories border. Texas Eastern Transmission and Columbia Gas
are affiliated in the venture. (Columbia Gas recently bought some North
Slope rights from Sohio.)

Mountain Pacific Pipeline, Limited is a fourth proposed pipeline system
to bring gas from Alaska and northern Canada. It is reported to have proposed a 1,100-mi 48-inch pipeline to Fort Laird, Northwest Territories, where
the line would split into two segments, one to western U.S. and Canada and
the other to central Canada and the U.S. The total cost estimate was given
as $1.8 million.

It should be recalled that the Canadian government has issued guide-
lines, made public by Minister of Energy J.J. Greene and Minister of Indian
Affairs and Northern Development Jean Cretien, concerning Canadian ownership
and participation in oil and gas pipelines from the Canadian North. It has
been specified that no more than one pipeline corridor from the North would
be licensed. Hence there is competition among the several pipeline planning
groups.

Thus far much of the planning has involved Alaskan oil and gas. If and
when proved sizeable reserves of oil/gas in the Mackenzie delta region are
outlined, the attention would also shift more to recoveries from that area.
As yet no plans have been announced for pipelines as a method of tapping
possible oil/gas finds in the Sverdrup Basin and in other remote areas in
the arctic islands. However, a group called The Gas Arctic Systems Study

Group has commissioned a preliminary assessment of the feasibility of transporting natural gas from Canada's arctic islands.[68]   The group has assigned
Pipeline Engineering and Management Services of Canada to study all possible
means of moving to market the gas reserves in the islands, where Panarctic
Oils has already made two significant discoveries. Among the alternatives
to be studied are a pipeline from the discovery areas on Melville and King
Christian islands to the western Canadian arctic mainland, and a pipeline
running southward along the Boothia Peninsula and the western shore of
Hudson Bay. A line angling to the west would link with Gas Arctic's proposed
line from Prudhoe Bay, Alaska to the Grande Prairie area of Alberta. The
Boothia line would connect with existing gas pipeline systems in the Great
Lakes area of Canada and the United States.

U.S.S.R. Arctic Resources

The area of interest extends about 4,500 mi from Norway to the Bering Strait. It includes the Kola Peninsula and White Sea area because of their impact on the Barents Sea activity and the arctic climate inland. Also included are the great basins of the major rivers emptying into the Arctic Ocean.

Energy Resources

The trends of the U.S.S.R. fuel production are shown in Table 18.[69] It shows the comparative importance of different fuels by reducing them to standard fuel units. The increase in relative importance of petroleum in the 1950's and 1960's was due mainly to the expansion of the Volga-Urals oil production. Natural gas became significant only after 1955, with the discovery of large gas fields and the completion of pipelines. The relative significance of coal production has been declining steadily since 1950.

TABLE 18

Fuel Structure of the U.S.S.R. (in percent)

	1940	1945	1950	1955	1960	1965
Petroleum	18.7	15.0	17.4	21.1	30.5	35.9
Natural Gas	1.9	2.3	2.3	2.4	7.9	15.6
Coal	59.1	62.2	66.1	64.8	53.9	42.9
Peat	5.7	4.9	4.8	4.3	2.9	1.7
Oil Shale	0.3	0.2	0.4	0.7	0.7	0.8
Firewood	14.3	15.4	9.0	6.7	4.1	3.1

Coal

Figure 74 shows the principal U.S.S.R. coal basins.[69] Total production has increased from 165.9 million metric tons in 1940 to 577.7 million in 1965. The Pechora Basin production in the arctic region, despite its large reserves, has been only about 18 million tons since 1958. Its production has been limited by high mining costs due to adverse climatic and working conditions. The limited coal mining at other arctic locations of Noril'sk, Sanger, Arkagala, and Zyryanka have been primarily for local use.

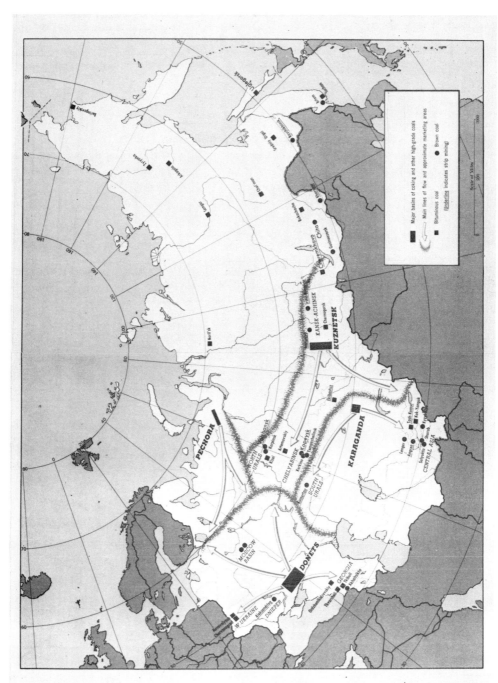

Figure 74. PRINCIPAL COAL BASINS OF THE U.S.S.R.

The increased importance of oil and gas production in the U.S.S.R. since 1955 has reduced the relative importance of the coal mining industry. This trend is likely to continue. In 1956, Soviet geologists claimed that their country possessed 55 percent of the world's coal supply.[70] Of those estimates, 85 percent consisted of "possible reserves" in the little-known basins of northern Siberia. The deposits of the Pechora Basin are estimated at 303 billion tons,[71] of Taimyr Basin at 583.5 billion, of Yenisey District at 221.7 billion, and of the Lena Basin at 2,647.0 billion. Total U.S.S.R. mineable coal reserves are estimated at 7.7 trillion tons.[70] Although the U.S.S.R. arctic coal reserves are enormous, it is unlikely that they will be worked extensively, except perhaps the Pechora Basin reserve, because of high production costs and the competitive advantages of oil and gas.

Electric Power

The total generating capacity of the U.S.S.R. has risen sharply since 1955, from 37 million kilowatts to 115 million in 1965. Most of the generating capacity is south of the arctic area.[69] (See Fig. 75.)

The Kola Peninsula depends largely on hydroelectric power for its industrial energy. Hydroelectric stations generated about 70 percent of the total electricity output of 6 billion kilowatt-hours in the mid-1960's. [69] Principal power systems are on the Niva, Tuloma, and Paz rivers. The peninsula has been selected for one of the 880,000-kilowatt central nuclear power stations of the pressurized water type. The station, under construction south of Murmansk, will help raise the electrical generating capacity of the Kola Peninsula from about 1.5 million kilowatts in the late 1960's to 2.5 million kilowatts sometime in the 1970's. A small 800-kilowatt tidal power test installation was completed in 1968 at Kislaya Guba. There are plans for a 320,000-kilowatt tidal station at Lumbovka Bay, on the north shore of the Kola Peninsula, 200 mi southeast of Murmansk.

Around the White Sea area, the power stations are hydroelectric. Power stations include the Vyg River system with a capacity of 230,000 kilowatts, the Kenn River system with a capacity of 250,000 kilowatts, and the Kovda-Kuma system with a total capacity of 300,000 kilowatts.[69] There are plans for a tidal power station at the mouth of the Mezen River.[69]

Electric power output in the Pechora Basin has been limited to coal-burning heat and power stations at Vorkuta. Plans have been made for the construction of a 1.5-million-kilowatt hydroelectric station at Ust'-Izhma, on the Pechora River at the mouth of the Izhma, a left tributary.[69] The feasible power resources from the Pechora, Vychegda, and Mezen rivers are estimated at 22 billion kilowatt hours during a year of average water flow.

The arctic region of western Siberia has had little power development. There were plans for a 6- to 7-million-kilowatt hydroelectric station on the Lower Ob just above Salekhard. However, this has been opposed because its vast lowland reservoir would flood future valuable farmlands, interfere with the development of other resources (such as oil, gas, and timber), and cause adverse effects on the regional water balance, climate, and soils.[69] Norilsk has a coal thermal electric station with a capacity of 200,000 kilowatts or more. This is to be supplemented in 1970 by the

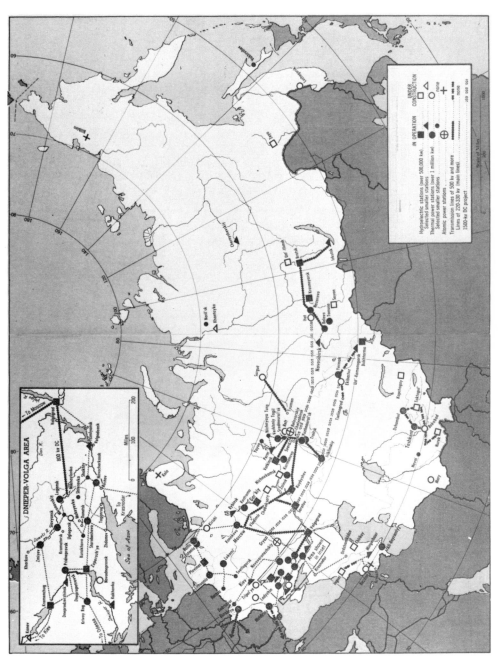

Figure 75. PRINCIPAL ELECTRIC POWER STATIONS AND TRANSMISSION LINES
OF THE U.S.S.R.

441,000-kilowatt hydroelectric station on the Khantayka River - one of the Soviet Union's northernmost hydroelectric plants.

Aykhal, in central Siberia, is served, as part of the diamond industry, by a 312,000-kilowatt hydroelectric station on the Vilyuy River at Cherny-Shevskiy. Farther east, a 17,000-kilowatt thermoelectric power station exists at Pevek using coal brought in by ship.[69] A floating 20,000-kilowatt power station moored at Zelenyy Mys burns coal from a deposit upstream on the Kolyma River. Four atomic power plants with a capacity of 12,000 kilowatts each are planned at Bilbino. A 12,000-kilowatt power station near Egvekinot serves the Iul'tin mining district burning coal from nearby seaboard coal mines.

Oil and Gas

Figure 76 shows principal oil fields and pipelines.

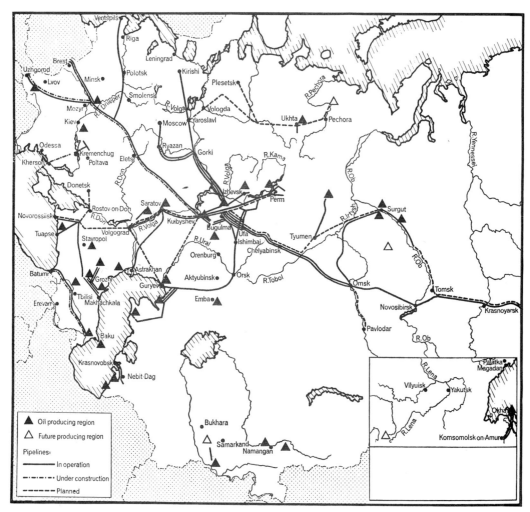

Figure 76. OIL INDUSTRY IN THE SOVIET UNION

Total U.S.S.R. production has been increasing since 1945 at a rate
which now places the U.S.S.R. in second place among the world's oil
producers.[69][72] Production figures in millions of metric tons are:

1945	19.5	1960	147.9
1950	37.9	1965	242.9
1955	70.8	1970	353.0

Recently disclosed targets for 1975 are as high as 480 to 500 million metric
tons, an increase from 1970 of nearly 50 percent. Refinery capacity and
output is to be correspondingly increased.[72]

Oil has been known in one locality in the Soviet Arctic since the second
half of the seventeenth century, in the Ukhta region of Komi ASSR, known as
the Tumano-Pechorskaya petroliferous province.[73] However, most of the
crude petroleum production in the U.S.S.R. has been from regions south of
the Arctic Circle. The situation has been changing in recent years and
forecasts for the future are of staggering dimensions. For example, it is
forecast that by 1975 the West Siberia basin will be the U.S.S.R.'s largest
producer, and that by 1980 it will be yielding 40 percent of the total
U.S.S.R. oil production.[74] Despite unusually high capital investment
expenses in arctic areas, the cost of western Siberian crude is already down
to the average for the U.S.S.R. as a whole, and by 1972 it is expected to
be the least expensive in the country.

Figure 77 shows the principal sedimentary basins favorable for
petroleum. Oil and gas exploration has been and is being pushed in several
arctic areas of the U.S.S.R. and the amounts of known or estimated potential
reserves on land and offshore have been increasing at a tremendous rate.[75]
The Soviet Minister for the petroleum industry, in an interview last year,
stated that, "The U.S.S.R. has Siberian oil coming out of its ears - - or
at least will have."[76] He forecast that 75 to 80 percent of the increase
in Soviet oil production in the next five years will come from Siberia.
Recent estimates are that of the 400,000-b/d jump in Russian crude production
in 1971, about 260,000 b/d, or 65 percent, will come from western Siberia.[77]
Western Siberian production is planned to reach 2 million barrels a day by
1975 and double that by 1980.[78] By 1980 it should be producing more than
40 percent of the total national output. A 1970 Soviet decree in fact envis-
aged a higher production by 1980, up to 230 to 260 million metric tons,
which was estimated as 40 percent of the probable total output at that
time.[79]

Like the Canadian arctic oil reserves, the U.S.S.R. reserves, known to
be great and assumed to be enormous, have not yet been established as
proved or fully known. Total reserve estimates are therefore reflections
of estimates based on the factors of geologic structures, application of
formulae, and similar well-known methods of calculating possible potential.

Siberia's major onshore oil province is the Ob-Yenisei river basin
between the Urals and the central Siberia platform. There are said to be
40 fields north of Tyumen, and Soviet geologists estimate that 75 billion
barrels of oil have been proved.[75] Peak output for that basin has been
projected as high as 10 million barrels per day.

Another source has stated that at least 40 billion barrels of "proved
plus probable" oil have been discovered in the Soviet Arctic. The ultimate
reserve, they state, will be more than three or four times these amounts.
They conclude that the Russian Arctic unquestionably is one of the richest

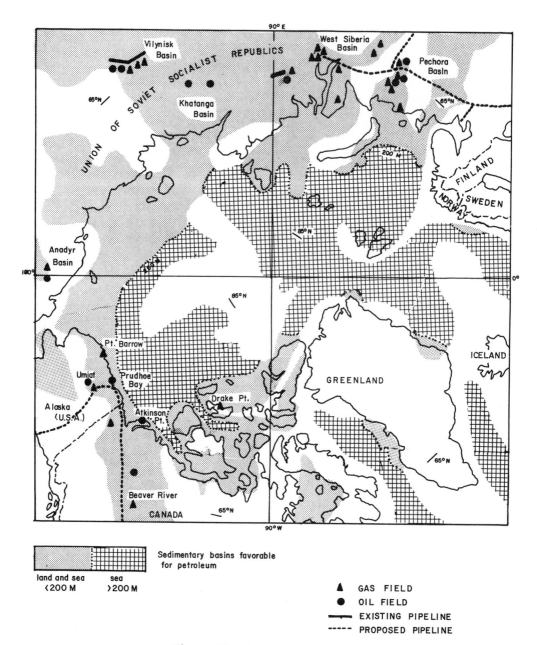

Figure 77. ARCTIC GAS AND OIL

hydrocarbon provinces on earth.[80] Soviet authorities are cited as having
stated that at least 40 percent of the U.S.S.R.'s potential oil reserves
are in arctic or near-arctic regions.[81] Although not fully known, the
offshore areas along the 4,500 mi of the U.S.S.R. arctic coast, from Norway
to the Bering Strait, are thought to embrace gigantic areas of geologically
favorable formations. Included are the Barents Sea, Kara Sea, and Laptev
Sea. The Pechora, West Siberia, and the Khatanga petroliferous basins
reportedly extend far out on the coastal shelves.[81] A University of Utah
geologist, A.J. Eardley, last year estimated that the offshore continental
shelf of U.S.S.R. Siberia contains a reserve of 200 billion barrels of
oil.[75] If the above estimates are valid, it would mean that the Soviet
Arctic, including onshore and offshore areas, may contain oil reserves near-
ing the half-trillion range. By comparison, the world published "proved"
reserves in 1969 totalled 540.6 billion barrels.[82]

Gas reserves in the Soviet Arctic are believed to be even more impressive. (See Fig. 78.) For example, it is reported that not less than 500

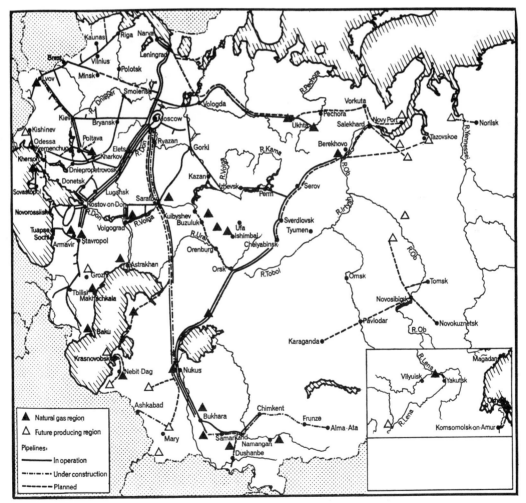

Figure 78. GAS INDUSTRY OF THE SOVIET UNION

trillion cu ft have already been proved.[80] It is conjectured that the
total may well run three or four times that amount. The offshore areas
alone are estimated to have 500 trillion cu ft.[75] Again, based on published estimates of potential reserves, the total for the Soviet Arctic
might reach the 2 to 3 quadrillion range.

The 2 to 3 quadrillion estimate may also be compared with the data
released by Soviet planning officials last year relating principally to the
West Siberian gas fields.[83] They reported that as of January 1, 1970 they
had 25 "untapped" or "virtually untapped" gas fields, each with at least 3.5
trillion cu ft of proved-plus-probable reserves. They placed the total
proved reserves at more than 290 trillion cu ft for the 24 fields and the
"probable" total at 637.3 to 672.6 trillion cu ft. Russia's total proved
reserves at the beginning of 1970 were 426.8 trillion cu ft, which was 15
trillion more than U.S. proved reserves as of that date. Russian officials
told the International Gas Industry Congress in Moscow last year that they
expect proved gas reserves to reach 760 to 882.5 trillion cu ft by 1980.[84]
At 1970's planned production rate - 6.9 trillion cu ft - Russia has almost
a 62-year proved gas supply, as compared with a 13.4-year supply for the
U.S. Western Siberia alone has 57 percent of the U.S.S.R.'s total. Alex
Sorokin, President of the International Gas Union and Deputy Minister of the
U.S.S.R.'s gas industry, reported at the Moscow Congress that potential
Soviet reserves now total 2.9 quadrillion cu ft, up from 2.5 quadrillion a
year earlier.[84] He stated that gas now accounts for nearly 20 percent of
the U.S.S.R.'s fuel output, and that he expected that percentage to rise to
35.2 by 1975. It would appear from Soviet sources that the potential 2
quadrillion cu ft of gas resources in the Soviet Arctic is a reasonably low
estimate.

Other Minerals

Figure 79 shows the metal industries for the Kola Peninsula and
central Siberia.

The Kola Peninsula has an integrated system from the mining to the output of finished metals for nickel and copper. Monchegorsk is the center of
the nickel-copper industry, with a smelter and a refinery. Its nearby mine
is largely depleted. The Pechenga complex is also approaching depletion,
but a new deposit is being developed east of Nickel. Iron ore is mined at
Olenegorsk and Kovdor, with a combined output of 6 million tons of concentrate in the mid-1960's. Olenegorsk proven reserves are placed at 300 million tons and indicated reserves at twice that amount.[71] Kovdor has the
U.S.S.R.'s largest deposit of vermiculite which is used in fire-resistant
building materials. Mica also is mined there. A commercial deposit of
columbium and tantalum is operated east of Kirovsk. The Pechora area also
has deposits of fluorspar and some lead ores.

Noril'sk, in central Siberia, is a center for the mining of nickel and
copper, polladium, platinum, selenium, tellurium, titanium, and canadium.
The Yarega titanium deposit has the potential as the most economic source
of raw material for a number of titanium-magnesium combines in the
U.S.S.R.[71]

Figure 80 shows the Soviet east arctic resources.[65] Tin mining is
concentrated in the basin of the Yana River. A diamond center is being
developed at Aykhal. Tin is also mined on the northeast coast near Pevek
and Iul'tin, which also produces tungsten. Gold mining occurs around
Bilibino and at Komsomolsky and Polyavnyy. A mercury deposit is worked
at Plomennyy.

KOLA PENINSULA METALS

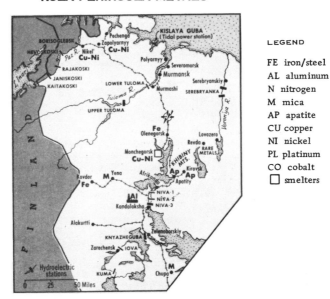

LEGEND

FE iron/steel
AL aluminum
N   nitrogen
M   mica
AP apatite
CU copper
NI nickel
PL platinum
CO cobalt
▢   smelters

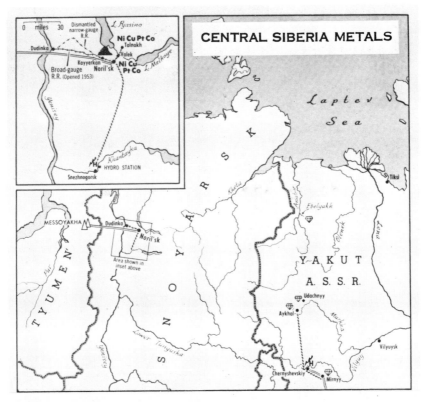

Figure 79. KOLA PENINSULA AND CENTRAL SIBERIAN METALS

The relative importance of the Soviet Union's metal industries in the Arctic is shown in Figures 81 through 85.[65] Most of the iron and steel industry is outside arctic U.S.S.R. The Kola Peninsula did supply 5.5 million metric tons of iron ore in 1965, compared to a total U.S.S.R. production of 153 million tons.

Of the ferroalloys, the Soviet Arctic does not supply any significant amounts of manganese, chromium, molybdenum, vanadium, and zirconium. The Kola Peninsula and Noril'sk supply two-thirds of the U.S.S.R.'s 80,000 to 90,000 tons of nickel. The arctic nickel deposits are now the Soviet Union's principal source of platinum-group metals. Virtually all of the cobalt is associated with nickel production, both in the Arctic and in the southern Urals, with a ratio of 1 ton of cobalt for every 70 tons of nickel. The large tungsten deposit at Iul'tin is supplemented by other deposits in the Caucasus and central Asia. The principal source of columbium and tantalum is the Kola Peninsula.

Of the base metals the Soviet Arctic does not supply any lead or zinc. Copper is a coproduct of nickel in the arctic mining centers of Noril'sk and the Kola Peninsula. However, copper is produced at many other areas with central Asia producing more than half the copper smelter output. The far eastern Arctic is a key source of tin at Ege-Khaya, Deputatskiy, and Iul'tin, supplemented by east Asian sources. Mercury production is concentrated in central Asia with a new deposit being developed in the far eastern Arctic at Plamennyy.

Of the light metals the Soviet Arctic is a significant producer only of aluminum. Nephelite concentrate, obtained as a byproduct of apatite production in the Kola Peninsula, is reduced at Volkhov and Pikakevo and then supplied to the aluminum mills at Kandalaksha. However, southern Siberia is expected to produce 65 percent of the planned 1970 output of aluminum, or 2 million tons.

Gold mining is concentrated in the Urals and in Siberia, including newly discovered placer deposits in the Kolyma district and around Bilibino in the Arctic. However, lode deposits are being developed elsewhere in central Asia. No uranium, asbestos, or graphite is processed in the Arctic. Diamond production is concentrated at Mirnyy, Aykhal, and Udachnyy in the eastern Arctic. Only minor amounts of fluorspar are worked at Amderma in the Pechora Basin in the Arctic, while most production occurs in central and east Asia. Muscovite sheet mica is obtained from the Kola Peninsula area and from the Mama River district of Irkutsk Oblast in eastern Siberia.

Industry, Forestry, and Agriculture

Despite having only 2 percent of the nation's population, the Soviet Arctic has a number of key industrial and mineral centers. On the other hand, the Soviet Arctic is not of significant importance in many areas of the Soviet economy. This includes industrial areas which are still concentrated in European Russia around the larger cities. Most of the electricity is produced south of the Arctic Circle. The iron and steel industry is concentrated in the Ukraine and Urals. The Soviet Arctic has not yielded to date significant quantities of important industrial metals such as manganese, chromium, molybdenum, vanadium, zirconium, lead, zinc, and magnesium; nor has it produced uranium, asbestos, or graphite.

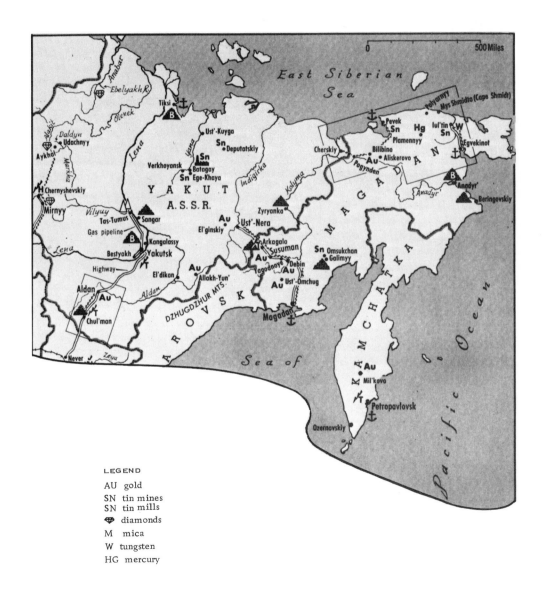

LEGEND

AU gold
SN tin mines
SN tin mills
◈   diamonds
M   mica
W   tungsten
HG mercury

Figure 80. EAST ARCTIC RESOURCES

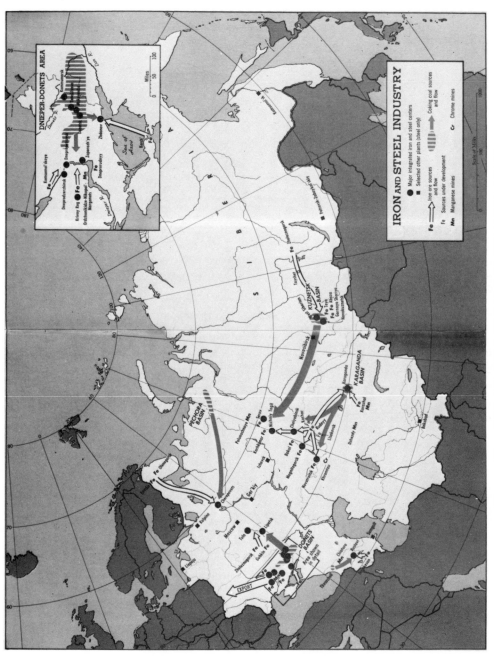

Figure 81.   IRON AND STEEL INDUSTRY IN THE SOVIET UNION

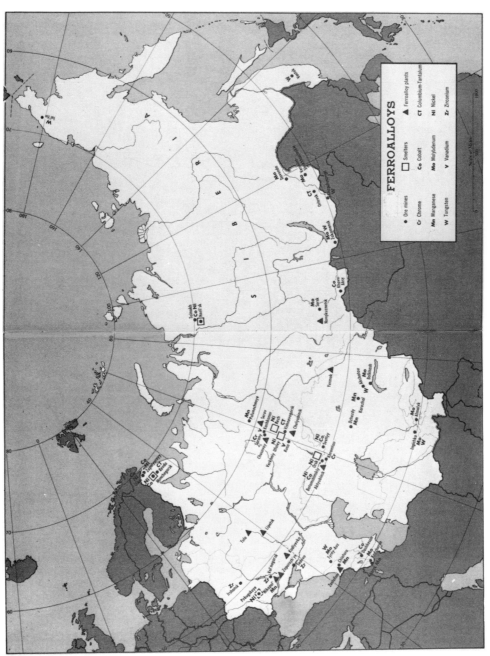

Figure 82.   FERROALLOYS IN THE SOVIET UNION

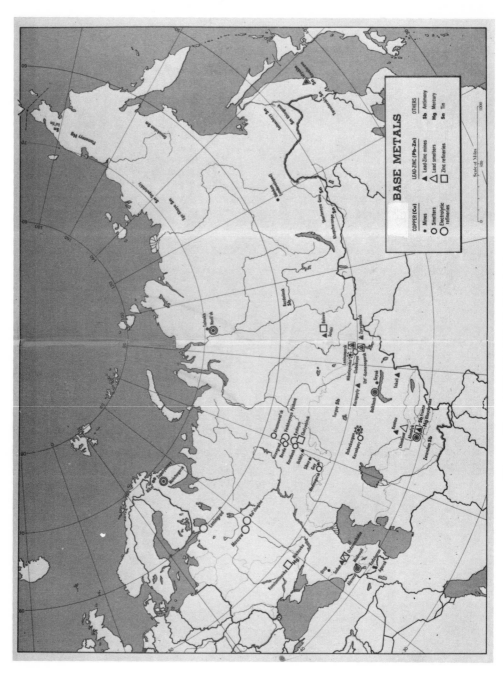

Figure 83.   BASE METALS IN THE SOVIET UNION

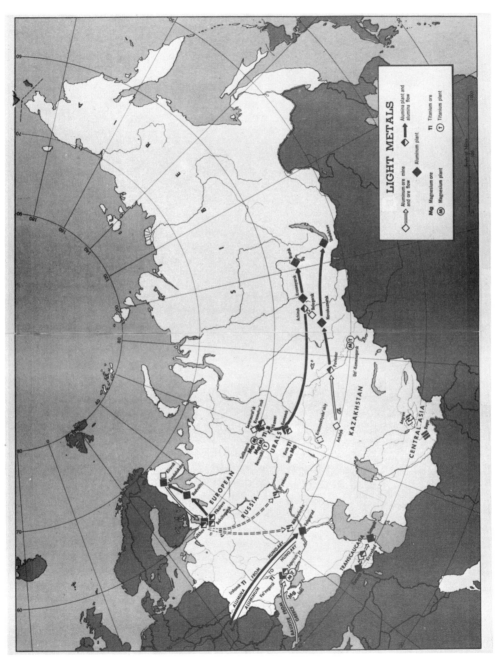

Figure 84. LIGHT METALS IN THE SOVIET UNION

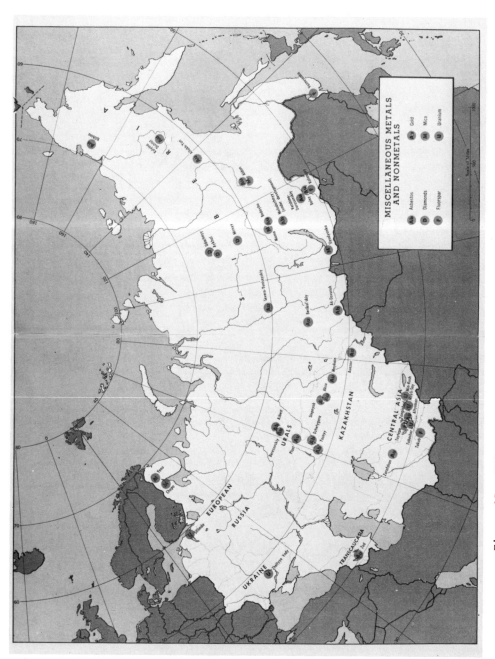

Figure 85. MESCELLANEOUS METALS AND NONMETALS IN THE SOVIET UNION

The machinery, synthetic rubber, nitrogen, chemical fibers, and consumer-goods industries are all well below the Arctic Circle near population centers. Farming in the Arctic is negligible except for limited areas in the southern parts of some river basins. Some cattle are raised in these same southern arctic areas. Reindeer herds are used for food and other products.

In the chemical industries, the Soviet Arctic plays an important role in fertilizers, but not at all for nitrogen, salts, alkalies, synthetic rubber, or chemical fibers.

The European North

The Murmansk Oblast has as much as 40 percent of the U.S.S.R.'s phosphorus resources (the chief apatite reserves), about 20 percent of the ceramic raw materials (feldspar, pegmatite), more than 95 percent of the kyanite, large reserves of abrasive materials (garnet).[71] The largest industrial center in the world bordering the Arctic Ocean is Murmansk. It is an ice-free, well-protected water area of great economic and strategic importance. As the northernmost open winter port of the U.S.S.R., it is the capital and educational center for the Kola Peninsula area. Murmansk is a center for shipbuilding, ocean trawling fleet, fish processing, and trans-ocean shipping and is the terminal of the Northern Sea Route.[85] Fishing accounts for about half of the Murmansk Oblast gross industrial product. The Murmansk coasts are ice-free most winters, due to the Norwegian Coastal Current extension of the Gulf Stream.

Archangel on the White Sea is the largest far-northern city in the world. It is a center for lumber industry and exports lumber, resin, turpentine, and furs. It has the largest saw mills of the U.S.S.R. Even though the harbor is frozen from November through May, requiring the use of icebreakers, it is an important port.

The Kola Peninsula and White Sea area also have a number of medium-size cities. Severodvinsk, Severmorsk, and Polyarnyy are Navy bases. Most of the other cities there are associated with the mining and lumber industries.

The rich apatite deposit of the Kola Peninsula is the principal raw material used at most Soviet superphosphate plants and accounts for 80 percent of the raw material used in superphosphate manufacture (Fig. 86).

In the Pechora Basin, the most important center is Vorkuta. It is a center for coal mining and geological research. Naryan-Mar is a port for both rivergoing and seagoing ships at the mouth of the Pechora and is an important timber port. Amderma on the arctic coast of the Kara Sea is a port on the Northern Sea Route and a research center for geologists and construction engineers.

Agricultural specialization by the individual oblasts and autonomous republics has been suggested as: dairy, beef, and poultry farming and (near cities) truck gardening in the southern part of the Karelian A.S.S.R.; dairy, pork, potato, and vegetable production in the southern part of Arkhangel'sk Oblast and Komi A.S.S.R.; and reindeer breeding, fur trapping, individual centers of farming, and livestock raising in the Murmansk Oblast and the northern parts of the Arkhangel'sk Oblast, Karelian, and Komi A.S.S.R.'s.[71]

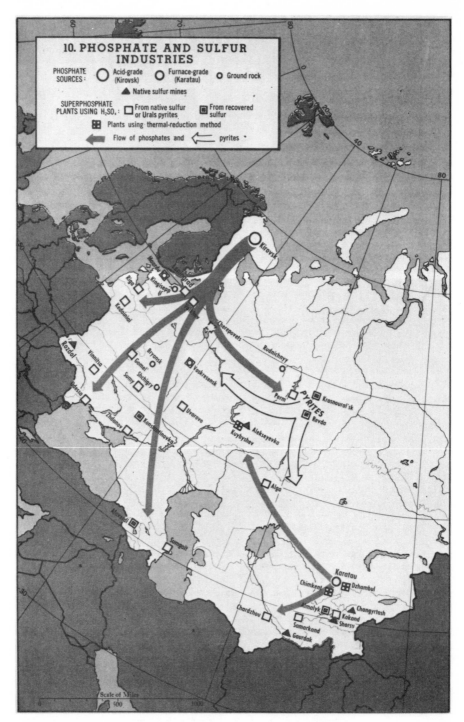

Figure 86.   PHOSPHATE AND SULFUR INDUSTRIES
OF THE SOVIET UNION

Total forest reserves of the Komi A.S.S.R. are 2.7 billion cubic meters. By 1970, the total volume of logging operations there could be brought up to 23 million cubic meters.[71] At the present time, Archangel Oblast, which holds first place in the U.S.S.R. shipments of timber, ships out 13 to 14 million metric tons of timber by rail.[71]

Western Siberian North

The west Siberian lowlands have timber reserves over an area exceeding 2 million square kilometers and are estimated at 8 billion cubic meters.[71] Future timber production could reach 28 million cubic meters annually.

Western Siberian agriculture is limited by the short growing season (at the latitude of Salekhard it is about 100 days), insufficient heat, prolonged north winds, and the threat of summer frost. Fast-ripening varieties of cereal crops (winter rye, oats, barley, and wheat), most fodder crops, potatoes, and vegetables can be grown in the Khanty-Mansi National Okrug. The total mean annual fish catch in the Ob-Irtysh Basin from 1955 to 1964 was one-third the catch for the U.S.S.R. and about 70 percent of the total catch for Siberia.

In the West Siberia Basin, the largest city is the metal mining center of Noril'sk. Salekhard is a river port at the mouth of the Ob and a center for the wood industry. Dudinka is at the mouth of the Yenisey River and serves as the port for Noril'sk. Dikson is an island off the mouth of the Yenisey and has been used as an anchorage and refueling point for ships on the Northern Sea Route. Igarka on the Yenisey is the largest timber center in Siberia.

Central and Eastern Siberian North

The central and eastern Siberian industrial centers consist mainly of small ports on the major rivers emptying into the Arctic Ocean and the industrial city of Yukutsk on the Lena River. Yukutsk is a center for coal mining and a natural gas field. Nordvik and Ambarchik are small anchorages and transshipment points. Tiksi at the mouth of the Lena River is the transshipment point for all goods coming in by sea to the Yakutskaya A.S.S.R. Pevek (700 mi east) is the port of the tin-mining region of western Chukotka.

Prospects for the Future

Concentrated in the Soviet European North in 1965 were: 100 percent of the national output of apatite concentrate, 17.5 percent of timber shipments, 12 percent of lumber production, 27.7 percent of the wood pulp, 18 percent of the paper, and 15.6 percent of the fish catch.[71] In the foreseeable future, the Soviet European North will extend its specialization in the timber, pulp and paper, woodworking, chemical, fuel, fishing, nonferrous metallurgy, and machine building sectors and expand its specialization in the titanium industry.[71] Specifically, the Archangel Oblast is expected to extend its specialization in the timber, pulp and paper, woodworking, and fishing industries and in machine building; a nonferrous metallurgy sector will emerge; and metalworking, manufacturing of building materials, and individual sectors of the food and clothing industries will be initiated.

The Murmansk Oblast is intensifying its specialization in nonferrous

The Murmansk Oblast is intensifying its specialization in nonferrous metallurgy and the chemical, mica, iron ore, and fishing industries, as well as developing metalworking, the production of building materials, and individual sectors of the food and clothing industries.

The Karelian A.S.S.R. undoubtedly will extend its specialization in the pulp, paper, woodworking, mica, and fishing industries; machine building; nonferrous metallurgy, and manufacturing of building materials. Individual sectors of the food and clothing industries and electric and thermal power production may also be expected to undergo further development.

The Komi A.S.S.R. almost certainly will intensify its specialization in the timber, pulp, paper, woodworking, coal, carbon black, gas and oil production, and oil refining industries, and expand its industrial specialization in the titanium and chemical industries. Production of electric power and building materials, as well as individual sectors of the clothing and food industries, will also be developed.

In western Siberia the main production will continue to be raw materials. Important reserves are oil, natural gas, timber, peat, coal, and iron ore. Rich reserves suggest that the region will specialize primarily in the production and partial processing of oil and gas, the shipment and chemical-mechanical processing of wood, and the petrochemical industry.

Central and eastern Siberia undoubtedly will continue the mining and production of nonferrous metals and minerals, such as gold, diamond, tin, mica, and coal.

Population

The population of the Soviet Arctic is greater by far than any other parts of the Arctic and is estimated to be about 4.5 million (see explanation below). This includes the river basins adjacent to the arctic coastline. Most of the population is concentrated in the Kola Peninsula and White Sea area, as shown in Figure 87.[86][87] Other population concentrations are along the Pechora, Ob, Yenisey, Lena, and Kolyma rivers that empty into the Arctic Ocean.

Table 19 shows the major U.S.S.R. cities in the Arctic.[86][88] Archangel and Murmansk both have populations of about 300,000. Six other cities have populations over 50,000 and 33 cities have populations of 10,000 and over. According to Izvestiya, October 2, 1966, Murmansk is expected to double its population by 1980.

The U.S.S.R. population in the arctic area was estimated, using the administrative divisions and populations in the mid-1960's as follows:[86][71]

Murmansk Oblast	)
Archangel Oblast	)
Karelian A.S.S.R.	)-- 3,700,000[71]
Komi A.S.S.R.	)
Nenets National Okrug	37,000
Yamal-Nenets National Okrug	64,000
Khanty-Mansi National Okrug	134,000
Taymr National Okrug	33,000
Evenki National Okrug	10,000
Yakut A.S.S.R.	527,000
Chukchi National Okrug	52,000
	4,557,000

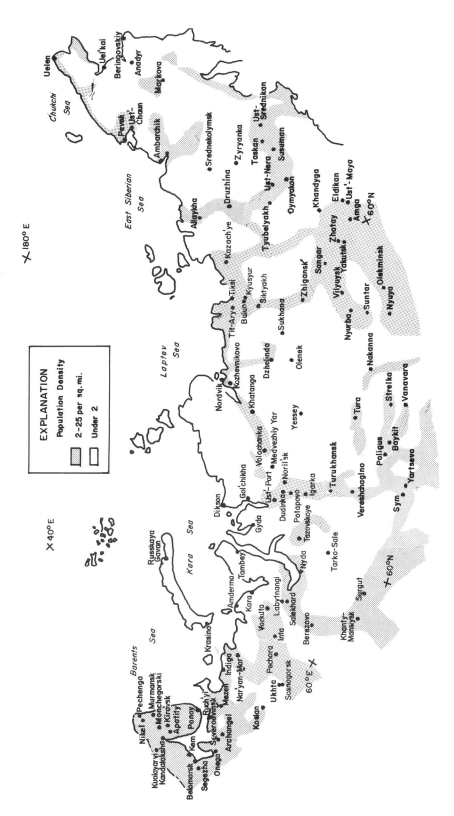

Figure 87. SOVIET ARCTIC POPULATION

It is estimated that in the mid-1960's the U.S.S.R. population in the arctic area was about 4.5 million. This amounted to about 2 percent of the total U.S.S.R. population.

It is estimated that there are nearly half a million military personnel in the Soviet Arctic Command, with many around the White Sea area and some in northern Siberia.[89] Russian census figures list military personnel at their place of recruitment, which in most cases is not the Soviet Arctic. In addition, there are probably an undetermined number of convicts and political prisoners in Siberia.

TABLE 19

Major U.S.S.R. Cities in the Arctic

City	Population	City	Population
Archangel	303,000	Naryan-Mar	11,400
Murmansk	272,000	Amderma	10,000
Noril'sk	124,000	Dikson	10,000
Yakutsk	89,000	Kem	10,000
Severodvinsk	78,657	Khatanga	10,000
Vorkuta	63,000	Kuolayurvi	10,000
Kirovsk	55,000	Yessey	10,000
Monchegorsk	54,000	Mezen	7,300
Kandalaksha	37,045	Pevek	5,800
Inta	36,154	Berezova	5,700
Ukhta	36,154	Olekminsk	5,500
Severomorsk	32,234	Turnkhansk	5,000
Pechora	30,586	Anadyr	4,600
Polyarnyy	30,000	Vilyuysk	3,600
Yartsevo	25,558	Nordvik	2,500
Vereshchagino	22,800	Ust'Maya	2,300
Khanty-Mansiysk	20,677	Tura	2,100
Apatity	19,938	Golchikha	1,300
Segezha	19,708	Verkhoyansk	1,200
Belomorsk	17,400	Tiksi	1,000
Dudinka	17,000	Allaykha	800
Onega	17,000	Ambarchik	800
Salekhard	16,567	Bulun	800
Nikel	16,305	Indiga	800
Igarka	14,300	Kazachye	800
Pechenga	13,200	Uelen	800

Transportation

The transportation in the U.S.S.R. Arctic is made up of sea, river, motor roads, and air modes as shown in Figures 88 and 89.[60][90] Rivers are the primary transportation routes for the arctic interior lands. These are tied together in the Arctic Ocean by the Northern Sea Route. To the south they are tied together by the Trans-Siberian and other railroads. Except for a motor road parallelling the railroad in the Kola Peninsula and Yakutsk in the far eastern part of Siberia, year-round roads are practically nonexistent in the Soviet Arctic.

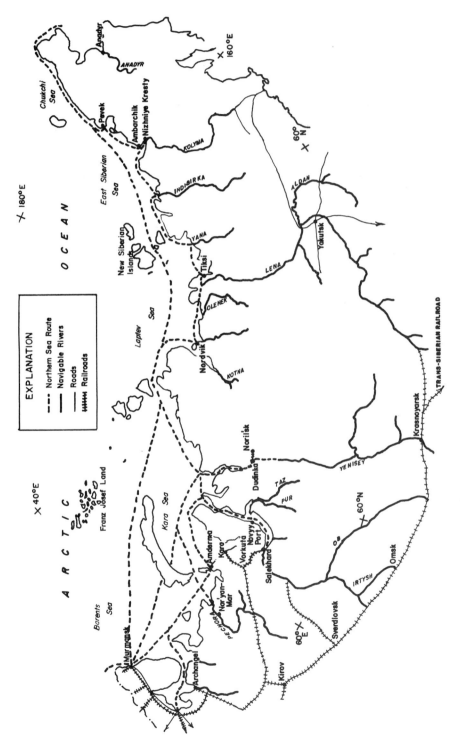

Figure 88.   MAJOR U.S.S.R. ARCTIC SURFACE ROUTES

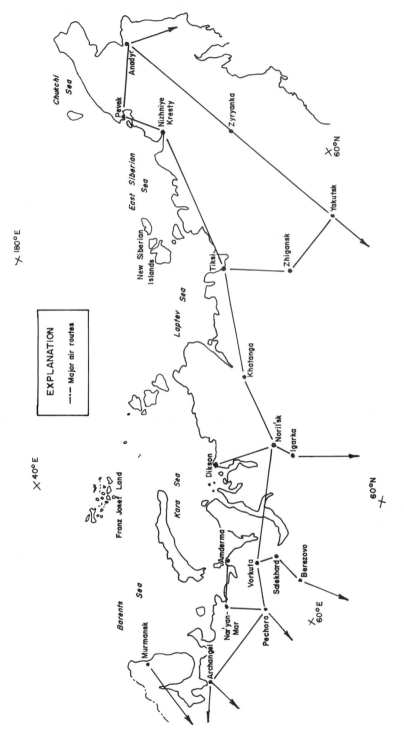

Figure 89.   MAJOR U.S.S.R. ARCTIC AIR ROUTES

Rivers

Most of the U.S.S.R. arctic rivers are navigable some distance inland part of the year. The Ob, Yenisey, and Lena rivers are navigable all the way to the Trans-Siberian Railway. However, they are frozen over a good portion of the year as follows:[91]

Ob - 220 days

Yenisey - 168 days

Lena (upper reaches) - 220 days

(lower reaches) - 275 days

A canal connects the White and Baltic seas permitting river traffic between Leningrad and Archangel. River and canal waterways are used extensively in the U.S.S.R. and their importance is constantly increasing - second only to railroads.

The rivers of the Pechora Basin provide excellent waterways for floating timber to pulp mills. Thus, Naryan-Mar on the southeast side of the Pechora River delta is a timber port of growing importance. The Siberian rivers are navigable their entire length for about four months only. During the winter months, when thick ice covers the rivers, over-snow vehicles and sledges are used.

The river freighting will be expanded in the future. On the Ob-Irtysh, the freight in 1980 is expected to be 35 million metric tons, three times the present figure.[57] This will be due to the oil and gas developments in the area.

Railroads

There is a well-developed network of railroads on the Kola Peninsula linking industrial and mining centers. The principal line runs from Murmansk to Belomorsk and then to Leningrad via Petrozavodsk or to Moscow via Vologda. The line extends north and west from Murmansk to Nikel. Branches extend from Olenegorsk to Monchegorsk, from Apitity to Kirovsk, and from Pinozero to Kovdor. Branches also extend to the Finnish border.

In the Pechora Basin, Vorkuta is linked to the main U.S.S.R. railroad network with a double-track electrified line. Northward the railroad extends to the port of Kara on the arctic coast of the Kara Sea.[90] Eastward the railroad crosses the northern Urals to Labytnangi, on the lower Ob opposite Salekhard.

In the Siberian Arctic, the only other railroad besides the previously mentioned one to Labytnangi is a short line between Dudinka on the Yenisey River and Noril'sk. A line was started in the early 1950's from the mouth of the Ob eastward to Igarka but later abandoned. Opening of oil and gas fields in this region may force its completion and possible extension to Dudinka.[59]

Northern Sea Route

The Northern Sea Route consists of a system of shipping lanes along the
arctic coasts of the U.S.S.R. from the straits between the Barents and Kara
seas to the Bering Strait. It is considered to include extensions to
Murmansk and Archangel at its western end and to Vladivostok at its eastern
end, as well as to branches at various ports along the navigable rivers
flowing into the Arctic Ocean. The principal seaports and river ports along
the route are Naryan-Mar on the Pechora River; Amderma at the southwestern
end of the Kara Sea; Novyy Port on the Gulf of Ob; Salekhard at the mouth of
the Ob River; Dikson, Dudinka, and Igarka on the Yenisey River; Nordvik at
the southwestern end of the Laptev Sea; Tiksi near the delta of the Lena
River; Kresty on the Kolyma River; and Ambarchik and Pevek at the southern
part of the East Siberian Sea.

The route is open up to 150 days per year with the aid of icebreakers
and the melting of fast ice by means of dark powder sprinkled on it. Two
new nuclear-powered icebreakers of the *Lenin* class are to be added in the
early 1970's; they are expected to prolong the shipping season to about
six months.[90] The route is now also open to foreign commerce on payment
of a fee for icebreaker and pilot services.

The Northern Sea Route is of economic and strategic importance to the
U.S.S.R. Freighting is estimated at 1.5 to 2 million metric tons, carried
by 200 to 300 ships.[59] Most freighting is not a through trip, but rather
from Murmansk to destinations on the eastern portion of the route. Ships
engaged in local traffic are often able to make two to three round trips a
season. The major freighting item is timber exported from Igarka on the
Yenisey (reaching 188,000 standards in 129 ships in 1967).[59] Next is
probably bringing general freight to Dudinka (for Noril'sk) and to Pevek and
the Kolma River for mining settlements inland. The through route from west
to east is used to transfer Navy ships such as cruisers, destroyers, and
submarines to and from bases in the Far East.

Air Routes

The major air routes in the U.S.S.R. Arctic are shown in Figure 89.[90]
[70][89] The larger cities such as Murmansk, Archangel, Vorkuta, and
Noril'sk have scheduled air service. Airlines, following the major rivers,
generally link all the main towns and mining centers. Special airlifts are
common in more important research areas.

Pipelines

Figure 90 shows the principal U.S.S.R. gas fields and pipelines.[69]
A 48-inch diameter gas pipeline connected the Vuktyl gas field in western
Siberia to the Moscow-Leningrad gas transmission system in 1969.[69] By
the late 1970's the west Siberian gas may be handled by transmission mains
of 80-inch and 100-inch lines to European Russia, the Baltic area,
Belorussia, the Urals, and the Ukraine and to countries of eastern
Europe.[69]

In eastern Siberia the natural gas field at Tas-Tumus is connected to
Yakutsk via a 250-mi-long pipeline to fuel a gas-turbine power station. The
pipeline has been extended to the Bestyakh-Pokrovsk area for supplying gas
to cement and lumber plants.

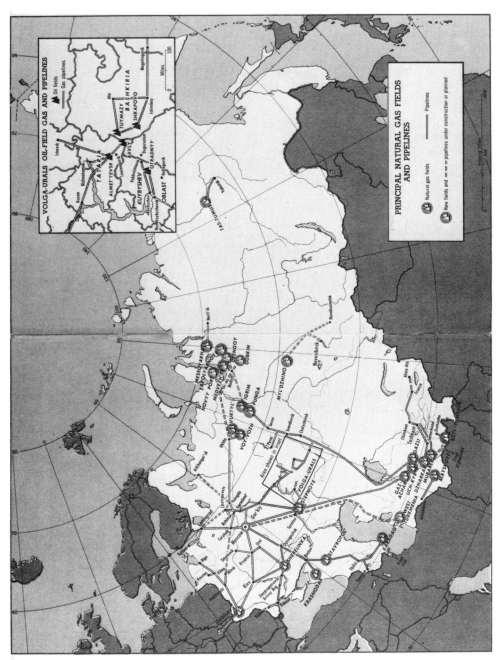

Figure 90.   PRINCIPAL NATURAL GAS FIELDS AND PIPELINES IN THE SOVIET UNION

Another gas pipeline is the 170-mi line built eastward across the Yenisey River to the mining center of Noril'sk.

In all, 39,000 mi of pipelines have been built to carry gas from the remote areas. Additional pipelines are planned, and the western Siberia throughput is expected to more than double by 1975.[72] It has recently (April 1971) been reported that Belgium may join three other west European countries as importers of Siberian natural gas. Austria, Italy, and West Germany are expected to begin receiving pipeline deliveries from Russia in 1973, and Belgium may extend the line from West Germany.[92] Soviet officials contend that the large-diameter pipelines can deliver Siberian gas to the Moscow area at one-third the cost of bringing in coal by railroad.[83] They also contend that west Siberian crude oil, even in the first stages of development, including high capital outlays, will cost about the same as Volga-Ural oil, which is the cheapest obtainable now.[83]

The U.S.S.R. has about 18,000 mi of oil pipelines.[76]

Scandinavian Arctic Resources

Arctic Scandinavia, if it were defined as the Scandinavian areas north of 60°, would embrace nearly all of Norway, Sweden, and Finland, plus all of Greenland and Iceland. If the Arctic Circle is used as the boundary, most of Sweden, Norway, and Finland fall south of the boundary and all of Iceland; and a part of southern Greenland also becomes non-arctic. If the criterion used is not a parallel of latitude but an area with "arctic conditions," primarily determined by water navigation conditions and accessability, the only parts of Scandinavia that are actually "arctic" are large parts of Greenland and Svalbard. Sweden, Finland, and Norway are in effect subarctic in parts and otherwise are temperate zone areas made so by the Gulf Stream. However, for purposes of this study the areas north of the Arctic Circle will be given attention as arctic areas.

Norway

Figure 91 shows the towns, railroads, and motor roads of arctic Scandinavia, including parts of Norway, Sweden, and Finland. The Norway area is generally mountainous, with an elevated coast strongly dissected by fjords and inlets. The coast and ports are ice-free.

Most of the population is concentrated in small towns along the coast or at the base of the fjords. About 100,000 of Norway's total population of 3.7 million live in northern Norway. Three towns, Bodø, Narvik, and Tromsø, have populations exceeding 10,000.

Mineral Resources

Aside from the fisheries off the coast, the major products of northern Norway are minerals, of which iron ore is the most significant. Norway's largest mine is located just south of Kirkenes, at the Norwegian-Soviet border on the Barents Sea. The mine produces about 2.5 million tons of iron concentrates per year.[90] Reserves are estimated at about 500 million tons of low-grade ore. The concentrates are shipped from Kirkenes port mainly to smelters in western Europe. A much greater quantity of iron ore is shipped from the port of Narvik, which receives the ore via railroad from the richer mines of northern Sweden. The rail-port capacity is 20 million tons per year.

At Sulitjelma, close to the Swedish border, there is a mining center producing copper concentrates and pyrites. The nearby port of Bodø serves as a shipping point.

Like the other Scandinavian countries, Norway has been considered poor in energy minerals. The only resource of even local consequence has been the coal on Svalbard. Production there has ranged upward of 450,000 tons annually, but 1968 production was down to 330,000 tons.[93] Recently the Norwegian energy resource picture has changed, due to the discovery of important oil resources by a Phillips consortium in the Norwegian sector of the North Sea. The so-called Ekofisk find is about to begin production

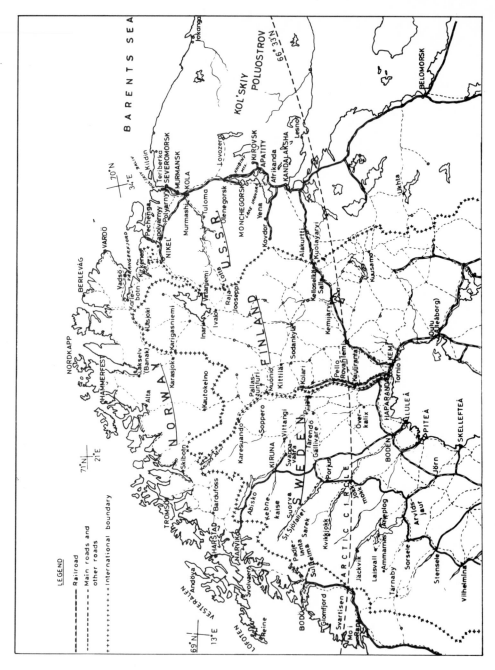

Figure 91.   MAP OF ARCTIC SCANDINAVIA AND THE KOLA PENINSULA

from a field which is 150 mi off the southwest Norwegian coast. The
field's potential has been estimated as more than 1 billion barrels.[94]
The Ekofisk find is not in the Arctic, but the find has spurred anew the
exploration in the Norwegian continental shelf areas between 62° and 83°
which includes Svalbard (the Spitsbergen Archipelago). Exploration has
previously been conducted in the Spitsbergen area by U.S., Norwegian,
Soviet, and French concerns since 1960, thus far without success. Soviet
interests have also operated coal mines on what, until recently, was
called West Spitsbergen (See Fig. 92).

Transportation

Motor roads connect all major towns on the mainland of northern
Norway. Roads also connect to southern Norway, to northern Finland, and,
via Finland, to Sweden. A railroad extends from southern Norway to Bodø
and the mining area of Sulitjelma, but does not reach the Narvik-Tromsø-
Hammerfest-Kirkenes towns farther north. Narvik is connected by rail to
the iron mines in northern Sweden. Airports exist at Kirkenes, Lakselv,
Hammerfest, Alta, Kautokeino, Tromsø, Bardufoss, Harstad, Narvik, Svolvaer,
Ballstad, and Bodø. Coastal steamers make daily calls at all the larger
and most of the smaller port towns from Bodø around North Cape to Kirkenes.

Meteorological stations are located on the Norwegian island of Jan
Mayen, 300 mi northeast of Iceland, and on Bear Island, located between
northern Norway and Spitsbergen.

Sweden

One-seventh of Sweden lies north of the Arctic Circle. All the area
is inland, with mountains to the north and west. The largest town is the
iron district town of Kiruna, with a population of 28,000. The permanent
population of arctic Sweden is estimated at 80,000, of a national total
of nearly 8 million. An ESRO Sounding Rocket Launching Range has been
active near Kiruna since 1966. It is operated by the European Space
Research Organization.

Mineral Resources

The principal mineral resource of arctic Sweden is iron ore, which
has been mined actively since 1888. Estimated reserves are 3,000 million
tons.[94] Ore fields are concentrated around Kiruna, Gallivare, and
Malmberget. Total capacity of the pelletizing plants in these areas is
4.4 million tons per year. Most of the iron-rich ore is exported - 25
million tons in 1968. Northern Sweden also has copper resources recently
being developed. In 1968 the Boliden Company opened an open-pit mine at
Aitik, 10 mi southeast of Gallivare. The 1968 production was 18,200 tons
of metal content ore. Production is scheduled to reach 2 million tons per
year, which will yield 20-35 tons of concentrate and 10,000 tons of recoverable copper.[95] Total reserves are estimated at 30 million tons open-pit
and 120 million tons additional underground to a depth of 300 meters. The
metal ore is said to extend to a depth of 600 meters (nearly 2,000 ft).[95]

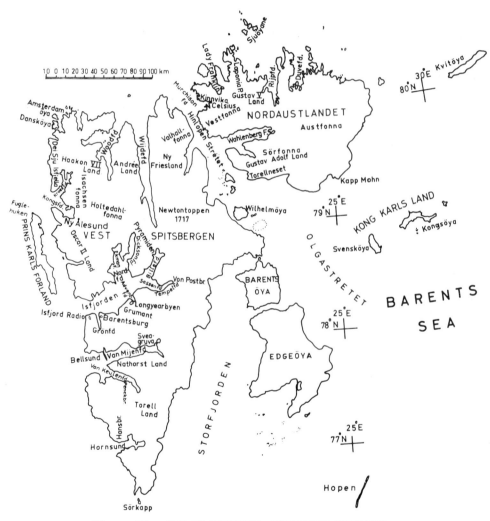

Figure 92. MAP OF SVALBARD, EXCLUDING BJORNOYA

Hydroelectric Power

There are several hydroelectric power plants in arctic Sweden, including those at Porjus and Harspranget. The economic hydroelectric potential of the area is estimated at 14,600 million kilowatt hours per year.[90] A one-million-kilowatt station is planned near the Norwegian border, in the vicinity of Narvik.

Transportation

Two Swedish railroads penetrate the Swedish Arctic - the Malmbanen railroad, which opened in 1888 and extends to the Norwegian port of Narvik, and the Inland railroad, which connects with southern Sweden. Good motor roads link the towns in the eastern half of arctic Sweden and connect with those to the south and to Finland. Kiruna has regular air service to southern Sweden.

Finland

One-quarter of Finland is located north of the Arctic Circle. Most of the area is lowland. The major town, Rovaniemi, which is actually just south of the Arctic Circle, has a population of about 25,000. Lesser towns are Kemijarvi, Ivalo, and Sodankyla. Arctic Finland has about 50,000 people out of a total population above 4.5 million.

Mineral Resources

Iron ore mining is an important industry in arctic Finland. Mines are located in the region of Kemijarvi and Kolari. Cobalt and gold have been found in the Kittila region, and limestone is found near Kolari.[96] Finland lost its richest arctic-area mineral resource to the U.S.S.R. by the territorial cession of the Petsamo region after World War II.

A Finnish company is developing a new iron deposit in the Kolari district and plans to begin production in 1974. Finnish Lapland also has some apatite deposits.[96]

Hydroelectric Power

The Finnish arctic area has potential for the generation of hydroelectric power, and a proposed net would provide 5,500 million kilowatt hours annually.[90]

Transportation

One railroad extends from Rovaniemi through the mining areas of Kemjarvi and then on to the U.S.S.R. border, where it connects with the Kola Peninsula Soviet rail network. A second railroad extends from southern Finland to Kolari, and Rovaniemi also has a rail connection with Oulu and points farther south. Motor roads connect all Finnish towns, and there are five road connections with Sweden, three with Norway, and four with the U.S.S.R. Rovaniemi and Ivalo have airline service with Kirkenes at the eastern tip of northern Norway and with Helsinki in southern Finland.

Connections with Murmansk have also existed.

Greenland

Greenland, which is constitutionally a part of Denmark, has the
northernmost land in the world, with Coffee Cup Island at 83°38'N, 33°52'W.
Eighty-four percent of Greenland is covered by a dome-shaped ice cap, as
is shown in Figure 93.[90] Most of Greenland is above the Arctic Circle
and has arctic conditions, with only 16 percent of the land ice-free.[97]
Most of the population - 40,000 of the total of about 50,000 - lives along
the southwest edge of the island, where the warmer ocean currents moderate
the climate.

Mineral Resources

Cryolite has been mined in southwest Greenland at Ivigtut for over a
century. At one time the production was of major economic importance, with
exports around 40-50 thousand tons per year.[90] The mine is now closed,
however. It is the only place in the world, aside from the U.S.S.R., where
a large deposit of the mineral has been found. Its main use is as a flux
in the electrolysis process of aluminum smelting.

However, Greenland has not lost its interest as a potential source of
valuable minerals. As may be noted, Greenland is by far the largest
unexplored land mass in the world that is politically stable.[98] Its
geologic, climatic, and logistics characteristics are similar to much of
arctic Canada; and it is not too difficult to explore. The recently
organized Geological Survey of Greenland (GGU) has set out to map the
country and to advise the Danish government on minerals policy. The entire
island has now been mapped. Prospecting will follow on much of the 185,000
sq mi that are uncovered coastal region. The minerals most anticipated are
oil, gas, lead, and zinc. A small lead-zinc deposit was, in fact, profit-
ably mined in the early 1950's near Mesters Veg on the east coast. Inland
from there a large molybdenum deposit was discovered. On the west coast a
small amount of low-grade coal has been mined from time to time.

Exploration during the past ten years has been mainly under Canadian
consortiums. Cominco, Ltd. controls a lead-zinc deposit on the west
coast. A production decision is anticipated by 1975.[98] Another Canadian
company (Renzy Mines) has a 2,000-sq-mi concession at Fiskenaesset on the
southwest coast, which is being examined for copper-nickel-platinum
sulphide mineralization. Low-grade chromite, which carries vanadium and
rutile, has also been found in the area. Possibilities of nickel, magnelite,
kimerlite, and fluorite, have also been reported. A Danish company has a
large concession on the east coast, embracing a molybdenum discovery. A
low-grade uranium mineralization on the south tip of Greenland is also
being investigated.

The most recent intense interest has developed in the offshore areas
along the west coast, where non-exclusive exploration concessions have
been granted for limited terms of years. The search is for oil and gas
and also for radioactive materials. A Canadian consortium is reported
to be spending $2.3 million in oil exploration in northern Greenland in
1971.[99] The oil company interest reportedly centers on the waters off
west Greenland, all the way from the northeast corner of Baffin Bay (Thule
area) into Labrador Sea off Cape Farvel at the southern tip of Greenland.[100]

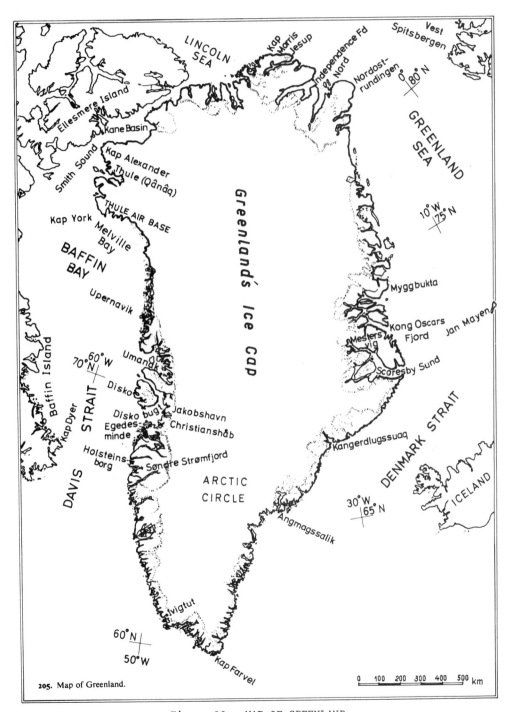

205. Map of Greenland.

Figure 93. MAP OF GREENLAND

U.S. and European companies have flown aeromagnetic surveys, and seismic
surveys have been made by two U.S. companies.[100] There are 19 companies
holding licenses, and activity has been spurred by the explorations
begun in 1969 in the Canadian Arctic Archipelago and by the Baffin Bay
geophysical investigations. The Danish government has not yet decided
on granting exclusive exploration or exploitation rights. A committee has
been drawing up recommendations to the government.

The ultimate result of the current activities off the west coast cannot
yet be forecast. Drilling is said to be at least three or four years away.
A one-year delay in the award of concessions is anticipated, and 1974
is the earliest target date for drilling.[101] Weather, wind, fog, and ice
are pointed to as negative factors which will also increase costs. Until
more is known about the potential oil and gas trapped in the area, one can
only note that the degree of oil company interest suggests the possibility
of further great petroleum finds in the Greenland-eastern Canada region of
the Arctic. The Alaskan, north Canadian, and Siberian oil resources that
are assuming such great potential importance, may be found to extend also
into the Greenland-northeastern Canada area.

Transportation

Conventional roads between towns do not exist in arctic Greenland, and
special snow vehicles are used for military transport on the ice sheet.
Shipping along the east coast is limited by ice conditions to a short
summer season. However, the west coast season is much longer for all
shipping. Several airfields exist: at Thule Air Base in northwest Greenland, Sondre Stromfjord (Sonderstrom) on the west coast, Nord at the
Arctic Ocean, Mestersvig on the east coast, and Godthaab and Julianehaab
on the southwest coast. The world's longest commercial helicopter routes
are maintained between Sondrektoven, Godthaab, and Sukkertoppen.

Future Significance of Arctic Resources

Less Promising Arctic Resources

If people are a significant resource, the Arctic gives little promise
of developing that resource in great quantity. The foregoing references
to arctic-area populations have simply emphasized the well-known fact
that those areas, with few exceptions, are very thinly populated. Large-
scale resource development may change this situation to some degree, but
it appears now that the most probable types of new economic activity in
the Arctic for the next few decades will be precisely those that will
require little manpower. Migration to the Arctic of many people for other
purposes cannot now be foreseen.

Agriculture is now a distantly minor activity in most arctic areas, and
relative costs-of-production factors, probably much more than higher transportation costs, are unlikely to change the picture.

Forest resources are absent, or nearly so, from almost all the genuinely
arctic areas, although the Arctic Circle is not in all circumpolar areas
north of the tree line. Nevertheless, the relatively slow growth of trees
in the forested arctic areas, the higher costs of production and transportation in most arctic places, and the fact that forests are a renewable
resource at lower cost in lower latitudes are among the important factors
that point to very minor forestry development in most of the Arctic.

Industry, except for specialty industries encouraged by the presence
of a suitable resource, is not now predictable for much of the Arctic.
Aside from native crafts, the cost factor again is discouraging, as is
the labor supply now and probably in the future. Efforts by the Soviets
and others to attract or force labor into the high Arctic have had some,
but not major, successes.

The fishing industry is a widespread and, in some waters, relatively
lucrative activity in the Arctic. It is yet to be established, however,
that the Arctic Ocean is teeming with edible fish, and most of the present
fish catch, except for example in the Gulf Stream waters north of
Norway and the western U.S.S.R., is in the somewhat warmer waters south of
the Arctic. The fishing industry prospects for most of the Arctic must
probably be rated as unpromising.

Hard Minerals of Significance

The country by country circumpolar survey has indicated the presence
of considerable deposits in the Arctic of numerous hard minerals, including
metals. It has also been noted that while some of the hard minerals
are now being produced in the Arctic, and that production in most arctic
areas is on the rise, the picture is not uniform. High production costs,
labor scarcity, transportation problems, and, in general, lower costs of
production outside the Arctic must give rise to caution in predicting
sharp increases in hard metal production across the board in the arctic
deposits. Heavy world demands may have the effect of raising prices on some

minerals to the point where arctic production becomes profitable. Copper
may well become such a mineral, and copper deposits of greater or lesser
amounts have been located, if not yet developed, in circumpolar areas such
as Alaska, Canada, Scandinavia, and the U.S.S.R. Iron ore deposits, if
accessible and rich enough in iron, may also be found worthy of development.
The Mary River deposit on Baffin Island is a good example of an extensive
rich ore deposit. The predicted cumulative demands for iron and steel in the
U.S. for the next three decades indicate, as stated, that the known reserves
are 40 percent short and that the supply will need to be augmented. It is
unlikely, under these circumstances, that the 139 million tons of Baffin
Island iron ore which grades 68 percent iron or better, will be left in the
ground. Soviet deposits at Olenegorsk, with even greater total reserves will
probably also be developed, although the Soviet iron ore production is now
concentrated in the Ukraine and other non-arctic areas. (See Fig. 81.)
Norway and Sweden are producing, and will undoubtedly continue to produce,
from their northern iron mines, but conditions there are not really arctic;
and the transportation problem is a simple one, due to the ice-free ports of
Narvik and Kirkenes close at hand.

     Other minerals that may well develop more critical supply and demand
situations have also been noted, such as mercury, lead and zinc, tin, tungsten, flourite, and perhaps gold. The near-term prospects for significant
increases in production from most arctic areas that have deposits of the
named metals are not great. During the period 1980 to 2000, however, the
demand curve may well cause more intense production efforts. Technological
advances both in mining and in transportation techniques could also lower
production and delivery costs to the point where arctic-situated mines become competitive. Again, the comparative richness of the ores becomes a
factor.

     In addition to the base and common metals one should also take account
of rare metals that may become significant. The arctic inventory of such
metals is not taken in this study.

     A high U.S. official has recently stated that the U.S. demand for
primary minerals will increase fourfold by the year 2000. Specifically, he
predicted a sixfold demand for aluminum and titanium; a fourfold demand for
tungsten and vanadium; a threefold demand for copper, sand and gravel, beryllium, fluorine, tantalum, and magnesium; and a doubling of demand for many
others.[18] Even if his prediction is borne out, the prospect that many of
the arctic area mineral deposits will lie undeveloped does not entirely disappear, but for some key metals major development may well occur if the projection is moved to the year 2000.

Energy Fuels

Known Resources and Consumption Rates

     Although we have noted coal deposits in Alaska, arctic U.S.S.R., and a
few other arctic locations, the prospect that arctic coal will become a critical energy resource to be developed in the next three decades appears to be
extremely dim. The fact that more inexpensively accessible deposits are rec-
koned as sufficient to meet world needs for upward of 400 years is likely to
offer little prospect for major arctic production. A reservation should be
made, however, that a country such as Japan, greatly in need of energy fuels,
may find it advantageous to bargain for the production of some coal from easily accessible Alaska, just as Norway has produced some coal in Spitsbergen.

The energy source which has risen most sharply in world production and consumption has its location in the deposits of oil and gas that have been found in great and small concentrations in all continents and in many parts of the coastal seabeds. The rise in world production and consumption will be seen from Tables 20, 21, 22, and 23.[82] It will be noted that world oil production increased during the period 1959-1969 from slightly over one billion tons a year to over two billion (1,012.2 million to 2,145.0 million). During the same period, consumption, naturally, has also doubled, going from 20.07 million barrels per day to 42.55 million barrels. The rate of increase, both in production and consumption, during that period has been greater in the eastern hemisphere than in the western, both production and consumption having tripled in the eastern hemisphere during the decade.

Table 24 shows world "published proved" oil reserves at the end of 1969.[82] Figure 94 shows the relative production on a regional basis and the world total for the decade 1959-1969, as well as the world reserves at the beginning and end of that decade.

Several facts of interest to the evaluation of potential arctic reserves as a factor in the energy picture during the coming decades emerge from the recent production and reserve tables. It should be noted at the outset that the statistics given are either recorded historical facts in the case of production figures or, on the "reserves" side, are of "published proved" reserves only. On the other hand, most of the estimates of arctic oil potential in this study have been of the estimated potential, rather than of the "proved" category.

We note, for example, that while world oil reserves increased by about 240 billion barrels during the 1960's (300 billion to 540 billion) or an 80 percent increase, the increase was accounted for largely by the oil finds in the Middle East and Africa. By 1970, those two areas accounted for 72.7 percent of the world's proved reserves; whereas the U.S. had barely 7 percent, Canada had less than 2 percent, and the U.S.S.R. and the eastern Europe-China area had 11 percent. In other words, the circumpolar-arctic countries, plus a number of eastern hemisphere countries, had only about 20 percent of the world total proved oil reserves.

We note, more particularly, that the U.S., which had produced approximately 100 billion barrels of oil during the 1960's, had a proved reserve of only 37.8 billion barrels at the beginning of the 1970's. The U.S.-Canadian total reserves by January 1, 1970 were less than half the U.S. production during the previous decade.

We note also from the consumption tables, that by 1969 the U.S. was consuming oil at the rate of about 5 billion barrels annually. The 1970 consumption rose to 5.4 billion barrels.[102] At the 1970 rate of U.S. consumption, assuming no imports, the 37.8 billion barrel "proved" U.S. reserves of January 1, 1970 would theoretically be exhausted by the end of 1976. Assuming a continued rise in national consumption rate, the January 1, 1970 U.S. reserves would not even cover 7 years' consumption. On a similarly hypothetical basis Canada's proven reserves as of the beginning of the 1970's would give 20 years' supply at the 1969 rate of consumption. The corresponding figure for the U.S.S.R., eastern Europe, and China would be 26 years. Considering that there are economic, political, and strategic bases for any nation, particularly an industrial, technically advanced country wishing to have its own, or at least dependable, sources of energy, it is not surprising that the recent explorations and discoveries of oil

TABLE 20

World Oil Production

MILLION TONS

COUNTRY/AREA	1959	1960	1961	1962	1963	1964	1965	1966	1967	1968	1969	1969 over 1959	1969 over 1964
NORTH AMERICA													
U.S.A.													
Crude Oil	350·3	350·3	356·7	364·1	374·5	379·2	387·6	412·0	437·5	452·9	457·7	+ 2·8%	+ 4·0%
Natural Gas Liquids	31·8	33·8	35·8	36·9	39·5	41·7	43·6	46·1	50·5	53·8	56·9	+ 6·0%	+ 6·5%
	382·1	384·1	392·5	401·0	414·0	420·9	431·2	458·1	488·0	506·7	514·6	+ 3·3%	+ 4·3%
Canada	25·4	26·4	31·3	35·7	38·2	40·8	45·6	49·4	54·1	58·2	64·2	+ 9·8%	+ 9·3%
Mexico	13·6	14·8	15·9	16·5	17·1	17·6	18·0	18·3	20·2	21·5	22·3	+ 5·3%	+ 5·3%
TOTAL NORTH AMERICA	421·1	425·3	439·7	453·2	469·3	479·3	494·8	525·8	562·3	586·4	601·1	+ 3·8%	+ 4·8%
CARIBBEAN													
Venezuela	143·5	148·8	152·3	167·6	170·1	177·4	182·1	176·9	185·9	189·7	189·1	+ 2·8%	+ 1·5%
Colombia	7·6	7·7	7·4	7·2	8·4	8·7	10·2	9·9	9·6	8·8	10·7	+ 3·8%	+ 4·5%
Trinidad	5·7	6·1	6·5	7·0	6·9	7·1	7·0	7·9	9·3	9·6	8·3	+ 3·8%	+ 3·3%
TOTAL CARIBBEAN AREA	156·8	162·6	166·2	181·8	185·4	193·2	199·3	194·7	204·8	208·1	208·1	+ 2·8%	+ 1·8%
SOUTH AMERICA													
Argentina	6·4	9·1	12·0	14·0	13·9	14·3	14·1	15·0	15·6	17·9	18·6	+11·0%	+ 5·3%
Brazil	3·3	4·1	4·8	4·6	5·1	4·4	4·7	5·8	7·1	8·0	8·3	+10·3%	+13·5%
Others	4·0	4·3	4·5	5·0	5·3	5·6	5·6	5·8	6·6	7·6	7·3	+ 6·8%	+ 5·8%
TOTAL SOUTH AMERICA	13·7	17·5	21·3	23·6	24·3	24·3	24·4	26·6	29·3	33·5	34·2	+ 9·8%	+ 7·3%
TOTAL WESTERN HEMISPHERE	591·6	605·4	627·2	658·6	679·0	696·8	718·5	747·1	796·4	828·0	843·4	+ 3·8%	+ 4·0%
WESTERN EUROPE													
France	1·6	2·0	2·2	2·4	2·5	2·8	3·0	2·9	2·8	2·7	2·5	+ 4·5%	− 2·5%
W. Germany	5·1	5·5	6·2	6·8	7·4	7·7	7·9	7·9	7·9	8·0	7·9	+ 4·5%	+ 0·5%
Austria	2·4	2·4	2·4	2·3	2·6	2·7	2·8	2·7	2·7	2·7	2·7	+ 1·5%	+ 0·8%
Others	4·8	5·4	6·0	6·2	6·6	8·4	8·4	8·6	9·4	9·6	10·3	+ 8·0%	+ 4·0%
TOTAL WESTERN EUROPE	13·9	15·3	16·8	17·7	19·1	21·6	22·1	22·1	22·8	23·0	23·4	+ 5·3%	+ 1·8%
MIDDLE EAST													
Iran	46·4	52·6	59·4	66·0	73·1	85·4	94·8	105·1	129·3	142·2	168·1	+13·8%	+14·5%
Iraq	41·8	47·5	49·0	49·2	56·7	61·7	64·4	68·0	60·1	74·3	74·9	+ 6·0%	+ 4·0%
Kuwait	69·5	81·9	82·7	92·2	97·2	106·7	109·0	114·4	115·2	122·1	129·5	+ 6·5%	+ 4·0%
Neutral Zone	6·1	7·3	9·5	13·0	16·7	18·8	19·1	22·3	21·7	22·1	23·3	+14·3%	+ 4·5%
Qatar	7·9	8·2	8·3	8·8	9·1	10·2	11·0	13·8	15·4	16·3	17·0	+ 8·3%	+10·5%
Saudi Arabia	54·2	62·1	69·2	75·8	80·5	86·2	100·8	119·4	129·2	140·9	148·6	+10·5%	+11·5%
Abu Dhabi	—	—	—	0·8	2·6	9·0	13·6	17·3	18·3	24·0	28·9	*	+26·3%
Others	2·1	2·2	2·2	2·2	2·4	2·5	2·8	3·3	6·5	17·2	24·0	+25·3%	+57·0%
TOTAL MIDDLE EAST	228·0	261·8	280·3	308·0	338·3	380·5	415·5	463·6	495·7	559·1	614·3	+10·5%	+10·3%
AFRICA													
Algeria	1·2	8·6	15·8	20·7	23·9	26·5	26·5	33·8	39·1	42·8	44·5	+43·5%	+11·0%
Libya	—	—	0·9	8·7	22·4	41·4	58·7	72·3	84·3	125·5	149·8	*	+29·5%
Other North Africa	3·3	3·4	3·9	4·8	5·8	6·6	6·6	7·0	8·6	14·6	19·6	+19·5%	+24·5%
Nigeria	0·5	0·9	2·8	3·5	3·8	6·0	13·7	20·7	16·2	6·9	26·6	+48·8%	+34·8%
Other West Africa	0·8	0·9	1·0	1·5	1·8	2·4	1·8	2·3	4·1	6·2	11·8	+31·0%	+37·0%
TOTAL AFRICA	5·8	13·8	24·4	39·2	57·7	82·9	107·3	136·1	152·3	196·0	252·3	+46·5%	+25·0%
SOUTH EAST ASIA													
Indonesia	19·1	20·6	21·4	23·1	22·5	23·3	23·8	23·5	25·5	29·7	35·3	+ 6·3%	+ 8·5%
Other S.E. Asia	5·4	4·6	4·2	4·0	4·0	3·6	3·9	4·7	5·6	6·2	6·9	+ 2·5%	+13·8%
TOTAL SOUTH EAST ASIA	24·5	25·2	25·6	27·1	26·5	26·9	27·7	28·2	31·1	35·9	42·2	+ 5·5%	+ 9·5%
U.S.S.R.	129·5	147·9	166·0	186·0	206·1	223·6	243·0	265·1	288·0	309·0	328·0	+ 9·8%	+ 8·0%
EASTERN EUROPE AND CHINA	17·2	19·3	20·0	21·8	22·4	24·2	25·2	26·7	27·0	29·7	30·0	+ 5·8%	+ 4·5%
OTHER EASTERN HEMISPHERE	1·7	1·8	2·0	3·1	3·5	4·2	5·1	7·0	8·2	9·7	11·4	+21·0%	+22·0%
TOTAL EASTERN HEMISPHERE	420·6	485·1	535·1	602·9	673·6	763·9	845·9	948·8	1,025·1	1,162·4	1,301·6	+12·0%	+11·3%
WORLD (excl. U.S.S.R., E.Europe, China)	865·5	923·3	976·3	1,053·7	1,124·1	1,212·9	1,296·2	1,404·1	1,506·5	1,651·7	1,787·0	+ 7·5%	+ 8·0%
WORLD	1,012·2	1,090·5	1,162·3	1,261·6	1,352·6	1,460·7	1,564·4	1,695·9	1,821·5	1,990·4	2,145·0	+ 7·8%	+ 8·0%

*Greater than 300%

TABLE 21

World Oil Production

THOUSAND BARRELS DAILY

COUNTRY/AREA	1959	1960	1961	1962	1963	1964	1965	1966	1967	1968	1969	Yearly Change 1969 over 1959	Yearly Change 1969 over 1964
NORTH AMERICA													
U.S.A.													
Crude Oil	7,055	7,035	7,185	7,330	7,540	7,615	7,805	8,295	8,810	9,095	9,215	+ 2·8%	+ 4·0%
Natural Gas Liquids	880	930	990	1,020	1,100	1,155	1,210	1,285	1,410	1,505	1,590	+ 6·0%	+ 6·5%
	7,935	7,965	8,175	8,350	8,640	8,770	9,015	9,580	10,220	10,600	10,805	+ 3·3%	+ 4·3%
Canada	520	540	645	735	790	850	935	1,015	1,110	1,195	1,325	+ 9·8%	+ 9·3%
Mexico	275	300	320	335	345	355	360	370	410	435	455	+ 5·3%	+ 5·3%
TOTAL NORTH AMERICA	8,730	8,805	9,140	9,420	9,775	9,975	10,310	10,965	11,740	12,230	12,585	+ 3·8%	+ 4·8%
CARIBBEAN													
Venezuela	2,770	2,845	2,920	3,225	3,270	3,395	3,505	3,400	3,575	3,640	3,640	+ 2·8%	+ 1·5%
Colombia	145	150	145	140	165	170	200	195	190	175	210	+ 3·8%	+ 4·5%
Trinidad	110	115	125	135	135	135	135	150	180	185	160	+ 3·8%	+ 3·3%
TOTAL CARRIBEAN AREA	3,025	3,110	3,190	3,500	3,570	3,700	3,840	3,745	3,945	4,000	4,010	+ 2·8%	+ 1·8%
SOUTH AMERICA													
Argentina	125	175	230	270	270	275	270	285	315	345	355	+11·0%	+ 5·3%
Brazil	65	80	95	95	105	90	95	115	145	165	170	+10·3%	+13·5%
Others	80	90	95	105	110	115	120	120	140	160	155	+ 6·8%	+ 5·8%
TOTAL SOUTH AMERICA	270	345	420	470	485	480	485	520	600	670	680	+ 9·8%	+ 7·3%
TOTAL WESTERN HEMISPHERE	12,025	12,260	12,750	13,390	13,830	14,155	14,635	15,230	16,285	16,900	17,275	+ 3·8%	+ 4·0%
WESTERN EUROPE													
France	30	40	45	50	50	55	60	60	55	55	50	+ 4·5%	− 2·5%
W. Germany	100	110	125	135	150	150	160	155	155	160	155	+ 4·5%	+ 0·5%
Austria	50	45	45	45	50	50	55	55	55	55	55	+ 1·5%	+ 0·8%
Others	95	105	115	120	125	160	160	165	180	185	200	+ 8·0%	+ 4·0%
TOTAL WESTERN EUROPE	275	300	330	350	375	415	435	435	445	455	460	+ 5·3%	+ 1·8%
MIDDLE EAST													
Iran	940	1,060	1,195	1,330	1,475	1,710	1,905	2,110	2,595	2,850	3,375	+13·8%	+14·5%
Iraq	850	955	990	995	1,160	1,255	1,315	1,390	1,225	1,510	1,525	+ 6·0%	+ 4·0%
Kuwait	1,380	1,620	1,645	1,830	1,930	2,115	2,170	2,275	2,290	2,420	2,575	+ 6·5%	+ 4·0%
Neutral Zone	120	135	175	245	315	360	355	420	420	425	450	+14·3%	+ 4·5%
Qatar	160	175	175	190	195	215	230	290	320	340	355	+ 8·3%	+10·5%
Saudi Arabia	1,100	1,245	1,390	1,525	1,630	1,730	2,025	2,395	2,600	2,830	2,995	+10·5%	+11·5%
Abu Dhabi	—	—	—	15	55	185	280	360	380	500	600	*	+26·3%
Others	50	45	45	45	45	50	60	65	130	340	480	+25·3%	+57·0%
TOTAL MIDDLE EAST	4,600	5,235	5,615	6,175	6,805	7,620	8,340	9,305	9,960	11,215	12,355	+10·5%	+10·3%
AFRICA													
Algeria	25	180	330	435	510	565	560	715	840	915	955	+43·5%	+11·0%
Libya	—	—	20	185	465	860	1,220	1,505	1,745	2,600	3,110	*	+29·5%
Other North Africa	65	65	75	90	110	130	125	130	170	290	395	+19·5%	+24·5%
Nigeria	10	20	55	70	75	120	275	420	320	140	545	+48·8%	+34·8%
Other West Africa	15	20	20	30	35	50	35	45	85	125	240	+31·0%	+37·0%
TOTAL AFRICA	115	285	500	810	1,195	1,725	2,215	2,815	3,160	4,070	5,245	+46·5%	+25·0%
SOUTH EAST ASIA													
Indonesia	380	415	430	460	455	470	480	475	515	600	715	+ 6·3%	+ 8·5%
Other S.E. Asia	110	95	80	80	80	75	80	95	115	125	140	+ 2·5%	+13·8%
TOTAL SOUTH EAST ASIA	490	510	510	540	535	545	560	570	630	725	855	+ 5·5%	+ 9·5%
U.S.S.R.	2,605	2,970	3,340	3,740	4,145	4,485	4,890	5,335	5,795	6,190	6,585	+ 9·8%	+ 8·0%
EASTERN EUROPE AND CHINA	345	385	400	440	450	485	505	535	545	595	605	+ 5·8%	+ 4·5%
OTHER EASTERN HEMISPHERE	35	35	40	65	70	85	105	140	170	195	230	+21·0%	+22·0%
TOTAL EASTERN HEMISPHERE	8,465	9,720	10,735	12,120	13,575	15,360	17,050	19,135	20,705	23,445	26,335	+12·0%	+11·3%
WORLD (excl. U.S.S.R., E. Europe, China)	17,540	18,625	19,745	21,330	22,810	24,545	26,290	28,495	30,650	33,560	36,420	+ 7·5%	+ 8·0%
WORLD	20,490	21,980	23,485	25,510	27,405	29,515	31,685	34,365	36,990	40,345	43,610	+ 7·8%	+ 8·0%

*Greater than 300%

TABLE 22

Oil Consumption and Trade

COUNTRY/AREA	1959	1960	1961	1962	1963	1964	1965	1966	1967	1968	1969	1969 over 1959	1969 over 1964
CONSUMPTION				THOUSAND BARRELS DAILY									
U.S.A.	9,420	9,660	9,810	10,230	10,550	10,820	11,300	11,850	12,280	13,080	13,810	+ 4·0%	+ 5·0%
Canada	820	860	880	930	1,000	1,070	1,150	1,220	1,290	1,380	1,440	+ 5·8%	+ 6·0%
Other Western Hemisphere	1,500	1,550	1,650	1,710	1,820	1,900	2,010	2,150	2,250	2,450	2,600	+ 5·8%	+ 6·5%
TOTAL WESTERN HEMISPHERE	11,740	12,070	12,340	12,870	13,370	13,790	14,460	15,220	15,820	16,910	17,850	+ 4·3%	+ 5·3%
Benelux	340	420	480	560	640	740	840	870	900	1,040	1,150	+13·0%	+ 9·3%
France	530	570	630	730	870	970	1,110	1,190	1,360	1,470	1,640	+12·5%	+11·0%
W. Germany	570	680	830	1,010	1,210	1,400	1,620	1,820	1,940	2,140	2,430	+15·8%	+11·3%
Italy	390	470	570	700	800	930	1,040	1,170	1,260	1,380	1,540	+15·3%	+10·3%
U.K.	850	990	1,060	1,130	1,240	1,360	1,510	1,590	1,680	1,820	1,960	+ 8·5%	+ 7·5%
Scandinavia	390	440	450	500	570	620	690	780	790	880	980	+10·0%	+ 9·8%
Others	450	520	560	660	780	910	1,030	1,150	1,310	1,480	1,640	+13·5%	+12·5%
TOTAL WESTERN EUROPE	3,520	4,090	4,580	5,290	6,110	6,930	7,840	8,570	9,240	10,210	11,340	+12·5%	+10·3%
Japan	450	590	810	950	1,250	1,490	1,770	1,990	2,370	2,800	3,290	+22·0%	+17·3%
Australasia	250	270	290	300	330	380	410	450	490	530	560	+ 8·5%	+ 8·0%
U.S.S.R., E. Europe, China	2,670	2,920	3,150	3,520	3,880	4,170	4,460	4,840	5,240	5,690	6,280	+ 9·0%	+ 8·5%
Other Eastern Hemisphere	1,440	1,540	1,710	1,790	1,910	2,040	2,160	2,370	2,730	2,990	3,230	+ 8·5%	+ 9·8%
TOTAL EASTERN HEMISPHERE	8,330	9,410	10,540	11,850	13,480	15,010	16,640	18,220	20,070	22,220	24,700	+11·5%	+10·5%
WORLD	20,070	21,480	22,880	24,720	26,850	28,800	31,100	33,440	35,890	39,130	42,550	+ 7·8%	+ 8·0%
MAIN PRODUCT DEMAND (Including Bunkers)													
U.S.A.													
Gasolines	4,270	4,340	4,410	4,570	4,830	4,910	5,110	5,370	5,560	5,920	6,140	+ 3·8%	+ 4·5%
Middle Distillates	2,180	2,300	2,370	2,540	2,600	2,620	2,720	2,850	3,030	3,280	3,430	+ 4·8%	+ 5·5%
Fuel Oil	1,430	1,430	1,400	1,380	1,360	1,410	1,510	1,610	1,680	1,710	1,870	+ 2·8%	+ 5·8%
TOTAL	7,880	8,070	8,180	8,490	8,790	8,940	9,340	9,830	10,270	10,910	11,440	+ 3·8%	+ 5·0%
WESTERN EUROPE													
Gasolines	750	810	940	1,030	1,150	1,320	1,530	1,740	1,870	2,080	2,270	+11·8%	+11·5%
Middle Distillates	980	1,130	1,280	1,540	1,840	2,040	2,330	2,580	2,800	3,190	3,590	+14·0%	+12·0%
Fuel Oil	1,270	1,520	1,700	1,970	2,220	2,550	2,850	3,090	3,230	3,500	3,850	+12·0%	+ 8·5%
TOTAL	3,000	3,460	3,920	4,540	5,210	5,910	6,710	7,410	7,900	8,770	9,710	+12·5%	+10·3%
EXPORTS													
U.S.A.	240	200	170	170	210	200	190	200	310	200	170	− 3·5%	− 3·3%
Caribbean	2,510	2,560	2,640	2,970	3,060	3,160	3,290	3,100	3,200	3,250	3,230	+ 2·5%	+ 0·5%
Other America	160	160	260	330	350	360	330	390	610	620	680	+15·5%	+13·5%
Middle East	4,170	4,710	5,090	5,570	6,150	6,930	7,690	8,570	9,140	10,440	11,520	+10·8%	+10·8%
North Africa	30	190	360	670	1,050	1,440	1,720	2,240	2,460	3,620	4,260	+64·0%	+24·3%
South East Asia	280	290	330	310	340	370	340	350	410	440	540	+ 6·8%	+ 7·8%
U.S.S.R., Eastern Europe	360	460	620	690	740	800	900	1,030	1,090	1,100	1,020	+11·0%	+ 5·0%
Others	190	240	310	290	300	360	530	670	690	730	1,220	+20·5%	+27·8%
WORLD	7,940	8,810	9,780	11,000	12,200	13,620	14,990	16,550	17,910	20,400	22,640	+11·0%	+10·8%
IMPORTS													
U.S.A.	1,780	1,820	1,920	2,080	2,120	2,260	2,470	2,570	2,540	2,810	3,170	+ 6·0%	+ 7·0%
Western Europe	3,560	4,160	4,520	5,290	6,070	6,900	7,600	8,580	9,250	10,480	11,740	+12·8%	+11·3%
Japan	460	680	870	930	1,220	1,470	1,720	2,000	2,400	3,060	3,460	+22·3%	+18·8%
Others	2,140	2,150	2,470	2,700	2,790	2,990	3,200	3,400	3,720	4,050	4,270	+ 7·3%	+ 7·5%
WORLD	7,940	8,810	9,780	11,000	12,200	13,620	14,990	16,550	17,910	20,400	22,640	+11·0%	+10·8%

TABLE 23

Oil Consumption and Trade

COUNTRY/AREA	1959	1960	1961	1962	1963	1964	1965	1966	1967	1968	1969	Yearly Change 1969 over 1959	Yearly Change 1969 over 1964
CONSUMPTION						MILLION TONS							
U.S.A.	460	473	478	498	513	527	549	576	596	636	668	+ 4·0%	+ 5·0%
Canada	41	43	44	46	47	52	57	61	62	66	69	+ 5·8%	+ 6·0%
Other Western Hemisphere	79	80	86	88	92	98	102	109	112	119	126	+ 5·8%	+ 6·5%
TOTAL WESTERN HEMISPHERE	580	596	608	632	652	677	708	746	770	821	863	+ 4·3%	+ 5·3%
Benelux	17	21	24	28	32	37	43	45	46	52	58	+13·0%	+ 9·3%
France	25	28	31	36	42	48	54	58	66	72	80	+12·5%	+11·0%
W. Germany	27	35	41	50	60	69	80	89	94	104	118	+15·8%	+11·3%
Italy	19	24	29	35	40	48	52	59	64	70	78	+15·3%	+10·3%
U.K.	43	50	53	57	62	67	75	79	83	89	96	+ 8·5%	+ 7·5%
Scandinavia	19	21	22	25	28	31	34	39	39	45	49	+10·0%	+ 9·8%
Others	23	26	28	33	39	45	52	58	66	74	81	+13·5%	+12·5%
TOTAL WESTERN EUROPE	173	205	228	264	303	345	390	427	458	506	560	+12·5%	+10·3%
Japan	23	30	41	49	63	75	90	99	118	138	162	+22·0%	+17·3%
Australasia	12	13	14	14	16	18	20	22	23	25	27	+ 8·5%	+ 8·0%
U.S.S.R., E. Europe, China	132	144	156	175	193	206	221	239	260	283	311	+ 9·0%	+ 8·5%
Other Eastern Hemisphere	71	77	85	90	95	102	109	118	136	150	162	+ 8·5%	+ 9·8%
TOTAL EASTERN HEMISPHERE	411	469	524	592	670	746	830	905	995	1,102	1,222	+11·5%	+10·5%
WORLD	991	1,065	1,132	1,224	1,322	1,423	1,538	1,651	1,765	1,923	2,085	+ 7·8%	+ 8·0%
MAIN PRODUCT DEMAND (Including Bunkers)													
U.S.A.													
Gasolines	184	187	190	197	208	212	220	231	240	256	265	+ 3·8%	+ 4·5%
Middle Distillates	106	112	115	123	126	128	132	139	147	159	166	+ 4·8%	+ 5·5%
Fuel Oil	78	79	77	76	75	77	83	88	92	94	102	+ 2·8%	+ 5·8%
TOTAL	368	378	382	396	409	417	435	458	479	509	533	+ 3·8%	+ 5·0%
WESTERN EUROPE													
Gasolines	31	35	40	44	50	57	65	75	80	90	98	+11·8%	+11·5%
Middle Distillates	47	55	62	75	89	99	113	125	136	155	174	+14·0%	+12·0%
Fuel Oil	68	83	93	107	121	139	157	169	176	191	209	+12·0%	+ 8·5%
TOTAL	146	173	195	226	260	295	335	369	392	436	481	+12·5%	+10·3%
EXPORTS													
U.S.A.	12	10	9	9	11	11	10	10	16	9	9	− 3·5%	− 3·3%
Caribbean	133	136	139	159	162	167	173	161	166	171	170	+ 2·5%	+ 0·5%
Other America	8	8	12	15	18	17	16	19	30	32	34	+15·5%	+13·5%
Middle East	207	234	252	277	306	345	383	426	455	519	567	+10·8%	+10·8%
North Africa	1	9	17	33	50	71	83	107	118	174	204	+64·0%	+24·3%
South East Asia	14	14	16	15	17	18	16	17	20	22	27	+ 6·8%	+ 7·8%
U.S.S.R., Eastern Europe	17	24	31	35	37	42	46	52	54	56	52	+11·0%	+ 5·0%
Others	9	12	16	14	14	16	25	33	34	35	60	+20·5%	+27·8%
WORLD	401	447	492	557	615	687	752	825	893	1,018	1,123	+11·0%	+10·8%
IMPORTS													
U.S.A.	93	95	99	108	110	117	127	133	131	147	162	+ 6·0%	+ 7·0%
Western Europe	178	206	224	265	303	346	378	426	458	519	580	+12·8%	+11·3%
Japan	22	34	43	48	62	75	88	103	120	153	170	+22·3%	+18·8%
Others	108	112	126	136	140	149	159	163	184	199	211	+ 7·3%	+ 7·5%
WORLD	401	447	492	557	615	687	752	825	893	1,018	1,123	+11·0%	+10·8%

TABLE 24

World "Published Proved" Oil Reserves at End 1969

COUNTRY/AREA	Thousand Million Tons	Share of Total	Thousand Million Barrels	Share of Total
U.S.A.	4·8	6·6%	37·8	7·0%
Canada	1·4	1·9%	10·5	1·9%
Caribbean	2·4	3·3%	17·1	3·2%
Other Western Hemisphere	1·7	2·3%	12·1	2·2%
TOTAL WESTERN HEMISPHERE	10·3	14·1%	77·5	14·3%
Western Europe	0·3	0·5%	2·4	0·5%
Africa	7·2	9·8%	54·8	10·1%
Middle East	45·4	62·0%	332·8	61·6%
U.S.S.R., E. Europe and China	8·2	11·2%	60·0	11·1%
Other Eastern Hemisphere	1·8	2·4%	13·1	2·4%
TOTAL EASTERN HEMISPHERE	62·9	85·9%	463·1	85·7%
WORLD (excl. U.S.S.R., etc.)	65·0	88·8%	480·6	88·9%
WORLD	73·2	100·0%	540·6	100·0%

SOURCE OF DATA

U.S.A. American Petroleum Institute.

Canada Canadian Petroleum Association.

All other areas Estimates published by the "Oil & Gas Journal"
(Worldwide Oil Issue 30th December 1969)

NOTES

1.   Proved reserves are generally taken to be the volume of oil remaining in the ground which geological and engineering information indicate with reasonable certainty to be recoverable in the future from known reservoirs under existing economic and operating conditions.

2.   The recovery factor, i.e. the relationship between proved reserves and total oil in place, varies according to local conditions and can vary in time with economic and technological changes.

3.   For the U.S.A. and Canada the data include oil which it is estimated can be recovered from proved natural gas reserves.

4.   The data exclude the oil content of shales and tar sands.

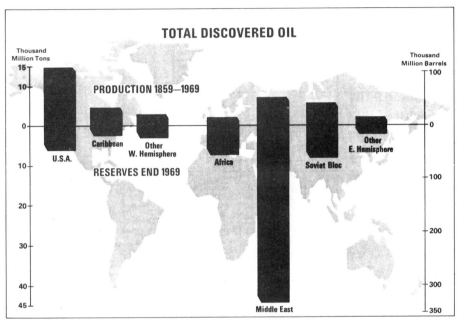

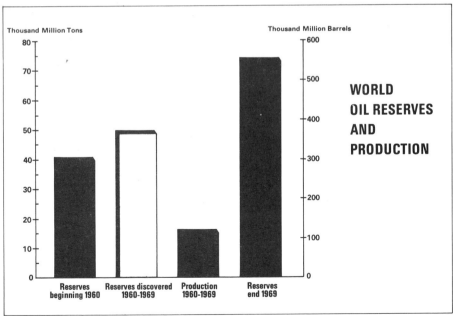

Figure 94

in the arctic regions of the U.S., Canada, and the U.S.S.R. have aroused
great enthusiasm in many quarters in each of the three countries. For
example, the president of a U.S. oil company has recently estimated that
the U.S. will consume 150 billion barrels of oil from 1970 to 1990, of a
total world consumption of 465 billion barrels.[103] With U.S. proved
reserves outside the Arctic at one-fourth his estimated requirement for
the next 20 years, it was his conclusion that visible reserves were
extremely low. Estimates of the future growth rate of U.S. oil consumption
have varied considerably, however, The rate of increase to 1980 forecast
in the Draft Environmental Impact Statement of the Department of the
Interior on the Trans-Alaska Pipeline resulted in a projected 1980 U.S.
annual consumption of 8.03 billion barrels. Other 1970 estimates have
ranged downward to about 6.5 billion barrels. The forecast rate of
increase for the decade ranged from above five percent to below three percent per year.

The potential U.S. interest in arctic gas finds is similarly related to
projected consumption rates and to the known reserves with which to meet
future demands. As has been noted, U.S. proved gas reserves as of
January 1, 1971 were about 290 trillion cu ft. U.S. consumption in 1970
was up seven percent, to a total of 22 trillion cu ft, and provided a
third of U.S. energy consumption. Again, if the 1970 rate of U.S. consumption is applied to proven U.S. reserves, the result is only about 13 years'
supply. Canadian consumption in 1969 was only 4.65 percent of U.S. consumption and Canada has been a potential source, rather than a heavy consumer,
of natural gas.

Potential North American Arctic Petroleum Reserves

Since a judgement concerning the potential significance of arctic North
American oil and gas must depend first of all upon the potential recoverable amounts that are there, a recapitulation is in order. As has been
stated, there is no universal agreement on the estimates. Probably the
most clearly sustainable are the potential crude oil reserves of the
Prudhoe Bay field on the North Slope of Alaska. For arctic North America
the following represent estimates of reserves ranging from conservative to
the most optimistic (See Fig. 95).

Oil Reserves Estimates:

	Low	High
Arctic Alaska	10 bil bbls*	60 bil bbls
Arctic Canada	50 bil bbls	256 bil bbls
Arctic North America	60 bil bbls	316 bil bbls

*Included in 1970 proved reserves

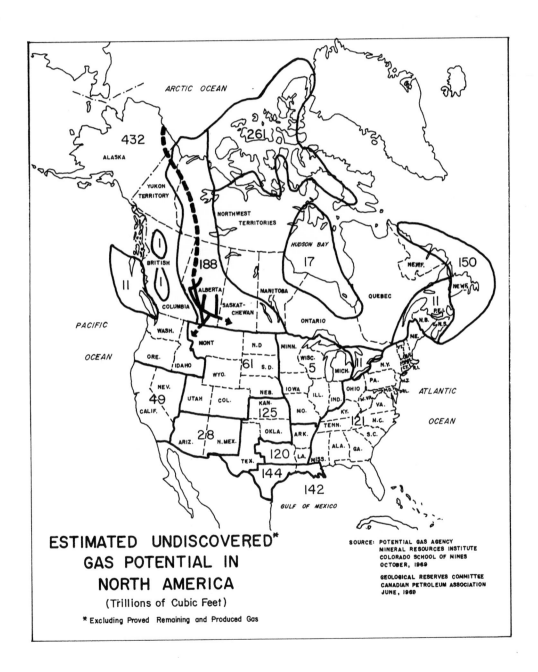

ESTIMATED UNDISCOVERED*
GAS POTENTIAL IN
NORTH AMERICA
(Trillions of Cubic Feet)

* Excluding Proved Remaining and Produced Gas

SOURCE: POTENTIAL GAS AGENCY
MINERAL RESOURCES INSTITUTE
COLORADO SCHOOL OF MINES
OCTOBER, 1969

GEOLOGICAL RESERVES COMMITTEE
CANADIAN PETROLEUM ASSOCIATION
JUNE, 1969

Figure 95

Gas Reserves Estimates:

	Low	High
Arctic Alaska	31 tril cu ft	432 tril cu ft
Arctic Canada	300 tril cu ft	725 tril cu ft
Arctic North America total	331 tril cu ft	1157 tril cu ft

We have noted that the U.S. plus Canadian annual rate of consumption of oil and gas as of 1970 was in the order of 6 billion barrels of oil and 23 trillion cu ft of gas. We have noted also that the 1970 proved U.S. reserves were 7 and 13 years respectively. Applying the lower estimated arctic potential reserves (331 trillion cu ft of gas and 60 billion barrels of oil) to the 1970 rate of consumption would extend the North American oil supply by 8 years and the gas supply by 14 years. On the basis of the high reserve estimates, however, the supplies would be extended by 51 years for oil and by 50 years for gas. Even assuming percentage annual rises in consumption at 3-5 percent, the higher estimates would be sufficient to cover U.S. and Canadian consumption for at least three decades. The North American Arctic addition to the present total world proved oil reserves would be nearly 60 percent of that total.

Factors Affecting North American Arctic Petroleum Development

Any attempt to forecast the future significance of the truly enormous estimated petroleum reserves of the arctic region (assuming that the high estimates are justified) naturally becomes a resultant of projecting past trends and adjusting for anticipated possible and probable changes that may affect that projection.

Looking at the past, one may note the following basic facts:[104]

1. World energy consumption has more than doubled during the 1960's.

2. Nearly all the increase has been met by oil and gas.

3. Oil is the most important fuel. This applies to nearly all countries.

4. There is a close relationship between energy consumption and the per-capita gross national product.

5. Nuclear power has not lived up to earlier promise. Technical and cost problems have retarded development.

Based largely on past and especially on more recent trends, it has been forecast that world energy demands will increase perhaps twofold by 1980 and threefold before the year 2000. In recent years it has been predicted, also, that the additional energy, at least for 1970-1985 period, will be met mainly by gas and oil. However, such long-term forecasts become of dubious value unless critical evaluation is made of factors that may enter the picture to change past trends. A number of such possible factors may be noted and given some preliminary assessment. Some of the factors may become so during the 1970's, and others may have a later bearing on the oil and gas demands.[104]

1. Rate of population growth may or may not be slowed.

2. The rate of economic growth in "underdeveloped" areas in terms of its effect on energy demand may be a factor, even though the growth is in turn dependent on energy input.

3. The timing of solutions to technical problems, some of them relating to more efficient utilization and recovery of energy supplies and especially to the problems of generating electricity economically by nuclear power, will affect the projection.

4. The rate of discovery of oil and gas and the comparable costs of retrieval with other sources of energy will be a major economic factor.

5. The extent to which the world coal reserves do or do not gain competitive status will be significant, because the coal reserves, as has been noted, are so enormous.

6. Both the technology and the economics of extracting energy fuels from tar sands and shales will affect the development of conventional petroleum sources.

7. The success and timing of "new" sources of energy such as solar power, tides, and geothermal energy in the types on which the President asked for speeded up research in his June 4, 1971 announcement on a long-range energy program, may affect the projection but are difficult to assess now.[105]

8. Further advances in the technology and engineering of economical safe transportation of energy fuels, including gas and oil, will be a factor especially significant in the Arctic.

9. It is not beyond the realm of possibility that the demands for pollution control and environmental protection will have a considerable bearing on the demands for oil. Changes in power-using vehicles and machinery may be made which throw emphasis to non-polluting or less pollutant forms of energy (solar, tidal, and geothermal energy have been mentioned as possible examples).

10. The effective demand for energy may also be affected by social, economic, or political maladjustments, such as economic depressions, wars, blockades, etc., which might either increase or diminish demands for certain fuels in certain areas.

Some Tentative General Conclusions

The evaluation of the significance, from 1971 to the year 2000, of the arctic petroleum resources must begin with two estimates - one, the estimate of the actual reserves that exist in the Arctic as recoverable amounts; and, two, the trend of effective demands for arctic gas and oil, which in turn will be affected by several economic factors such as the competitive position of oil and gas, both in terms of comparative cost and comparative

utility and on social acceptability. In this connection, it has been
stated that, "Of all the items that affect any development in the Arctic,
and especially the development of natural resources in the regions, transportation is easily the most important."[106] At the moment that statement has merit; but by 1985 or 1990 there may be other factors that are
equally or more critically important.

Whereas most of the above listed contingencies or variables may well
warrant great caution in forecasting for the last two decades of the
century, one may doubt whether the factors which now provide the impetus
for exploration of arctic oil and gas will seriously reduce that impetus
before 1980 and perhaps not even after that. Coal, as a competitor, has
been losing ground to oil and gas. In 1970, 76 percent of U.S. energy
came from oil and gas, as compared with 20 percent from coal. In the
U.S.S.R. the trend has been similar in recent years. The President has now
requested intensified development work on fast-breeder reactors, with the
aim of completing a demonstration reactor by 1980. (Apparently research on
nuclear fusion was not emphasized.) In a recent interview, Dr. John
McKetta, Chairman of the National Energy Policy Committee, which had been
commissioned and appointed by the Secretary of the Interior, predicted
that fast-breeder reactors would not produce a great increase in nuclear
energy until after 1990. He suggested that 10 percent of nuclear-powered
energy was a possible estimate for 1990.[107] Any substantial change in
world energy sources prior to 1990 cannot now be predicted with any confidence.

The total problem of forecasting the oil situation was recently
summarized by the Senior Editor of the *Oil and Gas Journal* as follows:[108]

> "The 1970's promise to become one vast headache for U.S.
> industry and government planners in trying to forecast oil and
> gas needs.

> "A rapidly changing life style in America, and the growing
> concern for the environment already are playing hob with old
> methods and tools of forecasting.

> "Add to this an increasing inefficiency in the nation's
> use of energy and a tightening supply. That means trouble. ...
> But at least one factor appears pretty certain: Oil will be
> the dominant supplier of a surge of U.S. energy demand in the
> decade."

If forecasting the energy picture for the 1970's is difficult, the
problem of looking ahead to the 1980's and 1990's is far greater. Dr.
Paul McCracken, Chairman of the President's Council of Economic Advisers,
has pointed out an additional worrisome fact about the energy situation -
the fact that since 1966 the total energy consumption has risen more rapidly
than real economic growth.[108]

Future North American Arctic Energy Development

A factor which has been largely responsible for the oil industry
willingness to make a substantial investment in Alaskan North Slope oil
development is, of course, the evident concentration of oil riches, with
anticipated daily wellhead flow far greater than from most fields in the
"lower 48." If other arctic Alaskan and Canadian reserves are equally

promising, that fact will greatly spur development, even though transportation costs and production costs per well are comparatively high.

A significant factor in the U.S.-Canadian arctic oil development
picture is the fact that, as indicated in the above summary, the arctic
Alaskan reserves may be found to be far less than the Canadian, while the
U.S. consumption rate now is more than 20 times greater and may well
continue to be. The U.S. interest in Canadian arctic petroleum is likely,
therefore, to be strong. The U.S. market for Canadian oil and gas will
probably be a major factor influencing the rate of Canadian development,
although it may eventually prove to be economical for Canada to supply its
eastern Canada market from its arctic oil, even if the current exploration
between Greenland and Baffin Island prove to be unproductive. In any
event, it seems clear now that Canadian arctic oil will be an important
aspect of any U.S.-Canadian joint energy policy agreement, if such agreement
is ever to be reached. Central to the North American energy policy
issue is, of course, the matter of imports from other western hemisphere
sources and, more particularly, from the eastern hemisphere. The weighing
of the forces which will affect import policy for the 1980's and 1990's
is perhaps not possible now, but the economic, political, national security,
and other arguments have already surfaced to some extent. The content of
the report of the 1970 "oil Import Question" by the Cabinet Task Force
on Oil Import Control, which emerged with divided counsel, is perhaps
indicative of the range and depth of views on the subject. The resolution
of U.S. and Canadian interests may prove to be a long and painful process.
However, unless there are breakthroughs in the field of new energy sources,
the prospect would seem to be that a common policy on North American arctic
oil development and distribution will be reached within the next 10 years.
Meanwhile, environmental concerns are, of course, a delaying factor in
the development of the oil reserves in Alaska and may also affect the
developments in arctic Canada.

Future Development of Soviet Arctic Energy Resources

As has been noted above, present estimates are that more than 40 percent of the U.S.S.R.'s potential oil reserves are in the arctic or near-
arctic regions. The estimates of arctic gas reserves in the U.S.S.R. are
even more impressive, ranging up to 2 or 3 quadrillion cu ft, or perhaps
five or six times the present proved U.S.S.R. reserves of 427 trillion cu
ft. In one respect the U.S.S.R.'s problems of arctic oil and gas development are simpler than the North American problem - the area is politically
controlled by one country alone. Another factor has been referred to also -
that the main centers of U.S.S.R. consumer demand for petroleum products
are in European Russia, which in turn could rather easily be connected by
pipeline to the populous industrialized areas of western Europe. Gas
pipelines are already projected to West Germany, Italy, and eventually to
Belgium. The continued explorations in the offshore North Sea areas may
produce gas and/or oil deposits that would have the effect of slowing down
the movement of Soviet gas and oil to western Europe. Price (cost) factors,
as well as political developments in the Middle East and Africa, will also
have significance for the timing and intensity of western European demand
for the U.S.S.R. oil and gas. The political factor is incalculable now
but may well prove to be relatively minor.

References

1. The Environmental Policy Division, Library of Congress, *The Economy, Energy, and the Environment,* Sept. 1, 1970.

2. Bureau of Mines, "Statistical Summary," *1969 Minerals Yearbook* (preprint), p.5-6.

3. U.S. Geological Survey, "Coal Resources of the Cape Lisborne-Colville River Region, Alaska," *GSA Bulletin,* 1242-E.

4. Bureau of Mines, "The Mineral Industry of Alaska," *1969 Minerals Yearbook.*

5. U.S. Geological Survey, *Mineral and Water Resources of Alaska, 1964.*

6. Bureau of Mines, *loc. cit.*

7. Federal Field Committee for Development Planning in Alaska, *Alaska Natives and the Land,* p. 377-395.

8. Univ. of Alaska, *Mineral Resources of Northern Alaska, 1969,* M.I.R.L. Rept. No. 16.

9. Federal Maritime Comm., *Alaska Trade Study,* July 1967.

10. Production figures from *Minerals Yearbook*; 1969 figures from *1969 Minerals Yearbook* (preprint).

11. *Oil and Gas Jour.,* Apr. 5, 1971, p. 38-39 and *Petrol. Press Serv.,* May 1971, p.183.

12. *Oil and Gas Jour.,* July 20, 1970, p.37.

13. Cabinet Task Force on Oil Import Control, *The Oil Import Question,* Feb. 1970, p.306.

14. *Oil and Gas Jour.,* Mar. 15, 1971, p.24. See also *The Humble Way,* First Quarter 1971, p.24-27.

15. *Oil and Gas Jour.,* Dec. 7, 1970, p.109.

16. Federal Maritime Commission, *op. cit.*

17. Frank N. Ikard, "The Energy Gap - A Search for Solutions," *Petrol. Today,* Winter 1971, p.13.

18. Hollis M. Dole, Dept. of the Interior press release, Feb. 1, 1971.

19. John C. Reed, *Resources Development, A Must,* unpubl. paper, 1971.

20. A.R. Tussing and G.R. Erickson, *Mining and Public Policy in Alaska* (Univ. of Alaska).

21. U.S. Dept. of Comm., *Statistical Abstract of the United States,* 1968 edition.

22. G.W. Wilson, "World Market Potential for Northern Resources," in *Arctic and Middle North Transportation,* B.F. Sater, ed. (Wash., D.C.: Arctic Inst. of N. Amer.) 1969.

23. Dole, *op. cit.*

24. Dept. of Labor, State of Alaska, *Alaska Economic Trends,* Nov. 1970, p.1.

25. Dept. of Labor, State of Alaska, *Alaska's Manpower Outlook - 1970's,* May 28, 1970.

26. Dept. of Labor, State of Alaska, *Alaska's Manpower Outlook - 1970's*, Feb. 3, 1971.

27. Dept. of Labor, State of Alaska, *Alaska's Manpower Outlook - 1970's*, May 28, 1970.

28. *Oil and Gas Jour.*, April 20, 1970, p.100.

29. *U.S. News and World Rept.*, Aug. 24, 1970, p. 28.

30. *Baltimore Sun*, Aug. 30, 1970.

31. U.S. Dept. of Transportation, *Long-Range Polar Objectives*, 1968.

32. *Oil and Gas Jour.*, May 11, 1970, p. 46 and June 9, 1969, p. 39.

33. *Wall Street Jour.*, April 2, 1970.

34. *Oceanology International*, June 1970.

35. *Petroleum Times*, Jan. 2, 1970.

36. *Oil and Gas Jour.*, Mar. 29, 1971.

37. *Report of the NORTH Commission to the Governor of Alaska*, June 24, 1970.

38. *Oil and Gas Jour.*, July 21, 1969, p. 48.

39. *Oil and Gas Jour.*, April 20, 1970, p. 140.

40. *Wall Street Jour.*, June 30, 1970.

41. Canadian Dept. of Indian Affairs and Northern Devel., *North of 60°*, Table 3-1.

42. *Polar Record*, Vol. 15, No. 95 (May 1970), p. 154.

43. Dominion Bureau of Statistics, *Canada 1970.*

44. J.C. Underhill, "The Future of Oil and Gas Development in the Canadian North," in Sater, ed., *op. cit.*

45. C.E. Forget, *Economic Development, Pollution Control and Sovereignty* (Montreal: Private Planning Assoc. of Canada), Feb. 1970.

46. "Canada's First Arctic Finds," *Petrol. Press Serv.*, April 1970.

47. *Oil and Gas Jour.*, April 12, 1971, p. 49.

48. *Oil and Gas Jour.*, Nov. 2, 1970, p. 48.

49. *Oil and Gas Jour.*, Mar. 8, 1971, p. 30.

50. *Oil and Gas Jour.*, Jan. 4, 1971, p. 105.

51. A.E. Pallister, *Oil and Gas Jour.*, Nov. 9, 1970, p.96 and R.G. McCrossan and R.M. Procter, *Oil and Gas Jour.*, Jan. 25, 1971, p.153.

52. *Exploration and Production in the Canadian Archipelago*, paper delivered at San Francisco, Feb. 1, 1971, p. 34.

53. Canadian Imperial Bank of Commerce, *Commercial Letter*, Sept. 1969, p. 2.

54. Cited by the Mineral Industry of Canada in *The Minerals Yearbook, 1969,* Vol. IV.

55. *Oil and Gas Jour.,* Aug. 31, 1970, p. 56.

56. *Northwest Territories,* p. 5-6 (Canadian Government publication).

57. U.S. Coast Guard, "Northern Transportation in Canada," *Polar Transportation Requirements Study Rept.,* App. G (from info. compiled by J.C. Reed and Arctic Inst. of No. Amer.), 1968.

58. "Canada's Heartland, The Prairie Provinces," *National Geographic,* Oct. 1970.

59. Dominion Bureau of Statistics, *Canada 1970.*

60. J.E. Sater, *The Arctic Basin* (Wash., D.C.: Arctic Inst. of N. Amer.), 1969.

61. Canadian Gov. Travel Bureau, *Canada and Northern United States Highway Map,* 1968.

62. Northern Transportation Company Limited.

63. R.A. Bandeen, "Railways in Northern Resource Development," in Sater, ed., *op. cit.*

64. W.S. Hall, "Northern River Navigation on the Mackenzie Watershed of Canada," *ibid.*

65. O.M. Solandt, "Keynote Address," *ibid.*

66. Panarctic Oils, Ltd., *Annual Report, 1970,* p. 11.

67. *Oil and Gas Jour.,* Jan. 11, 1971, p. 26.

68. *Financial Post,* April 17, 1971.

69. T. Shabad, *Basic Indus. Resources of the U.S.S.R.* (New York: Col. Univ. Press), 1969.

70. R.C. Kinsbury and R.N. Taafe, *An Atlas of Soviet Affairs* (Praeger Press), 1968.

71. Natl. Res. Council of Canada, *Problems of the North,* trans. *Problemy Severa,* 1967.

72. *Oil and Gas Jour.,* Mar. 1, 1971, p. 22.

73. *Polar Record,* Vol. 11, No. 73 (Jan. 1963).

74. *Oil and Gas Jour.,* April 20, 1970, p. 122, 128, and 127.

75. *Oil and Gas Jour.,* Dec. 28, 1970, p. 173.

76. *Oil and Gas Jour.,* Aug. 24, 1970.

77. *Oil and Gas Jour.,* Jan. 4, 1971, p. 40.

78. T. Armstrong, "Oil and Natural Gas in North-West Siberia," *Polar Record,* Vol. 14, No. 92, p. 616.

79. *Petrol. Press Serv.,* Sept., 1970, p. 322.

80. A.A. Meyerhoff, I.A. Mamantov, and T. Shabad, *Russian Arctic Petroleum Provinces,* unpubl. paper read at Second Int. Symp. on Arctic Geol., San Francisco, Feb., 1971.

81. *Oil and Gas Jour.*, April 20, 1970, p. 128.

82. British Petrol. Co., *BP Statistical Rev. of the World Oil Industry 1969.*

83. *Oil and Gas Jour.*, Sept. 7, 1970, p. 51-53.

84. *Oil and Gas Jour.*, July 6, 1970, p. 72.

85. T. Armstrong, *Russian Settlement in the North* (Cambridge Univ. Press), 1965.

86. After van Allen.

87. Glavnoe Upravlenie Geodezii e Kartografic, *Atlas SSSR*, 1962.

88. *Rand McNally New Cosmopolitan World Atlas*, 1968 edition.

89. T.J. Laforest, "Strategic Significance of North Sea Route," *U.S. Naval Institute Proceedings*, 1967.

90. R. Thoren, *Picture Atlas of the Arctic* (Elsevier Publishers), 1969.

91. V.P. Petrov, "Soviet Canals," *U.S. Naval Institute Proceedings*, July 1967.

92. "Newsletter," *Oil and Gas Jour.*, April 19, 1971.

93. The Minerals Industry of Norway, *1968 Minerals Yearbook*, Vol. IV, p. 561.

94. *Oil and Gas Jour.*, July 27, 1970, p.86 and *New York Times*, May 17, 1971, p. 53.

95. The Mineral Industry of Sweden, *1968 Minerals Yearbook*, p. 688.

96. The Minerals Industry of Finland, *1969 Minerals Yearbook* (preprint), p. 8-9.

97. National Geographic Society, *National Geographic Atlas of the World*, p. 83.

98. R.A. Geisler, "Unknown Greenland Catches Miners' Eyes," *Northern Miner*, Mar. 4, 1971.

99. "Newsletter," *Oil and Gas Jour.*, Dec. 14, 1970.

100. *Oil and Gas Jour.*, Nov. 23, 1970, p. 35.

101. *Oil and Gas Jour.*, Nov. 30, 1970, p. 93.

102. Bureau of Mines, Dept. of the Interior news release, Mar. 9, 1971.

103. Wayne Glenn, *Oil and Gas Jour.*, Mar. 8, 1971, p. 34.

104. William Jamieson, *Long Term Future Requirements*, paper presented to Fifth Northern Development Conf., Edmonton, Nov. 1970.

105. *New York Times*, June 5, 1971.

106. A.N. Edginton, D.L. Campbell, and N.A. Cleland, *Exploration and Production in the Canadian Archipelago*, paper delivered at Second Int. Symp. on Arctic Geology, San Francisco, February 1971.

107. *World Oil, International Edition*, Mar. 1971, p. 71.

108. *Oil and Gas Jour.*, Feb. 11, 1971, p. 33.

ACKNOWLEDGEMENTS

For their cooperation in granting permission to reproduce maps and figures grateful acknowledgement is made to the following:

Air University Review - Figure 12
The Alberta Gas Trunk Line Limited - Figure 95
Columbia University Press - Figures 74, 75, 79, 80, 81, 82,
        83, 84, 85, 86, and 90
Elsevier Publishing Company - Figures 33, 34, 38, 39, 40, 41,
        64, 91, 92, 93, and Table 2
Northern Transportation Company Limited - Figure 73
Panarctic Oils Limited - Figure 68
Petroleum Press Service - Figures 69, 76, and 78
Petroleum Publishing Company - Figure 65
The Queen's Printer - Figures 67, 71, 72
Scott Polar Research Institute - Figure 70 and Table 14.